D1504158

The Brooklyn Reader

Expository Writing Department
NYU Polytechnic School of Engineering

Custom Edition for New York University

Edited by
Jono Mischkot
Elisa Linsky
Pat C. Hoy II

Pearson Learning Solutions, 501 Boylston Street, Suite 900, Boston, MA 02116
A Pearson Education Company
www.pearsoned.com

Printed in the United States of America

3 4 5 6 7 8 9 10 VOZN 17 16 15

000200010271904577

TF/CB

ISBN 10: 1-269-75590-0
ISBN 13: 978-1-269-75590-0

Copyright Acknowledgments

Contents

Observation

Science and the Humanities

Research & Scientific Reasoning

Technology

Supplemental Table of Contents

eReader

Observation

Science and the Humanities

Research & Scientific Reasoning

Technology

Preface

The Brooklyn Reader is the required text for all students of the Expository Writing Program at NYU Polytechnic School of Engineering, satisfying two semesters of the following required courses:

- *Writing the Essay* is the foundational writing course, providing instruction and practice in critical reading, creative thinking, and clear writing. It offers additional instruction in analyzing and interpreting written texts, the use of written texts as evidence, the development of ideas, and the writing of both exploratory and argumentative essays. The course stresses exploration, inquiry, reflection, analysis, revision, and collaborative learning.

- *Advanced College Essay* builds on *Writing the Essay* and provides advanced instruction in analyzing and interpreting written texts from a variety of academic disciplines, using written texts as evidence, developing ideas, conducting academic research, and writing persuasive essays. It stresses analysis, inductive reasoning, reflection, revision, and collaborative learning. The course is tailored for students in the School of Engineering so that readings and essay writing focus on issues that are pertinent to the sciences.

Observation

Animal Communication
and Human Language

Emile Benveniste

To apply the notion of language to the animal world is admissible only at the price of misusing terms. We know that it has been impossible until now to prove that animals enjoy, even in a rudimentary form, a means of expression endowed with the characteristics and functions of human speech. All serious observations made of animal communities, all attempts to establish or verify, by means of various technical devices, any form of speech comparable to that of man have failed. It does not seem that animals which emit certain kinds of calls are thereby displaying any behavior from which we may infer that they are conveying "spoken" messages to one another. The fundamental conditions for a strictly linguistic communication seem to be lacking even in the higher animal world.

The case of the bees, however, is different. At any rate, it has become apparent lately that it may turn out to be different. Everything confirms the belief that the bees possess the means of communicating with one another—a fact which has been observed for a long time. The amazing organization of their colonies, the differentiation and coordination of their activities, their capacity for reacting collectively to unforeseen circumstances, lead us to suppose that they are capable of exchanging real messages. The attention of observers has been drawn particularly to the way in which the bees are informed when one of them has discovered a source of food. Consider, e.g., a foraging bee discovering on its flight a sugar solution, placed at a certain point experimentally in order to attract its attention. It will drink of it, and while it feeds, the experimenter carefully puts a mark on it. Then it flies back to the hive. A few seconds later a flight of bees arrives on the spot, all from the same hive. The bee which discovered the food is not among them. It must have informed the others, and the information must have been quite precise since they are able to reach the spot without any guide, although it often is at a considerable distance from the hive and always out of the bees' sight. There is no error or hesitation in locating it. If the foraging bee has chosen one particular flower among others which could have also attracted it, then the bees arriving on the scene after its return fly to the same flower, neglecting all others. It seems clear that the scouting bee has indicated to its fellow bees the spot whence it has come. But how?

This fascinating problem has baffled observers for a long time. We owe it to Karl von Frisch (professor of zoology at the University of Munich) and to the experiments he conducted for some thirty years, that we are now in the possession of principles which enable us to solve the problem. His research has revealed the method of communication among bees. Working with a transparent hive, he has observed the conduct of the bee returning after the discovery of honey. It is immediately surrounded by the others. The excitement in the hive is great. They stretch out their antennae toward it to collect the pollen with which it is laden or they drink the nectar which it disgorges. Then, followed by the others, the scouting bee proceeds to perform dances. This is the critical moment and constitutes the act of communication. The bee performs two different dances, according to the kind of information it intends to convey. In the one dance it traces horizontal circles from right to left, then from left to right, in succession (round dance). In the other dance (wagging dance) it wags its abdomen continually and cuts what appears to be a figure eight in the following manner: it flies straight, then makes a full left turn, flies straight again, and begins a full turn to the right, etc. After the dances, one or several bees leave the hive and go straight to the supply spot visited by the first bee. Once they have had their fill they regain the hive, where they, in turn, perform the same dances. This causes fresh departures so that, after a few coming and goings, some hundreds of bees swarm to the spot where the forager discovered the food.

The round dance and the wagging dance, then, appear to be the actual message which announces the discovery to the hive. The difference between the two dances still awaited an explanation. Frisch thought that it refers to the nature of the food: the round dance announcing the nectar, the wagging dance the pollen. These facts and their interpretation, first presented in 1923, have been much publicized, and even popularized, in the meantime. It is easy to appreciate the lively interest which they have aroused. Nevertheless, they do not entitle us to ascribe to the bees a language in the strict sense of the word.

This position, however, was changed completely as a result of further experiments by Karl von Frisch, extending and correcting his first observations. He announced his findings in 1948 in technical journals and summarized them in 1950 in a small volume presenting a series of lectures he had delivered in the United States. After conducting, literally, thousands of experiments with truly admirable patience and ingenuity, he succeeded in determining the real meaning of the dances. The essential new information which he provided is that the dances indicate the distance from the hive to the food and not, as he thought at first, the nature of the food. The round dance announces that the food site must be sought close by within the radius of approximately a hundred meters

4

from the hive. The bees fly out hovering not far from the hive until they have found the spot. The other dance performed by the foraging bee, in which it wags its abdomen and cuts figures of eight, indicates that the point is at a greater distance, between a hundred meters and six kilometers. This message contains two distinct pieces of information, one about the distance, the other about the direction. The distance is indicated by the number of figures traced in a given time. It varies always in inverse proportion to their frequency. For example, the bee describes nine to ten complete cycles of the dance in fifteen seconds when the distance is a hundred meters, seven for two hundred meters, four and a half for one kilometer, and only two for six kilometers. The greater the distance, the slower the dance. As for the direction in which the food is to be sought, this is indicated by the axis of the figure eight and its relation to the sun. According to its inclination right or left this axis gives the angle which the site forms with the sun. By virtue of their particular sensitiveness to polarized light, the bees are capable of finding their bearings even when the sky is overcast. In practice there exist slight variations, in measuring the distance, between one bee and another or between one hive and another, but the variations do not affect the choice of the dance. This interpretation is the result of approximately four thousand experiments which other zoologists, at first inclined to be sceptical, have repeated and confirmed in Europe and in the United States. We now have the means of ascertaining that it is in fact the dance with its two variations which the bees use to inform their fellow bees about a discovery and to guide them to the spot by giving information about direction and distance. The nature of the food, furthermore, is disclosed to the other bees by the scent on the scouting bee or by the nectar which it has drunk and which they now absorb from it. Then they take wing and infallibly reach the spot. The experimenter thus can predict the behavior of the hive and verify the information given, according to the type and rhythm of the dance.

The importance of these discoveries for the study of animal psychology need not be stressed. We should like to dwell here on a less obvious aspect of the problem, which Frisch, intent on describing objectively his experiments, has not touched on. We are, for the first time, in a position to ascertain with precision the methods of communication used in an insect colony. We can, likewise, for the first time envisage the working of an animal "language." It may be well to examine briefly if and in what sense it can or cannot be called a language and how these observations on the bees could help us to find, by contrast or resemblance, a definition of human speech.

The bees appear to be capable of giving and receiving real messages which contain several data. They can register reports concerning the position and distance of a certain object. They can store these data in some kind of "memory." They can, furthermore, communicate them by means of symbols, using different somatic movements. Indeed, the most remarkable thing is that they show an aptitude for symbolizing: there is undoubtedly a "conventional" relation between their behavior and the facts it conveys. This relation is perceived by the other bees in the terms in which it is transmitted to them and becomes an actuating force.

So far we find among bees the very conditions without which no language is possible, i.e., the capacity for formulating and interpreting a "sign" which refers to a certain "reality," the memory of an experience undergone, and the ability to decompose the remembered experience.

The message passed on contains three items of information, or, more precisely, only three have been identified until now: the existence of a source of food, its distance, and its direction. These elements could be arranged in a somewhat different way. The round dance indicates simply the presence of food and merely implies the fact that it is not far away. It is based on the mechanical principle of "all or nothing." The other dance conveys a real communication. The existence of food, this time, is implicit in two data (distance and direction) which are explicitly announced. There are thus several points of resemblance with human language. An effective, though rudimentary, symbolism is brought into play. Through it objective data are turned into formalized gestures conveying variable elements and an invariable "meaning." We are faced here with a language in the strict sense of the term, considering not only the way it functions but also the medium in which it takes place: the system is operative within a given community, and each member of the community is capable of using and of understanding it.

But the differences between the bee language and human language are considerable, and they help us to understand the truly distinctive characteristics of the latter. It should be noted, above all, that the bee's message consists entirely of physical motion, a dance, without the intervention of any "vocal" organ, whereas there can be no real language without the exercise of voice. This leads us to another difference of a physical nature. Effectuated as it is without the exercise of voice, by means of gestures only, communication between bees necessarily occurs under conditions which permit visual perception, i.e., in daylight. It cannot be made effective in darkness. Human language is not subject to this limitation.

A very important difference exists, furthermore, with regard to the circumstances in which the communication is made. The bee's message does not call for any reply from those to whom it is addressed, except that it evokes a particular behavior which is not strictly an answer. This means that the language of the bees lacks the dialogue which is distinctive of human speech. We speak to others who speak to us: such is the nature of human intercourse. This reveals yet another contrast. Because the bees are incapable of dialogue, the communication concerns only a certain objective fact. No "linguistic" information is involved, there being no reply. For a reply is a linguistic reaction to a linguistic manifestation. Moreover, the bee's message cannot be reproduced by another bee which has not seen for itself what the first bee has announced. There is no indication, for example, that a bee goes off to another hive with the message it has received in its own hive. This would constitute a kind of transmission or relay. Human language is different; for in the dialogue the reference to the objective experience and the reaction to its linguistic manifestation mix freely and without limitation. The bee does not construe a message from another message. Each bee, once advised by the scouting bee's dance, flies out and feeds at the spot indicated, reproducing the same information on its return, not with reference to the first message but with reference to the fact it has just verified itself. Now the characteristic of language is to produce a substitute for experience which can be passed on *ad infinitum* in time and space. This is the nature of our symbolism and the basis of linguistic tradition.

If we now consider the content of the message it is easy to see that it always concerns only one fact, namely, food, and that the only variations of this theme concern the question of space. The contrast with the boundless possibilities of human language is obvious. Furthermore, the behavior which expresses the bee's message is a special form of symbolism. It consists in tracing off an objective situation of fact, the only situation which can be translated into a message, without any possibility of variation or transposition. In human language, on the contrary, the symbol as such does not trace out the facts of experience in the sense that there is no necessary relationship between the objective reference and the linguistic form.

Many more distinctions could be made here from the standpoint of human symbolism, the nature and function of which have as yet been little studied. But the difference is already sufficiently indicated.

Finally, one more feature of the communication among bees should be mentioned which distinguishes it sharply from human language. The bee's message cannot be analyzed. We can see in it only an overall reference to a total content; the only possible differentiation pertains to the spatial position of the reported object. But it is impossible to resolve this content into its constituent "morphemes" and to make each morpheme correspond to an element of what has been enounced. This is precisely where the distinctive character of human speech manifests itself. Each enunciation made by man can be reduced to elements which combine easily and freely according to definite laws so that a small number of morphemes admits of a great number of combinations. Hence proceeds the variety of human language—which has the capacity of expressing everything. A more searching analysis of language reveals that this restricted number of morphemes, or elements of meaning, can be reduced to even less numerous "phonemes," or elements of articulation, devoid of meaning. It is the selective and distinctive grouping of these elements of articulation which produces the sense units. These "empty" phonemes, organized in systems, constitute the basis of every language. It is evident that no such constituent parts can be isolated in the language of the bees. It cannot be reduced to identifiable and distinctive elements.

All these observations bring out the essential difference between the method of communication discovered among bees and our human language. This difference can be stated summarily in one phrase which seems to give the most appropriate definition of the manner of communication used by the bees: it is not a language but a signal code. All the characteristics of a code are present: the fixity of the subject matter, the invariability of the message, the relation to a single set of circumstances, the impossibility of separating the components of the message, and its unilateral transmission. Nevertheless, it is significant that this code, the only form of language found so far among animals, is the property of insects which live in a society. Society is likewise the condition of human language. One of the most interesting aspects of the discoveries of Karl von Frisch is that, apart from the insights into the life of the insect world, he has indirectly enlightened us as to the conditions of human language and its underlying symbolism. It is likely that further progress of this research will bring a further penetration of the possibilities and nuances of this form of communication. But the mere discovery of its existence, its nature, and its way of functioning is a contribution toward a better understanding of the origins of language and the definition of man.

At the Dam

Joan Didion

Since the afternoon in 1967 when I first saw Hoover Dam, its image has never been entirely absent from my inner eye. I will be talking to someone in Los Angeles, say, or New York, and suddenly the dam will materialize, its pristine concave face gleaming white against the harsh rusts and taupes and mauves of that rock canyon hundreds or thousands of miles from where I am. I will be driving down Sunset Boulevard, or about to enter a freeway, and abruptly those power transmission towers will appear before me, canted vertiginously over the tailrace. Sometimes I am confronted by the intakes and sometimes by the shadow of the heavy cable that spans the canyon and sometimes by the ominous outlets to unused spillways, black in the lunar clarity of the desert light. Quite often I hear the turbines. Frequently I wonder what is happening at the dam this instant, at this precise intersection of time and space, how much water is being released to fill downstream orders and what lights are flashing and which generators are in full use and which just spinning free.

I used to wonder what it was about the dam that made me think of it at times and in places where I once thought of the Mindanao Trench, or of the stars wheeling in their courses, or of the words *As it was in the beginning, is now and ever shall be, world without end, amen.* Dams, after all, are commonplace: we have all seen one. This particular dam had existed as an idea in the world's mind for almost forty years before I saw it. Hoover Dam, showpiece of the Boulder Canyon project, the several million tons of concrete that made the Southwest plausible, the *fait accompli* that was to convey, in the innocent time of its construction, the notion that mankind's brightest promise lay in American engineering.

Of course the dam derives some of its emotional effect from precisely that aspect, that sense of being a monument to a faith since misplaced. "They died to make the desert bloom," reads a plaque dedicated to the 96 men who died building this first of the great high dams, and in context the worn phrase touches, suggests all of that trust in harnessing resources, in the meliorative power of the dynamo, so central to the early Thirties. Boulder City, built in 1931 as the construction town for the dam, retains the ambience of a model city, a new town, a toy triangular grid of green lawns and trim bungalows, all fanning out from the

9

Reclamation building. The bronze sculptures at the dam itself evoke muscular citizens of a tomorrow that never came, sheaves of wheat clutched heavenward, thunderbolts defied. Winged Victories guard the flagpole. The flag whips in the canyon wind. An empty Pepsi-Cola can clatters across the terrazzo. The place is perfectly frozen in time.

But history does not explain it all, does not entirely suggest what makes that dam so affecting. Nor, even, does energy, the massive involvement with power and pressure and the transparent sexual overtones to that involvement. Once when I revisited the dam I walked through it with a man from the Bureau of Reclamation. For a while we trailed behind a guided tour, and then we went on, went into parts of the dam where visitors do not generally go. Once in a while he would explain something, usually in that recondite language having to do with "peaking power," with "outages" and "dewatering," but on the whole we spent the afternoon in a world so alien, so complete and so beautiful unto itself that it was scarcely necessary to speak at all. We saw almost no one. Cranes moved above us as if under their own volition. Generators roared. Transformers hummed. The gratings on which we stood vibrated. We watched a hundred-ton steel shaft plunging down to that place where the water was. And finally we got down to that place where the water was, where the water sucked out of Lake Mead roared through thirty-foot penstocks and then into thirteen-foot penstocks and finally into the turbines themselves. "Touch it," the Reclamation said, and I did, and for a long time I just stood there with hands on the turbine. It was a peculiar moment, but so explicit as to suggest nothing beyond itself.

There was something beyond all that, something beyond energy, beyond history, something I could not fix in my mind. When I came up from the dam that day the wind was blowing harder, through the canyon and all across the Mojave. Later, toward Henderson and Las Vegas, there would be dust blowing, blowing past the Country-Western Casino FRI & SAT NITES and blowing past the Shrine of Our Lady of Safe Journey STOP & PRAY, but out at the dam there was no dust, only the rock and the dam and a little greasewood and a few garbage cans, their tops chained, banging against a fence. I walked across the marble star map that traces a sidereal revolution of the equinox and fixes forever, the Reclamation man had told me, for all time and for all people who can read the stars, the date the dam was dedicated. The star map was, he had said, for when we were all gone and the dam was left. I had not thought much of it when he said it, but I thought of it then, with the wind whining and the sun dropping behind a mesa with the finality of a sunset in space. Of course that was the image I had seen always, seen it without quite realizing what I saw, a dynamo finally free of man, splendid at last in its absolute isolation, transmitting power and releasing water to a world where no one is.

Joan Didion
1970

Seeing

Annie Dillard

W hen I was six or seven years old, growing up in Pittsburgh, I used to take a precious penny of my own and hide it for someone else to find. It was a curious compulsion; sadly, I've never been seized by it since. For some reason I always "hid" the penny along the same stretch of sidewalk up the street. I would cradle it at the roots of a sycamore, say, or in a hole left by a chipped-off piece of sidewalk. Then I would take a piece of chalk, and, starting at either end of the block, draw huge arrows leading up to the penny from both directions. After I learned to write I labeled the arrows: SURPRISE AHEAD or MONEY THIS WAY. I was greatly excited, during all this arrow-drawing, at the thought of the first lucky passer-by who would receive in this way, regardless of merit, a free gift from the universe. But I never lurked about. I would go straight home and not give the matter another thought, until, some months later, I would be gripped again by the impulse to hide another penny.

It is still the first week in January, and I've got great plans. I've been thinking about seeing. There are lots of things to see, unwrapped gifts and free surprises. The world is fairly studded and strewn with pennies cast broadside from a generous hand. But—and this is the point—who gets excited by a mere penny? If you follow one arrow, if you crouch motionless on a bank to watch a tremulous ripple thrill on the water and are rewarded by the sight of a muskrat kit paddling from its den, will you count that sight a chip of copper only, and go your rueful way? It is dire poverty indeed when a man is so malnourished and fatigued that he won't stoop to pick up a penny. But if you cultivate a healthy poverty and simplicity, so that finding a penny will literally make your day, then, since the world is in fact planted in pennies, you have with your poverty bought a lifetime of days. It is that simple. What you see is what you get.

I used to be able to see flying insects in the air. I'd look ahead and see, not the row of hemlocks across the road, but the air in front of it. My eyes would focus along that column of air, picking out flying insects. But I lost interest, I guess, for I dropped the habit. Now I can see birds. Probably some people can look at the grass at their feet and discover all the crawling

11

creatures. I would like to know grasses and sedges—and care. Then my least journey into the world would be a field trip, a series of happy recognitions. Thoreau, in an expansive mood, exulted, "What a rich book might be made about buds, including, perhaps, sprouts!" It would be nice to think so. I cherish mental images I have of three perfectly happy people. One collects stones. Another—an Englishman, say—watches clouds. The third lives on a coast and collects drops of seawater, which he examines microscopically and mounts. But I don't see what the specialist sees, and so I cut myself off, not only from the total picture, but from the various forms of happiness.

Unfortunately, nature is very much a now-you-see-it, now-you-don't affair. A fish flashes, then dissolves in the water before my eyes like so much salt. Deer apparently ascend bodily into heaven; the brightest oriole fades into leaves. These disappearances stun me into stillness and concentration; they say of nature that it conceals with a grand nonchalance, and they say of vision that it is a deliberate gift, the revelation of a dancer who for my eyes only flings away her seven veils. For nature does reveal as well as conceal: now-you-don't-see-it, now-you-do. For a week last September migrating red-winged blackbirds were feeding heavily down by the creek at the back of the house. One day I went out to investigate the racket; I walked up to a tree, an Osage orange, and a hundred birds flew away. They simply materialized out of the tree. I saw a tree, then a whisk of color, then a tree again. I walked closer and another hundred blackbirds took flight. Not a branch, not a twig budged: the birds were apparently weightless as well as invisible. Or, it was as if the leaves of the Osage orange had been freed from a spell in the form of red-winged blackbirds; they flew from the tree, caught my eye in the sky, and vanished. When I looked again at the tree the leaves had reassembled as if nothing had happened. Finally I walked directly to the trunk of the tree and a final hundred, the real diehards, appeared, spread, and vanished. How could so many hide in the tree without my seeing them? The Osage orange, unruffled, looked just as it had looked from the house, when three hundred red-winged blackbirds cried from its crown. I looked downstream where they flew, and they were gone. Searching, I couldn't spot one. I wandered downstream to force them to play their hand, but they'd crossed the creek and scattered. One show to a customer. These appearances catch at my throat; they are the free gifts, the bright coppers at the roots of trees.

It's all a matter of keeping my eyes open. Nature is like one of those line drawings of a tree that are puzzles for children: Can you find hidden in the leaves a duck, a house, a boy, a bucket, a zebra, and a boot? Specialists can find the most incredibly well-hidden things. A book I read when I was young recommended an easy way to find caterpillars to rear: you simply find some fresh caterpillar droppings, look up, and there's your caterpillar. More recently an author advised me to set my mind at ease about those piles of cut stems on the ground in grassy fields. Field mice make them; they cut the grass down by degrees to reach the seeds at the head. It seems that when the grass is tightly packed, as in a field of ripe grain, the blade won't topple at a single cut through the stem; instead, the cut stem simply drops vertically, held in the crush of grain. The mouse severs the bottom again and again, the stem keeps dropping an inch at a time, and finally the head is low enough for the mouse to reach the seeds. Meanwhile, the mouse is positively littering the field with its little piles of cut stems into which, presumably, the author of the book is constantly stumbling.

If I can't see these minutiae, I still try to keep my eyes open. I'm always on the lookout for antlion traps in sandy soil, monarch pupae near milkweed, skipper larvae in locust leaves. These things are utterly common, and I've not seen one. I bang on hollow trees near water, but so far no flying squirrels have appeared. In flat country I watch every sunset in hopes of seeing the green ray. The green ray is a seldom-seen streak of light that rises from the sun like a spurting fountain at the moment of sunset; it throbs into the sky for two seconds and disappears. One more reason to keep my eyes open. A photography professor at the University of Florida just happened to see a bird die in midflight; it jerked, died, dropped, and smashed on the ground. I squint at the wind because I read Stewart Edward White: "I have always maintained that if you looked closely enough you could *see* the wind—the dim, hardly-made-out, fine debris fleeing high in the air." White was an excellent observer, and devoted an entire chapter of *The Mountains* to the subject of seeing deer: "As soon as you can forget the naturally obvious and construct an artificial obvious, then you too will see deer."

But the artificial obvious is hard to see. My eyes account for less than one percent of the weight of my head; I'm bony and dense; I see what I expect. I once spent a full three minutes looking at a bullfrog that was so unexpectedly large I couldn't see it even though a dozen enthusiastic campers were shouting directions. Finally I asked, "What color am I looking for?" and a fellow said, "Green." When at last I picked out the frog, I saw what painters are up against: the thing wasn't green at all, but the color of wet hickory bark.

The lover can see, and the knowledgeable. I visited an aunt and uncle at a quarter-horse ranch in Cody, Wyoming. I couldn't do much of anything useful, but I could, I thought, draw. So, as we all sat around the kitchen table after supper, I produced a sheet of paper and drew a horse. "That's one lame horse," my aunt volunteered. The rest of the family joined in: "Only place to saddle that one is his neck"; "Looks like we better shoot the poor thing, on account of those terrible growths." Meekly, I slid the pencil and paper down the table. Everyone in that family, including my three young cousins, could draw a horse. Beautifully. When the paper came back it looked as though five shining, real quarter horses had been corralled by mistake with a papier-mâché moose; the real horses seemed to gaze at the monster with a steady, puzzled air. I stay away from horses now, but I can do a creditable goldfish. The point is that I just don't know what the lover knows; I just can't see the artificial obvious that those in the know construct. The herpetologist asks the native, "Are there snakes in that ravine?" "No sir." And the herpetologist comes home with, yes sir, three bags full. Are there butterflies on that mountain? Are the bluets in bloom, are there arrowheads here, or fossil shells in the shale?

Peeping through my keyhole I see within the range of only about thirty percent of the light that comes from the sun; the rest is infrared and some little ultraviolet, perfectly apparent to many animals, but invisible to me. A nightmare network of ganglia, charged and firing without my knowledge, cuts and splices what I do see, editing it for my brain. Donald E. Carr points out that the sense impressions of one-celled animals are *not* edited for the brain: "This is philosophically interesting in a rather mournful way, since it means that only the simplest animals perceive the universe as it is."

A fog that won't burn away drifts and flows across my field of vision. When you see fog move against a backdrop of deep pines, you don't see the fog itself, but streaks of clearness floating across the air in dark shreds. So I see only tatters of clearness through a pervading obscurity. I can't distinguish the fog from the overcast sky; I can't be sure if the light is direct or reflected. Everywhere darkness and the presence of the unseen appalls. We estimate now that only one atom dances alone in every cubic meter of intergalactic space. I blink and squint. What planet or power yanks Halley's Comet out of orbit? We haven't seen that force yet; it's a question of distance, density, and the pallor of reflected light. We rock, cradled in the swaddling band of darkness. Even the simple darkness of night whispers suggestions to the mind. Last summer, in August, I stayed at the creek too late.

Where Tinker Creek flows under the sycamore log bridge to the tear-shaped island, it is slow and shallow, fringed thinly in cattail marsh. At this spot an astonishing bloom of life supports vast breeding populations of insects, fish, reptiles, birds, and mammals. On windless summer evenings I stalk along the creek bank or straddle the sycamore log in absolute stillness, watching for muskrats. The night I stayed too late I was hunched on the log staring spellbound at spreading, reflected stains of lilac on the water. A cloud in the sky suddenly lighted as if turned on by a switch; its reflection just as suddenly materialized on the water upstream, flat and floating, so that I couldn't see the creek bottom, or life in the water under the cloud. Downstream, away from the cloud on the water, water turtles smooth as beans were gliding down with the current in a series of easy, weightless push-offs, as men bound on the moon. I didn't know whether to trace the progress of one turtle I was sure of, risking

14

sticking my face in one of the bridge's spider webs made invisible by the gathering dark, or take a chance on seeing the carp, or scan the mudbank in hope of seeing a muskrat, or follow the last of the swallows who caught at my heart and trailed it after them like streamers as they appeared from directly below, under the log, flying upstream with their tails forked, so fast.

But shadows spread, and deepened, and stayed. After thousands of years we're still strangers to darkness, fearful aliens in an enemy camp with our arms crossed over our chests. I stirred. A land turtle on the bank, startled, hissed the air from its lungs and withdrew into its shell. An uneasy pink here, an unfathomable blue there, gave great suggestion of lurking beings. Things were going on. I couldn't see whether that sere rustle I heard was a distant rattlesnake, slit-eyed, or a nearby sparrow kicking in the dry flood debris slung at the foot of a willow. Tremendous action roiled the water everywhere I looked, big action, inexplicable. A tremor welled up beside a gaping muskrat burrow in the bank and I caught my breath, but no muskrat appeared. The ripples continued to fan upstream with a steady, powerful thrust. Night was knitting over my face an eyeless mask, and I still sat transfixed. A distant airplane, a delta wing out of nightmare, made a gliding shadow on the creek's bottom that looked like a stingray cruising upstream. At once a black fin slit the pink cloud on the water, shearing it in two. The two halves merged together and seemed to dissolve before my eyes. Darkness pooled in the cleft of the creek and rose, as water collects in a well. Untamed, dreaming lights flickered over the sky. I saw hints of hulking underwater shadows, two pale splashes out of the water, and round ripples rolling close together from a blackened center.

At last I stared upstream where only the deepest violet remained of the cloud, a cloud so high its underbelly still glowed feeble color reflected from a hidden sky lighted in turn by a sun halfway to China. And out of that violet, a sudden enormous black body arced over the water. I saw only a cylindrical sleekness. Head and tail, if there was a head and tail, were both submerged in cloud. I saw only one ebony fling, a headlong dive to darkness; then the waters closed, and the lights went out.

I walked home in a shivering daze, up hill and down. Later I lay open-mouthed in bed, my arms flung wide at my sides to steady the whirling darkness. At this latitude I'm spinning 836 miles an hour round the earth's axis; I often fancy I feel my sweeping fall as a breakneck arc like the dive of dolphins, and the hollow rushing of wind raises hair on my neck and the side of my face. In orbit around the sun I'm moving 64,800 miles an hour. The solar system as a whole, like a merry-go-round unhinged, spins, bobs, and blinks at the speed of 43,200 miles an hour along a course set east of Hercules. Someone has piped, and we are dancing a tarantella until the sweat pours. I open my eyes and I see dark, muscled forms curl out of water, with flapping gills and flattened eyes. I close my eyes and I see stars, deep stars giving way to deeper stars, deeper stars bowing to deepest stars at the crown of an infinite cone.

"Still," wrote van Gogh in a letter, "a great deal of light falls on everything." If we are blinded by darkness, we are also blinded by light. When too much light falls on everything, a special terror results. Peter Freuchen describes the notorious kayak sickness to which Greenland Eskimos are prone. "The Greenland fjords are peculiar for the spells of completely quiet weather, when there is not enough wind to blow out a match and the water is like a sheet of glass. The kayak hunter must sit in his boat without stirring a finger so as not to scare the shy seals away. . . . The sun, low in the sky, sends a glare into his eyes, and the landscape around moves into the realm of the unreal. The reflex from the mirror-like water hypnotizes him, he seems to be unable to move, and all of a sudden it is as if he were floating in a bottomless void, sinking, sinking, and sinking. . . . Horror-stricken, he tries to stir, to cry out, but he cannot, he is completely paralyzed, he just falls and falls." Some hunters are especially cursed with this panic, and bring ruin and sometimes starvation to their families.

Sometimes here in Virginia at sunset low clouds on the southern or northern horizon are completely invisible in the lighted sky. I only know one is there because I can see its reflection in still water. The first time I discovered this mystery I looked from cloud to no-cloud in bewilderment, checking my bearings over and over, thinking maybe the ark of the covenant was just passing by south of Dead Man Mountain. Only much later did I read the explanation: polarized light from the sky is very much weakened by reflection, but the light in clouds isn't polarized. So invisible clouds pass among visible clouds, till all slide over the mountains; so a greater light extinguishes a lesser as though it didn't exist.

In the great meteor shower of August, the Perseid, I wail all day for the shooting stars I miss. They're out there showering down, committing harakiri in a flame of fatal attraction, and hissing perhaps at last into the ocean. But at dawn what looks like a blue dome clamps down over me like a lid on a pot. The stars and planets could smash and I'd never know. Only a piece of ashen moon occasionally climbs up or down the inside of the dome, and our local star without surcease explodes on our heads. We have really only that one light, one source for all power, and yet we must turn away from it by universal decree. Nobody here on the planet seems aware of this strange, powerful taboo, that we all walk about carefully averting our faces, this way and that, lest our eyes be blasted forever.

Darkness appalls and light dazzles; the scrap of visible light that doesn't hurt my eyes hurts my brain. What I see sets me swaying. Size and distance and the sudden swelling of meanings confuse me, bowl me over. I straddle the sycamore log bridge over Tinker Creek in the summer. I look at the lighted creek bottom: snail tracks tunnel the mud in quavering curves. A crayfish jerks, but by the time I absorb what has happened, he's gone in a billowing smokescreen of silt. I look at the water: minnows and shiners. If I'm thinking minnows, a carp will fill my brain till I scream. I look at the water's surface: skaters, bubbles, and leaves sliding down. Suddenly, my own face, reflected, startles me witless. Those snails have been tracking my face! Finally, with a shuddering wrench of the will, I see clouds, cirrus clouds. I'm dizzy, I fall in. This looking business is risky.

Once I stood on a humped rock on nearby Purgatory Mountain, watching through binoculars the great autumn hawk migration below, until I discovered that I was in danger of joining the hawks on a vertical migration of my own. I was used to binoculars, but not, apparently, to balancing on humped rocks while looking through them. I staggered. Everything advanced and receded by turns; the world was full of unexplained foreshortenings and depths. A distant huge tan object, a hawk the size of an elephant, turned out to be the browned bough of a nearby loblolly pine. I followed a sharp-shinned hawk against a featureless sky, rotating my head unawares as it flew, and when I lowered the glass a glimpse of my own looming shoulder sent me staggering. What prevents the men on Palomar from falling, voiceless and blinded, from their tiny, vaulted chairs?

I reel in confusion; I don't understand what I see. With the naked eye I can see two million light-years to the Andromeda galaxy. Often I slop some creek water in a jar and when I get home I dump it in a white china bowl. After the silt settles I return and see tracings of minute snails on the bottom, a planarian or two winding round the rim of water, roundworms shimmying frantically, and finally, when my eyes have adjusted to these dimensions, amoebae. At first the amoebae look like muscae volitantes, those curled moving spots you seem to see in your eyes when you stare at a distant wall. Then I see the amoebae as drops of water congealed, bluish, translucent, like chips of sky in the bowl. At length I choose one individual and give myself over to its idea of an evening. I see it dribble a grainy foot before it on its wet, unfathomable way. Do its unedited sense impressions include the fierce focus of my eyes? Shall I take it outside and show it Andromeda, and blow its little endoplasm? I stir the water with a finger, in case it's running out of oxygen. Maybe I should get a tropical aquarium with motorized bubblers and lights, and keep this one for a pet. Yes, it would tell its fissioned descendants, the universe is two feet by five, and if you listen closely you can hear the buzzing music of the spheres.

Oh, it's mysterious lamplit evenings, here in the galaxy, one after the other. It's one of those nights when I wander from window to window looking for a sign. But I can't see. Terror and a beauty insoluble are a ribband of blue woven into the fringes of garments of things both great and small. No culture explains, no bivouac offers real haven or rest. But it could be that we are not seeing something. Galileo thought comets were an optical illusion. This is fertile ground: since we are certain that they're not, we can look at what our scientists have been saying with fresh hope. What if there are *really* gleaming, castellated cities hung upside-down over the desert sand? What limpid lakes and cool date palms have our caravans always passed untried? Until, one by one, by the blindest of leaps, we light on the road to these places, we must stumble in darkness and hunger. I turn from the window. I'm blind as a bat, sensing only from every direction the echo of my own thin cries.

I chanced on a wonderful book by Marius von Senden, called *Space and Sight*. When Western surgeons discovered how to perform safe cataract operations, they ranged across Europe and America operating on dozens of men and women of all ages who had been blinded by cataracts since birth. Von Senden collected accounts of such cases; the histories are fascinating. Many doctors had tested their patients' sense perceptions and ideas of space both before and after the operations. The vast majority of patients, of both sexes and all ages, had, in von Senden's opinion, no idea of space whatsoever. Form, distance, and size were so many meaningless syllables. A patient "had no idea of depth, confusing it with roundness." Before the operation a doctor would give a blind patient a cube and a sphere; the patient would tongue it or feel it with his hands, and name it correctly. After the operation the doctor would show the same objects to the patient without letting him touch them; now he had no clue whatsoever what he was seeing. One patient called lemonade "square" because it pricked on his tongue as a square shape pricked on the touch of his hands. Of another postoperative patient, the doctor writes, "I have found in her no notion of size, for example, not even within the narrow limits which she might have encompassed with the aid of touch. Thus when I asked her to show me how big her mother was, she did not stretch out her hands, but set her two index-fingers a few inches apart." Other doctors reported their patients' own statements to similar effect. "The room he was in . . . he knew to be but part of the house, yet he could not conceive that the whole house could look bigger"; "Those who are blind from birth . . . have no real conception of height or distance. A house that is a mile away is thought of as nearby, but requiring the taking of a lot of steps. . . . The elevator that whizzes him up and down gives no more sense of vertical distance than does the train of horizontal."

For the newly sighted, vision is pure sensation unencumbered by meaning: "The girl went through the experience that we all go through and forget, the moment we are born. She saw, but it did not mean anything but a lot of different kinds of brightness." Again, "I asked the patient what he could see; he answered that he saw an extensive field of light, in which everything appeared dull, confused, and in motion. He could not distinguish objects." Another patient saw "nothing but a confusion of forms and colours." When a newly sighted girl saw photographs and paintings, she asked, " 'Why do they put those dark marks all over them?' 'Those aren't dark marks,' her mother explained, 'those are shadows. That is one of the ways the eye knows that things have shape. If it were not for shadows many things would look flat.' 'Well, that's how things do look,' Joan answered. 'Everything looks flat with dark patches.' "

But it is the patients' concepts of space that are most revealing. One patient, according to his doctor, "practiced his vision in a strange fashion; thus he takes off one of his boots, throws it some way off in front of him, and then attempts to gauge the distance at which it lies; he takes a few steps towards the boot and tries to grasp it; on failing to reach it, he moves on a step or two and gropes for the boot until he finally gets hold of it." "But even at this stage, after three weeks' experience of seeing," von Senden goes on, " 'space,' as he conceives it, ends with visual space, i.e., with colour-patches that happen to bound his view. He does not yet have the notion that a larger object (a chair) can mask a smaller one (a dog), or that the latter can still be present even though it is not directly seen."

In general the newly sighted see the world as a dazzle of color-patches. They are pleased by the sensation of color, and learn quickly to name the colors, but the rest of seeing is tormentingly difficult. Soon after his operation a patient "generally bumps into one of these colour-patches and observes them to be substantial, since they resist him as tactual objects do. In walking about it also strikes him—or can if he pays attention—that he is continually passing in between the colours he sees, that he can go past a visual object, that a part of it then steadily disappears from view; and that in spite of this, however he twists and turns—whether entering the room from the door, for example, or returning back to it—he always has a visual space in front of him. Thus he gradually comes to realize that there is also a space behind him, which he does not see."

The mental effort involved in these reasonings proves overwhelming for many patients. It oppresses them to realize, if they ever do at all, the tremendous size of the world, which they had previously conceived of as something touchingly manageable. It oppresses them to realize that they have been visible to people all along, perhaps unattractively so, without their knowledge or consent. A disheartening number of them refuse to use their new vision, continuing to go over objects with their tongues, and lapsing into apathy and despair. "The child can see, but will not make use of his sight. Only when pressed can he with difficulty be brought to look at objects in his neighbourhood; but more than a foot away it is impossible to bestir him to the necessary effort." Of a twenty-one-year-old girl, the doctor relates, "Her unfortunate father, who had hoped for so much from this operation, wrote that his daughter carefully shuts her eyes whenever she wishes to go about the house, especially when she comes to a staircase, and that she is never happier or more at ease than when, by closing her eyelids, she relapses into her former state of total blindness." A fifteen-year-old boy, who was also in love with a girl at the asylum for the blind, finally blurted out, "No, really, I can't stand it any more; I want to be sent back to the asylum again. If things aren't altered, I'll tear my eyes out."

Some do learn to see, especially the young ones. But it changes their lives. One doctor comments on "the rapid and complete loss of that striking and wonderful serenity which is characteristic only of those who have never yet seen." A blind man who learns to see is ashamed of his old habits. He dresses up, grooms himself, and tries to make a good impression. While he was blind he was indifferent to objects unless they were edible; now, "a sifting of values sets in . . . his thoughts and wishes are mightily stirred and some few of the patients are thereby led into dissimulation, envy, theft and fraud."

On the other hand, many newly sighted people speak well of the world, and teach us how dull is our own vision. To one patient, a human hand, unrecognized, is "something bright and then holes." Shown a bunch of grapes, a boy calls out, "It is dark blue and shiny. . . . It isn't smooth, it has bumps and hollows." A little girl visits a garden. "She is greatly astonished, and can scarcely be persuaded to answer, stands speechless in front of the tree, which she only names on taking hold of it, and then as 'the tree with the lights in it.' " Some delight in their sight and give themselves over to the visual world. Of a patient just after her bandages were removed, her doctor writes, "The first things to attract her attention were her own hands; she looked at them very closely, moved them repeatedly to and fro, bent and stretched the fingers, and seemed greatly astonished at the sight." One girl was eager to tell her blind friend that "men do not really look like trees at all," and astounded to discover that her every visitor had an utterly different face. Finally, a twenty-two-year-old girl was dazzled by the world's brightness and kept her eyes shut for two weeks. When at the end of that time she opened her eyes again, she did not recognize any objects, but, "the more she now directed her gaze upon everything about her, the more it could be seen how an expression of gratification and astonishment overspread her features; she repeatedly exclaimed: 'Oh God! How beautiful!' "

I saw color-patches for weeks after I read this wonderful book. It was summer; the peaches were ripe in the valley orchards. When I woke in the morning, color-patches wrapped round my eyes, intricately, leaving not one unfilled spot. All day long I walked among shifting color-patches that parted before me like the Red Sea and closed again in silence, transfigured, whenever I looked back. Some patches swelled and loomed, while others vanished utterly, and dark marks flitted at random over the whole dazzling sweep. But I couldn't sustain the illusion of flatness. I've been around for too long. Form is condemned to an eternal danse macabre with meaning: I couldn't unpeach the peaches. Nor can I remember ever having seen without understanding; the color-patches of infancy are lost. My brain then must have been smooth as any balloon. I'm told I reached for the moon; many babies do. But the color-patches of infancy swelled as meaning filled them; they arrayed themselves in solemn ranks down distances which unrolled and stretched before me like a plain. The moon rocketed away. I live now in a world of shadows that shape and distance color, a world where space makes a kind of terrible sense. What gnosticism is this, and what physics? The fluttering patch I saw in my nursery window—silver and green and shape-shifting blue—is gone; a row of Lombardy poplars takes its place, mute, across the distant lawn. That humming oblong creature pale as light that stole along the walls of my room at night, stretching exhilaratingly around the corners, is gone, too, gone the night I ate of the bittersweet fruit, put two and two together and puckered forever my brain. Martin Buber tells this tale: "Rabbi Mendel once boasted to his teacher Rabbi Elimelekh that evenings he saw the angel who rolls away the light before the darkness, and mornings the angel who rolls away the darkness before the light. 'Yes,' said Rabbi Elimelekh, 'in my youth I saw that too. Later on you don't see these things any more.'"

Why didn't someone hand those newly sighted people paints and brushes from the start, when they still didn't know what anything was? Then maybe we all could see color-patches too, the world unraveled from reason, Eden before Adam gave names. The scales would drop from my eyes; I'd see trees like men walking; I'd run down the road against all orders, hallooing and leaping.

Seeing is of course very much a matter of verbalization. Unless I call attention to what passes before my eyes, I simply won't see it. It is, as Ruskin says, "not merely unnoticed, but in the full, clear sense of the word, unseen." My eyes alone can't solve analogy tests using figures, the ones which show, with increasing elaborations, a big square, then a small square in a big square, then a big triangle, and expect me to find a small triangle in a big triangle. I have to say the words, describe what I'm seeing. If Tinker Mountain erupted, I'd be likely to notice. But if I want to notice the lesser cataclysms of valley life, I have to maintain in my head a running description of the present. It's not that I'm observant; it's just that I talk too much. Otherwise, especially in a strange place, I'll never know what's happening. Like a blind man at the ball game, I need a radio.

When I see this way I analyze and pry. I hurl over logs and roll away stones; I study the bank a square foot at a time, probing and tilting my head. Some days when a mist covers the mountains, when the muskrats won't show and the microscope's mirror shatters, I want to climb up the blank, blue dome as a man would storm the inside of a circus tent, wildly dangling, and with a steel knife claw a rent in the top, peep, and, if I must, fall.

But there is another kind of seeing that involves a letting go. When I see this way I sway transfixed and emptied. The difference between the ways of seeing is the difference between walking with and without a camera. When I walk with a camera, I walk from shot to shot, reading the light on a calibrated meter. When I walk without a camera, my own shutter opens, and the moment's light prints on my own silver gut. When I see this second way I am above all an unscrupulous observer.

It was sunny one evening last summer at Tinker Creek; the sun was low in the sky, upstream. I was sitting on the sycamore log bridge with the sunset at my back, watching the shiners the size of minnows who were feeding over the muddy sand in skittery schools. Again and again, one fish, then another turned for a split second across the current and flash! the sun shot out from its silver side. I couldn't watch for it. It was always just happening somewhere else, and it drew my vision just as it disappeared: flash, like a sudden dazzle of the thinnest blade, a sparking over a dun and olive ground at chance intervals from every direction. Then I noticed white specks, some sort of pale petals, small, floating from under my feet on the creek's surface, very slow and steady. So I blurred my eyes and gazed towards the brim of my hat and saw a new world. I saw the pale white circles roll up, roll up, like the world's turning, mute and perfect, and I saw the linear flashes, gleaming silver, like stars being born at random down a rolling scroll of time. Something broke and something opened. I filled up like a new wineskin. I breathed an air like light; I saw a light like water. I was the lip of a fountain the creek filled forever; I was ether, the leaf in the zephyr; I was flesh-flake, feather, bone.

When I see this way I see truly. As Thoreau says, I return to my senses. I am the man who watches the baseball game in silence in an empty stadium. I see the game purely; I'm abstracted and dazed. When it's all over and the white-suited players lope off the green field to their shadowed dugouts, I leap to my feet; I cheer and cheer.

But I can't go out and try to see this way. I'll fail, I'll go mad. All I can do is try to gag the commentator, to hush the noise of useless interior babble that keeps me from seeing just as surely as a newspaper dangled before my eyes. The effort is really a discipline requiring a lifetime of dedicated struggle; it marks the literature of saints and monks of every order East and West, under every rule and no rule, discalced and shod. The world's spiritual geniuses seem to discover universally that the mind's muddy river, this ceaseless flow of trivia and trash, cannot be dammed, and that trying to dam it is a waste of effort that might lead to madness. Instead you must allow the muddy river to flow unheeded in the dim channels of consciousness; you raise your sights; you look along it, mildly, acknowledging its presence without interest and gazing beyond it into the realm of the real where subjects and objects act and rest purely, without utterance. "Launch into the deep," says Jacques Ellul, "and you shall see."

The secret of seeing is, then, the pearl of great price. If I thought he could teach me to find it and keep it forever I would stagger barefoot across a hundred deserts after any lunatic at all. But although the pearl may be found, it may not be sought. The literature of illumination reveals this above all: although it comes to those who wait for it, it is always, even to the most practiced and adept, a gift and a total surprise. I return from one walk knowing where the killdeer nests in the field by the creek and the hour the laurel blooms. I return from the same walk a day later scarcely knowing my own name. Litanies hum in my ears; my tongue flaps in my mouth Ailinon, alleluia! I cannot cause light; the most I can do is try to put myself in the path of its beam. It is possible, in deep space, to sail on solar wind. Light, be it particle or wave, has force: you rig a giant sail and go. The secret of seeing is to sail on solar wind. Hone and spread your spirit till you yourself are a sail, whetted, translucent, broadside to the merest puff.

When her doctor took her bandages off and led her into the garden, the girl who was no longer blind saw "the tree with the lights in it." It was for this tree I searched through the peach orchards of summer, in the forests of fall and down winter and spring for years. Then one day I was walking along Tinker Creek thinking of nothing at all and I saw the tree with lights in it. I saw the backyard cedar where the mourning doves roost charged and transfigured, each cell buzzing with flame. I stood on the grass with the lights in it, grass that was wholly fire, utterly focused and utterly dreamed. It was less like seeing than like being for the first time seen, knocked breathless by a powerful glance. The flood of fire abated, but I'm still spending the power. Gradually the lights went out in the cedar, the colors died, the cells unflamed and disappeared. I was still ringing. I had been my whole life a bell, and never knew it until at that moment I was lifted and struck. I have since only very rarely seen the tree with the lights in it. The vision comes and goes, mostly goes, but I live for it, for the moment when the mountains open and a new light roars in spate through the crack, and the mountains slam.

Take the F

Ian Frazier

Brooklyn, New York, has the undefined, hard-to-remember shape of a stain. I never know what to tell people when they ask me where in it I live. It sits at the western tip of Long Island at a diagonal that does not conform neatly to the points of the compass. People in Brooklyn do not describe where they live in terms of north or west or south. They refer instead to their neighborhoods, and to the nearest subway lines. I live on the edge of Park Slope, a neighborhood by the crest of a low ridge that runs through the borough. Prospect Park is across the street. Airplanes in the landing pattern for LaGuardia Airport sometimes fly right over my building; every few minutes, on certain sunny days, perfectly detailed airplane shadows slide down my building and up the building opposite in a blink. You can see my building from the plane—it's on the left-hand side of Prospect Park, the longer patch of green you cross after the expanse of Green-Wood Cemetery.

We moved to a co-op apartment in a four-story building a week before our daughter was born. She is now six. I grew up in the country and would not have expected ever to live in Brooklyn. My daughter is a city kid, with less sympathy for certain other parts of the country. When we visited Montana, she was disappointed by the scarcity of pizza places. I overheard her explaining—she was three or four then—to a Montana kid about Brooklyn. She said, "In Brooklyn, there is a lot of broken glass, so you have to wear shoes. And, there is good pizza." She is stern in her judgment of pizza. At the very low end of the pizza-ranking scale is some pizza she once had in New Hampshire, a category now called New Hampshire pizza. In the middle is some O.K. pizza she once had in the Bronx Zoo, which she calls zoo pizza. At the very top is the pizza at the pizza place where the big kids go, about two blocks from our house.

Our subway is the F train. It runs under our building and shakes the floor. The F is generally a reliable train, but one spring as I walked in the park I saw emergency vehicles gathered by a concrete-sheathed hole in the lawn. Firemen lifted a metal lid from the hole and descended into it. After a while, they reappeared, followed by a few people, then dozens of people, then a whole lot of people—passengers from a disabled F train, climbing one at a time out an exit shaft. On the F, I sometimes see large women in straw hats reading a newspaper

25

called the *Caribbean Sunrise*, and Orthodox Jews bent over Talmudic texts in which the footnotes have footnotes, and groups of teenagers wearing identical red bandannas with identical red plastic baby pacifiers in the corners of their mouths, and female couples in porkpie hats, and young men with the silhouettes of the Manhattan skyline razored into their short side hair from one temple around to the other, and Russian-speaking men with thick wrists and big wristwatches, and a hefty, tall woman with long, straight blond hair who hums and closes her eyes and absently practices cello fingerings on the metal subway pole. As I watched the F-train passengers emerge among the grass and trees of Prospect Park, the faces were as varied as usual, but the expressions of indignant surprise were all about the same.

Just past my stop, Seventh Avenue, Manhattan-bound F trains rise from underground to cross the Gowanus Canal. The train sounds different—lighter, quieter—in the open air. From the elevated tracks, you can see the roots of many houses stretching back up the hill to Park Slope, and a bumper crop of rooftop graffiti, and neon signs for Eagle Clothes and Kentile Floors, and flat expanses of factory roofs where seagulls stand on one leg around puddles in the sagging spots. There are fuel-storage tanks surrounded by earthen barriers, and slag piles, and conveyor belts leading down to the oil-slicked waters of the canal. On certain days, the sludge at the bottom of the canal causes it to bubble. Two men fleeing the police jumped in the canal a while ago; one made it across, the other quickly died. When the subway doors open at the Smith–Ninth Street stop, you can see the bay, and sometimes smell the ocean breeze. This stretch of elevated is the highest point of the New York subway system. To the south you can see the Verrazono-Narrows Bridge, to the north the World Trade towers. For just a few moments, the Statue of Liberty appears between passing buildings. Pieces of a neighborhood—laundry on clotheslines, a standup swimming pool, a plaster saint, a satellite dish, a rectangle of lawn—slide by like quickly dealt cards. Then the train descends again; growing over the wall just before the tunnel is a wisteria bush, which blooms pale blue every May.

I have spent days, weeks on the F train. The trip from Seventh Avenue to midtown Manhattan is long enough so that every ride can produce its own minisociety of riders, its own forty-minute Ship of Fools. Once a woman an arm's length from me on a crowded train pulled a knife on a man who threatened her. I remember the argument and the principals, but mostly I remember the knife—its flat, curved wood-grain handle inlaid with brass fittings on each end, its long, tapered blade. Once a man sang the words of the Lord's Prayer to a mournful, syncopated tune, and he fitted the mood of the morning so exactly that when he asked for money at the end the riders reached for their wallets and purses as if he'd pulled a gun. Once a big white kid with some friends was teasing a small old Hispanic lady, and when he got off the train I looked at him through the window and he slugged it hard next to my face. Once a thin woman and a fat woman sitting side by side had a long and loud conversation about someone they intended to slap silly: "Her butt be in the *hospital!*" "Bring out the ar-*tillery!*" The terminus of the F in Brooklyn is at Coney Island, not far from the beach. At an off hour, I boarded the train and found two or three passengers, and walking around on the floor, a crab. The passengers were looking at the crab. Its legs clicked on the floor like varnished fingernails. It moved in this direction, then that, trying to get comfortable. It backed itself under a seat, against the wall. Then it scooted out just after some new passengers had sat down there, and they really screamed. Passengers at the next stop saw it and laughed. When a boy lifted his foot as if to stomp it, everybody cried, "Noooh!" By the time we reached Jay Street–Borough Hall, there were maybe a dozen of us in the car, all absorbed in watching the crab. The car doors opened and a heavyset woman with good posture entered. She looked at the crab; then, sternly, at all of us. She let a moment pass. The she demanded, "*Whose is that?*" A few stops later, a short man with a mustache took a manila envelope, bent down, scooped the crab into it, closed it, and put in his coat pocket.

The smells in Brooklyn: coffee, fingernail polish, eucalyptus, the breath from laundry rooms, pot roast, Tater Tots. A woman I know who grew up here says she moved away because she could not stand the smell of cooking food in the hallway of her parents' building. I feel just the opposite. I used to live in a converted factory above an Army-Navy store, and I like being in a place that smells like people live there. In the mornings, I sometimes wake to the smell of toast, and I still don't know exactly whose toast it is. And I prefer living in a borough of two and a half million inhabitants, the most of any borough in the city. I think of all the rural places, the pine-timbered canyons and within-commuting-distance farmland, that we are preserving by not living there. I like the immensities of the borough, the unrolling miles of Easter Parkway and Ocean Parkway and Linden Boulevard, and the dishevelled outlying parks strewn with tree limbs and with shards of glass held together by liquor-bottle labels, and the tough bridges—the Williamsburg and the Manhattan—and the gentle Brooklyn Bridge. And I like the way the people talk; some really do have Brooklyn accents, really do say "dese" and "dose." A week or two ago, a group of neighbors stood on a street corner watching a peregrine falcon on a building cornice contentedly eating a pigeon it had caught, and the sunlight came through its tail feathers, and a woman said to a man, "Look at the tail, it's so ah-range," and the man replied, "Yeah, I soar it." Like many Americans, I fear living in a nowhere, in a place that is no-place; in Brooklyn, that doesn't trouble me at all.

Everybody, it seems, is here. At Grand Army Plaza, I have seen traffic tieups caused by Haitians and others rallying in support of President Aristide, and by St. Patrick's Day parades, and by Jews of the Lubavitcher sect celebrating the birthday of their Grand Rebbe with a slow procession of ninety-three motor homes—one for each year of his life. Local taxis have bumper stickers that say

"Allah Is Great"; one of the men who made the bomb that blew up the World Trade Center used an apartment just a few blocks from me. When an election is held in Russia, crowds line up to cast ballots at a Russian polling place in Brighton Beach. A while ago, I volunteer-taught reading at a public elementary school across the park. One of my students, a girl, was part Puerto Rican, part Greek, and part Welsh. Her looks were a lively combination, set off by sea-green eyes. I went to a map store in Manhattan and bought maps of Puerto Rico, Greece, and Wales to read with her, but they didn't interest her. A teacher at the school was directing a group of students to set up chairs for a program in the auditorium, and she said to me, "We have a problem here—each of these kids speaks a different language." She asked the kids to tell me where they were from. One was from Korea, one from Brazil, one from Poland, one from Guyana, one from Taiwan. In the program that followed, a chorus of fourth and fifth graders sang "God Bless America," "You're a Grand Old Flag," and "I'm a Yankee-Doodle Dandy."

People in my neighborhood are mostly white, and middle class or above. People in neighborhoods nearby are mostly not white, and mostly middle class or below. Everybody uses Prospect Park. On summer days, the park teems with sound— the high note is kids screaming in the water sprinklers at the playground, the midrange is radios and tape players, and the bass is idling or speeding cars. People bring lawn furniture and badminton nets and coolers, and then they barbecue. Charcoal smoke drifts into the neighborhood. Last year, local residents upset about the noise and litter and smoke began a campaign to outlaw barbecuing in the park. There was much unfavorable comment about "the barbecuers." Since most of the barbecuers, as it happens, are black or Hispanic, the phrase "Barbecuers Go Home," which someone spray-painted on the asphalt at the Ninth Street entrance to the park, took on a pointed, unkind meaning. But then park officials set up special areas for barbecuing, and the barbecuers complied, and the controversy died down.

Right nearby is a shelter for homeless people. Sometimes people sleep on the benches along the park, sometimes they sleep in the foyer of our building. Once I went downstairs, my heart pounding, to evict a homeless person who I had been told was there. The immediate, unquestioning way she left made me feel bad; later I always said "Hi" to her and gave her a dollar when I ran into her. One night, late, I saw her on the street, and I asked her her last name (by then I already knew her first name) and for a moment she couldn't recall it. At this, she shook her head in mild disbelief.

There's a guy I see on a bench along Prospect Park West all the time. Once I walked by carrying my year-old son, and the man said, "Someday he be carrying you." At the local copy shop one afternoon, a crowd was waiting for copies and faxes when a man in a houndstooth fedora came in seeking signatures for a petition to have the homeless shelter shut down. To my surprise, and his, the people in the copy shop instantly turned on him. "I suppose because they're poor they shouldn't even have a place to sleep at night," a woman said as he backed out the door. On the park wall across the street from my building, someone has written in black marker:

Cops protect citizens
Who protect us from cops.

Sometimes I walk from my building downhill and north, along the Brooklyn waterfront, where cargo ships with scuffed sides and prognathous bows lean overhead. Sometimes I walk by the Brooklyn Navy Yard, its docks now too dormant to attract saboteurs, its long expanses of chain-link fence tangled here and there with the branches of ailanthus trees growing through. Sometimes I head southwest, keeping more or less to the high ground—Bay Ridge—along Fifth Avenue, through Hispanic neighborhoods that stretch in either direction as far as you can see, and then through block after block of Irish. I follow the ridge to its steep descent to the water at the Verrazano Narrows; Fort Hamilton, an Army post dating from 1814, is there, and a small Episcopal church called the Church of the Generals. Robert E. Lee once served as a vestryman of this church, and Stonewall Jackson was baptized here. Today the church is in the shade of a forest of high concrete columns supporting an access ramp to the Verrazano-Narrows Bridge.

Sometimes I walk due south, all the way out Coney Island Avenue. In that direction, as you approach the ocean, the sky gets bigger and brighter, and the buildings seem to flatten beneath it. Dry cleaners advertise "Tallis Cleaned Free with Every Purchase Over Fifteen Dollars." Then you start to see occasional lines of graffiti written in Cyrillic. Just past a Cropsey Avenue billboard welcoming visitors to Coney Island is a bridge over a creek filled nearly to the surface with metal shopping carts that people have tossed there over the years. A little farther on, the streets open onto the beach. On a winter afternoon, bundled-up women sit on the boardwalk on folding chairs around a portable record player outside a restaurant called Gastronom Moscow. The acres of trash-dotted sand are almost empty. A bottle of Peter the Great vodka lies on its side, drops of water from its mouth making a small depression in the sand. A man with trousers rolled up to his shins moves along the beach, chopping at driftwood with an axe. Another passerby says, "He's vorking hard, that guy!" The sunset unrolls light along the storefronts like tape. From the far distance, little holes in the sand at the water's edge mark the approach of a short man wearing hip boots and earphones and carrying a long-handled metal detector. Treasure hunters dream of the jewelry that people must have lost here over the years. Some say that this is the richest treasure beach in the Northeast. The man stops, runs the metal detector again over a spot, digs with a clamming shovel, lifts some sand, brushes through it with a gloved thumb, discards it. He goes on, leaving a trail of holes behind him.

I like to find things myself, and I always try to keep one eye on the ground as I walk. So far I have found seven dollars (a five and two ones), an earring in the shape of a strawberry, several personal notes, a matchbook with a 900 number to call to hear "prison sex fantasies," and two spent .25-calibre shells. Once on Carroll Street, I saw a page of text on the sidewalk, and I bent over to read it. It was page 91 from a copy of "Anna Karenina." I read the whole page. It described Vronsky leaving a gathering and riding off in a carriage. In a great book, the least fragment is great. I looked up and saw a woman regarding me closely from a few feet away. "You're reading," she said wonderingly. "From a distance, I t'ought you were watchin' ants."

My favorite place to walk is the Brooklyn Botanic Garden, not more than fifteen minutes away. It's the first place I take out-of-towners, who may not associate Brooklyn with flowers. In the winter, the garden is drab as pocket lint, and you can practically see all the way through from Flatbush Avenue to Washington Avenue. But then in February or March a few flowerings begin, the snowdrops and the crocuses, and then the yellow of the daffodils climbs Daffodil Hill, and then the magnolias—star magnolias, umbrella magnolias, saucer magnolias—go off all at once, and walking among them is like flying through cumulus clouds. Then the cherry trees blossom, some a soft and glossy red like makeup, others pink as a dessert, and crowds fill the paths on the weekends and stand in front of the blossoms in their best clothes and have their pictures taken. Security guards tell people, "No eating, no sitting on the grass—this is a garden, not a park." There are traffic jams of strollers, and kids running loose. One security guard jokes into his radio, "There's a pterodactyl on the overlook!" In the pond in the Japanese Garden, ducks lobby for pieces of bread. A duck quacks, in Brooklynese, "Yeah, yeah, yeah," having heard it all before.

Then the cherry blossoms fall, they turn some paths completely pink next to the grass's green, and the petals dry, and people tread them into a fine pink powder. Kids visit on end-of-school-year field trips, and teachers yell "Shawon, get back on line!" and boys with long T-shirts printed from neck to knee with an image of Martin Luther King's face run by laughing and swatting at one another. The yellow boxes that photographic film comes in fall on the ground, and here and there an empty bag of Crazy Calypso potato chips. The lilacs bloom, each bush with a scent slightly different from the next, and yellow tulips fill big round planters with color so bright it ascends in a column, like a searchlight beam. The roses open on the trellises in the Rose Garden and attract a lively air traffic of bees, and June wedding parties, brides and grooms and their subsidiaries, adjust themselves minutely for photographers there. A rose called the Royal Gold smells like a new bathing suit, and is as yellow.

In our building of nine apartments, two people have died and six have been born since we moved in. I like our neighbors—a guy who works for Off-Track Betting, a guy who works for the Department of Correction, a woman who works for Dean Witter, an in-flight steward, a salesperson of subsidiary rights at a publishing house, a restaurant manager, two lawyers, a retired machinist, a Lebanese-born woman of ninety-five—as well as any I've ever had. We keep track of the bigger events in the building with the help of Chris, our downstairs neighbor. Chris lives on the ground floor and often has conversations in the hall while her foot props her door open. When our kids are sick, she brings them her kids' videos to watch, and when it rains she gives us rides to school. One year, Chris became pregnant and had to take a blood-thinning medicine and was in and out of the hospital. Finally, she had a healthy baby and came home, but then began to bleed and didn't stop. Her husband brought the baby to us about midnight and took Chris to the nearest emergency room. Early the next morning, the grandmother came and took the baby. Then for two days nobody heard anything. When we knocked on Chris's door we got no answer and when we called we got an answering machine. The whole building was expectant, spooky, quiet. The next morning I left the house and there in the foyer was Chris. She held her husband's arm, and she looked pale, but she was returning from the hospital under her own steam. I hugged her at the door, and it was the whole building hugging her. I walked to the garden seeing glory everywhere. I went to the Rose Garden and took a big Betsy McCall rose to my face and breathed into it as if it were an oxygen mask.

The Art of Science

Alan Lightman

I vividly remember the occasion, years ago, when I took my two-year-old daughter to the ocean the first time. It was a mild, hazy day in June. We parked our car a half-mile from the water and walked the rest of the way. A speckled pink crab shell lying on the sand caught her attention. Then, a few hundred yards farther on, we heard the long roll of the waves. And I could tell that my daughter was curious about what made that sound she had never heard before.

Holding her up with one arm, I pointed to the sea. Her eyes followed along my arm, across the sand and then out to the vast, blue-green of the sea. For a moment she hesitated. I wasn't sure whether she would be puzzled or frightened by that first sight of infinity. Then she broke out into a radiant smile and giggled with pleasure. It was as if she already understood something about the sea, as if the sea were both unexpected and expected at the same time. I knew how she felt. This seemingly contradictory combination of qualities is exactly what I have experienced in my most creative moments: a stunning surprise joined with a feeling of rightness and inevitability.

It has been my good fortune to have worked both as a physicist and as a novelist. And I have found that the "creative moment" feels the same in both professions. Indeed this particular sensation, one of the deepest and most beautiful of human experiences, provides the basis for a powerful understanding between the scientist and the artist—an understanding that Charles Percy Snow (also a physicist and a novelist) overlooked in his grim differentiation between "the two cultures."

Creativity, of course, eludes easy grasp. Like a timid forest animal, it quickly darts behind a tree when you stare at it. How does one articulate that sense of the expected and unexpected at once? Where does it come from? How does one prepare for discovery? Most difficult of all to describe is the creative moment, that luscious instant when an idea, or an insight, or an unorthodox understanding, suddenly gels. I say "instant," but whenever I experience the creative moment, in science or in art, I lose all sense of time. I also lose all sense of my body, my ego, my surroundings. I forget who I am and where I am. I dissolve into the imagined world. I become pure spirit. Perhaps it is part of the essence of this delicate

33

and mysterious experience that it cannot be understood. Certainly, the sensations cannot be trapped and defined while in motion.

Despite these difficulties, writers, musicians, actors and other artists often attempt to describe their creative process. Scientists, however, rarely do. In a paper written for *Nature* in 1920 but never published, Einstein mentions the "happiest thought of my life," when he suddenly realised that the force of gravity disappears for a person falling freely through space. That simple but profound insight became the foundation of his general theory of relativity.

Max von Laue, in his Nobel Prize Lecture of 1915, briefly describes a meeting with another scientist one evening in February 1912 when they discussed the behaviour of long-wavelength electromagnetic waves in crystals. During that conversation, von Laue was "suddenly struck" by the image of short-wavelength waves traversing an atomic lattice, producing telltale interference patterns. And so was created the new field of X-ray diffraction. In *The Double Helix*, exceptional for its detailed and personal story of discovery, Jim Watson writes that "my mouth fell open and my pulse began to race" the instant he saw Rosalind Franklin's new X-ray diffraction picture of DNA, realising that the patterns could arise only from a double-helical structure.

But accounts like these are few. Such comments by scientists often amount to only a sentence or two, and they hardly ever describe the emotional and psychological sensations of creating.

My own first experience with the creative moment in science occurred when I was a graduate student in physics in the early 1970s. After waffling around with course work for a year, I had finally settled into some genuine research. My first couple of research problems were tidy and brief. Then I fastened onto a more open-ended investigation, something that held the distinct possibility of leading me off a cliff. My project, inconsequential in the grand sweep of science, was to prove or disprove the conjecture that known experiments required all theories of gravity to be geometrical in form.

After the initial period of study and work, I had succeeded in writing down all the equations I thought relevant. Then I hit a wall. I knew something was amiss, because a simple result at an early stage of the calculation was not coming out right. But I could not find my error. And I didn't even know what kind of error it was. Perhaps one of the equations was wrong. Or maybe the equations were right and I was making a silly arithmetic mistake. Or perhaps the conjecture was false, but would require an especially devious counter-example to disprove it. Or maybe I had misconceived the investigation from the beginning. Day after day I checked each equation, paced back and forth in my little, windowless office, but I didn't know what I was doing wrong—what I had missed. This confusion and failure went on for months. I began keeping cans of tuna in my desk drawer and eating my meals in the office.

34

Author first experience of creative moment X

Then one morning, I remember that it was a Sunday, I woke at about five o'clock and couldn't get back to sleep. I felt terribly excited. Something strange was happening in my mind. I was thinking about my research problem, and I was seeing deeply into it. I was seeing it in ways I never had before. I felt that my head was lifting off my shoulders. I felt weightless. And I had absolutely no sense of self. It was an experience completely without ego, without any thought about consequences or approval or fame.

definition of ego XI

The ego, so important to our sense of consciousness and identity, is in some ways a kind of friction, a drag, and it magically slips away when we're creating. For me, the best analogy is what sometimes happens when I'm sailing a round-bottomed boat in strong wind. Normally the hull stays down in the water and the drag greatly limits the speed of the boat. But in high wind, every once in a while the hull lifts out of the water and the drag disappears. It feels like a great hand has suddenly grabbed hold and flung me across the surface like a skimming stone. It's called planing.

XII

So I woke up at five in the morning to find myself planing. Although I had no sense of my ego, I did have a feeling of rightness. I had a strong sensation of seeing deeply into this problem and understanding it and knowing that I was right—a certain kind of inevitability. With these sensations surging through me, I tiptoed out of my bedroom, almost reverently, afraid to disturb whatever strange magic was going on in my head, and went to the kitchen. There I sat down at my ramshackle, faux-wood kitchen table. I got out the pages of my calculations, by now curling and stained. A tiny bit of daylight was starting to seep through the window.

XIII

I was oblivious to myself, my body and everything around me, though I was completely alone. I don't think any other person in the world would have been able to help me at that moment, and I didn't want any help. I had all these sensations and revelations in my head, and being alone with all that was an essential part of it. *of the creative moment*

XIV

I sat down at the table and began working. Somehow I had reconceptualised the project. I immediately spotted the error in my thinking and began anew. I'm not sure how this rethinking happened, but it didn't occur by going from one equation to the next. After a while at the kitchen table, I solved my research problem. I had proved that the conjecture was true. Feeling stunned and powerful, I strode out of the room. Suddenly I heard a noise and looked up at the clock on the wall and saw that it was two o'clock in the afternoon.

creative moment as novelist XV

The experience I've just described is quite similar to the creative moments I've had as a novelist. I write in two places. One is an island in Maine. From my writing desk, I can see spruce trees and cedars and a pine needle path that goes down a hill from my house to the ocean. The other place I write is a small storage room, without windows, attached to the garage of my house in Massachusetts.

There, my view is a rough plaster wall. Both places have served me equally well in my writing, because after twenty minutes I disappear into the imaginary world I am creating.

I had an extraordinary moment with my last novel, *The Diagnosis*. I was stuck on a character called Melissa, the wife of my protagonist. Just as I had been stuck on my equations in the physics problem. Being desperately stuck is apparently one of the best goads to creativity. After several drafts of the novel, the character was still wrong. In one draft, she was too mechanical and hard, in another she was a stereotypic alcoholic, in another her affection for her husband seemed false. When she spoke, her words didn't sound real. I could never hear her speaking with her own voice. She always spoke with my voice, or said what I wanted her to say, or what I thought she should be saying. She wasn't alive, even though I had been trying to breathe life into her for more than two years. Then one day, when I was discussing her with a friend, I suddenly felt myself inside of her. Unconsciously, I stopped talking because the universe had lifted. I was no longer myself. I was her. And I was suffering. I began to cry. I sat there numb, for how long I don't know. After that moment I was able to write her.

Similar accounts of the creative process have appeared in dozens of interviews with writers in *The Paris Review* over the past two or three decades. In Janet Sonenberg's book *The Actor Speaks* (Crown Trade Paperbacks, 1996), two dozen leading actors describe their acting techniques. From John Turturro: "Once the scene's dynamic is starting to occur, I'll go with it and then try to shift it, too, just like you would in life. The shifting is important. Then, if I can get to the point when that's happening and I don't know what I'm doing, that's inspiration. I've done all my work and then I try to achieve this other, living dimension, the human dimension. It ceases being my work and it becomes living."

The research and hard work. The prepared mind. The being stuck. The sudden shift. The letting go of control. The letting go of self. The pattern seems almost universal.

I am not sure why scientists have been more reluctant than artists to write about their creative moments. But I believe that a major factor must be the understanding of objectivity in science. What is most important in science is the final, dispassionate, impersonal result: the law of nature that would be known by smart Martians, or the experience that can be duplicated in any laboratory in the world. Max Delbruck, in his Nobel Prize Lecture of 1969, put it well: "A scientist's message is not devoid of universality, but its universality is disembodied and anonymous. While the artist's communication is linked forever with its original form, that of the scientist is modified, amplified, fused with the ideas and results of others and melts into the stream of knowledge and ideas which forms our culture."

Somehow, this understanding of science, which I share in most ways, has spawned the more dubious notion that any sign of personal struggle or emotionality in the individual scientist will compromise the whole enterprise. Thus, scientists are trained to write in the passive voice, humour in journal articles is usually frowned upon, and until recent years there has been a substantial stigma against scientists "popularising" their work for the public. (In the 19th century, Carl Friedrich Gauss—one of the greatest mathematicians of all time—took pains to destroy all written traces of his heuristic methods and winding paths, so that his theorems and proofs appear to have been born fully formed and perfect, like Athena from the head of Zeus.) All these admonitions, in subtle and not subtle ways, reflect the deep-seated idea that the scientist must wear sterile gloves at all times.

By now it is well known that this notion is false. It is certainly true that scientists, with the exception of behavioural scientists, study objects that reside outside the emotions while for artists the emotional life lies at the centre. But the process of doing science is human. Individual scientists have all the passions, the prejudices and biases, the psychological hills and valleys of other creative people. Indeed, as chemist Michael Polanyi so forcefully describes in his book *Personal Knowledge* (University of Chicago Press, 1974), these personal passions are probably essential for the success of science. The objectivity and method of science come not so much from the individual scientist as from the community of scientists, who are always eager to criticise and test each other's work.

Acknowledging the passions and struggles and creative moments of individual scientists will not diminish the discipline at all. Instead, it will help strengthen the understanding between scientists and others.

Spring

Gretel Ehrlich

W e have a nine-acre lake on our ranch and a warm spring that feeds it all winter. By mid-March the lake ice begins to melt where the spring feeds in, and every year the same pair of mallards come ahead of the others and wait. Though there is very little open water, they seem content. They glide back and forth through a thin estuary, brushing watercress with their elegant, folded wings, then tip end-up to eat and, after, clamber onto the lip of ice that retreats, hardens forward, and retreats again.

Mornings, a transparent pane of ice lies over the meltwater. I peer through and see some kind of waterbug—perhaps a leech—paddling like a sea turtle between green ladders of lakeweed. Cattails and sweet grass from the previous summer are bone dry, marked with black mold spots, and bend like elbows into the ice. They are swords that cut away the hard tenancy of winter. At the wide end, a mat of dead water plants has rolled back into a thick, impregnable breakwater. Near it, bubbles trapped under the ice are lenses focused straight up to catch the coming season.

It's spring again, and I wasn't finished with winter. That's what I said at the end of summer too. I stood on the ten-foot-high haystack and yelled, "No!" as the first snow fell. We had been up since four in the morning, picking the last bales of hay from the oat field by hand, slipping under the weight of them in the mud, and by the time we finished the stack, six inches of snow had fallen.

It's spring, but I was still cataloguing the different kinds of snow: snow that falls dry but is rained on; snow that melts down into hard crusts; wind-driven snow that looks blue; powder snow on hard pack on powder—a Linzer torte of snow. I look up. The troposphere is the five-mile-wide sleeve of air out of which all our weather shakes. A bank of clouds drives in from the south. Where in it, I wonder, does a snowflake take on its thumbprint uniqueness? Inside the cloud, where schools of flakes like schools of fish are flung this way and that? What gives the snowflake its needle, plate, column, branching shapes—the battering wind or the dust particles around which water vapor clings?

Near town the river ice breaks up and lies stacked in industrial-sized hunks on the banks—big as railway cars—and is flecked black by wheeling hurricanes of plowed topsoil. That's how I feel when winter breaks up inside me: heavy, upended, inert against the flow of a new season. I had thought about ice during the cold months too. How it is movement betrayed, water seized in the moment of falling. In November, ice thickened over the lake like a cataract and from the air looked like a Cyclops: one bad eye. Under its milky spans over irrigation ditches, the sound of water running south was muffled. One solitary spire of ice hung noiselessly against dark rock at the falls, as if mocking or mirroring the broomtail comet on the horizon. Then, in February, I tried for words not about ice but words hacked from it—the ice at the end of the mind, so to speak—and failed.

Those were winter things, and now it is spring, though one name can't describe what, in Wyoming, is a three-part affair: false spring, the vernal equinox, and the spring in June, when flowers come and the grass grows.

Spring means restlessness. The physicist I've been talking to all winter says if I look more widely, deeply, and microscopically all at once, I might see how springlike the whole cosmos is. What I see as order and stillness, the robust, time-bound determinacy of my life, is really a mirage suspended above chaos. "There's a lot of random jiggling going on everywhere," he tells me. Winter's tight sky hovers. Under it, hayfields are green, then white, then green growing under white. The confinement I've felt since November resembles the confinement of subatomic particles, I'm told. A natural velocity finally shows itself. Particles move and become waves.

Sap rises in trees and in me, and the hard knot of perseverance I cultivated to meet winter dissipates; I walk away from the obsidian of bitter nights. Now snow comes wet and heavy, but the air it traverses feels light. I sleep less and dream not of human entanglements but of animals I've never seen: a caterpillar fat as a man's thumb, made of linked silver tubes, has two heads—one human, one a butterfly's.

Last spring at this time I was coming out of a bout with pneumonia. I went to bed on January 1 and didn't get up until the end of February. Winter was a cocoon in which my gagging, basso cough shook the dark figures at the end of my bed. Had I read too much Hemingway? Or was I dying? I'd lie on my stomach and look out. Nothing close-up interested me. All engagements of mind—the circumlocutions of love interests and internal gossip—appeared false. Only my body was true. And my body was trying to close down, go out the window without me.

I saw things out there. Our ranch faces south down a long treeless valley whose vanishing point is two gray hills folded one in front of the other like two hands, beyond which is space, cerulean air, pleated clouds, and red mesas standing up like breaching whales in a valley three thousand feet below. Afternoons, our young horses played, rearing up on back legs and pawing oh so carefully at each other, reaching around, ears flat back, nipping manes and withers. One of those times their falsetto squeals looped across the pasture and hung, but when I tried to intone their sounds of delight, I found my lungs had no air.

It was thirty-five below zero that night. Our plumbing froze and because I was very weak my husband had to bundle me up and help me to the outhouse. Nothing close at hand seemed to register with me: neither the cold nor the semicoziness of an uninsulated house. But the stars were lurid. For a while I thought I saw dead horses, eating one another's manes and tails, spinning above my head in the icefall.

Scientists talk animatedly about how insignificant we humans are when placed against the time scale of geology and the cosmos. I had heard it a hundred times but never felt it truly. Back in bed, I felt the black room was a screen through which parts of my body traveled, leaving the rest behind. I thought I was a sun flying over a barge whose iron holds soaked me up until I became rust, floating on a bright river. A ferocious loneliness took hold of me. That night a luscious, creamy fog rolled in like a roll of fat hugging me, but it was snow.

Recuperation is like spring: dormancy and vitality collide. In any year I'm like a bear, a partial hibernator. During January thaws I stick my nose out and peruse the frozen desolation as if reading a book whose language I don't know. In March I'm ramshackle, weak in the knees, giddy, dazzled by broken-backed clouds, the passing of Halley's comet, the on-and-off strobe of sun. Like a sheepherder, I x out each calendar day as if time were a forest through which I could clear-cut a way to the future. The physicist straightens me out on this point too. The notion of "time passing," like a train through a landscape, is an illusion, he says. I hold the Big Ben clock taken from a dead sheepherder's wagon. The clock measures intervals of time, not the speed of time, and the calendar is a scaffolding we hang as if time were rushing water we could harness. Time-bound, I hinge myself to a linear bias—cause and effect all laid out in a neat row.

Julius Caesar had a sense of humor about time. The Roman calendar with its kalends, nones, and ides—counting days—changed according to who was in power. Caesar serendipitously added days, changed the names of certain months, and when he was through, the calendar was so skewed, January fell in autumn.

Einsteinian time is too big for even Julius Caesar to have touched. It stretches and shrinks and dilates. Indecipherable from space, time is not one thing but an infinity of space-times, overlapping and interfering. There is no future that is not now, no past that is not now. Time includes every moment.

It's the Ides of March today.

I've walked to a hill a mile from the house. It's not really a hill but a mountain slope that heaves up, turns sideways, and comes straight down to a foot-wide creek. Everything I can see from here used to be a flatland covered with shallow water. "Used to be" means several hundred million years ago, and the land itself was not really "here" at all but part of a continent floating near Bermuda. On top is a fin of rock, a marine deposition from Jurassic times created by small waves moving in and out from the shore.

I've come here for peace and quiet and to see what's going on in this secluded valley away from ranch work and sorting corrals, but what I get is a slap on the ass by a prehistoric wave, gains and losses in altitude and aridity, outcrops of mud composed of rotting volcanic ash which fell continuously for ten thousand years, a hundred million years ago. The soils are a geologic flag—red, white, green, and gray. On one side of the hill, mountain mahogany gives off a scent like orange blossoms; on the other, colonies of sagebrush root wide in ground the color of Spanish roof tiles. And it still looks like the ocean to me. "How much truth can a man stand, sitting by the ocean, all that perpetual motion . . . ," Mose Allison, the jazz singer, sings.

The wind picks up and blusters. Its fat underbelly scrapes uneven ground, twisting toward me like taffy, slips up over the mountain and showers out across the Great Plains. The sea smell it carried all the way from Seattle has long since been absorbed by pink gruss—the rotting granite that spills down the slopes of the Rockies. Somewhere over the Midwest the wind slows, tangling in the hair of hardwood forests, and finally drops into the corridors of cities, past Manhattan's World Trade Center, ripping free again as it skims the Atlantic's green swell.

Spring jitterbugs inside me. Spring *is* wind, symphonic and billowing. A dark cloud pops like a blood blister, spraying red hail down. The sky widens, breaking itself. Wind concusses. It is a cloth that sails so birds have something to fly on.

A message reports to my brain, but I can't believe my eyes. The sheet of wind had a hole in it: an eagle just fell out of the sky as if down the chute of a troubled airplane. Landed, falling. Is there a leg broken? The sides of this narrow valley, a seashore 170,000 years ago, now lift like a medic's litter to catch up this bird.

Hopping, she flaps seven feet of wing and sways near a dead fawn whose carcass had recently been feasted upon. When I approached, all I could see of the animal was a rib cage rubbed red with fine tissue and the decapitated head laying peacefully against sagebrush, eyes closed.

Friends who have investigated eagles' nests have literally feared for their lives. An eagle's talons are a powerful jaw. Their grip is so strong the talons can slice through flesh to bone in one motion.

I had come close to seeing what was wrong, to seeing what I could do. An eagle with a bum leg will starve to death, but when I approached again she lifted her wings threateningly and, craning her neck, first to one side, then to the other, she stared hard, giving me "the eagle eye." Best to leave her alone. My husband dragged a road-killed deer up the mountain slope so she could eat, and I brought a bucket of water.

A golden eagle is not golden but black with yellow spots on the neck and wings. Looking at her, I had wondered how feathers—the rachis, vane, and quill—came to be.

Birds are glorified flying lizards. Positioned together, feathers are like hundreds of smaller wings, evolved from reptilian scales. Ancestral birds had thirteen pairs of cone-shaped teeth that grew in separate sockets like a snake's, rounded ribs, and bony tails. Archaeopteryx was half bird, half dinosaur, and glided instead of flying; ichthyornis was a fish-bird, a relative of the pelican; diatryma was a seven-foot-tall giant with a huge beak and with wings so absurdly small they must have been useless, though later the wing bone sprouted from them. *Aquila chrysaëtos*, the modern golden eagle, has seven thousand contour feathers, no teeth, and weighs about one pound. I think about the eagle on the hill. How big she was, how each time she spread her wings it was like a thought stretching between two seasons.

Back at the house, I relax with a beer. At 5:03 the vernal equinox occurs. I go outside and stand in the middle of a hayfield with my eyes closed. The universe is restless, but I want to feel celestial equipoise: twelve hours of daylight, twelve of dark, and the earth ramrod straight on its axis. Straightening my posture to resist the magnetic tilt back into dormancy, spiritual and emotional reticence, I imagine the equatorial sash, now nose-to-nose with the sun, sizzling like a piece of bacon, and the earth slowly tilting.

In the morning I walk to the valley. The eagle isn't there. The hindquarters of the road-killed deer have been eaten. Coyote tracks circle the carcass. Did they have eagle for dinner too?

Afternoon. I return. Far up on the opposite hill I see her, flapping and hopping to the top. When I stop, she stops and turns her head. Even at two hundred yards, I can feel the heat of her stare.

Later, looking through my binoculars, I try to see the world with eagle eyes. After glassing the crescent moon, I dream it has grown full and doubled. One moon is pink and spins fast; the other is an eagle's head, turning slowly in the opposite direction. Then both moons descend, and it is day.

At first light I clamber up the hill. Now the dead deer my husband brought is only a hoop of ribs, two forelegs, and hair. The eagle is not here or along the creek or on either hill. I climb the slope and sit. After a long wait she careens out from the narrow slit of the red-walled canyon whose creek drains into this valley. Surely it's the same bird. Flying by, she cocks her head and looks at me. I smile. What is a smile to her? Now she is not flying but lifting above the planet, far from me.

Late March. The emerald of the hayfields brightens. A flock of gray-capped rosy finches who overwintered here swarms a leafless apple tree, then falls from the smooth boughs like cut grass. The tree was planted by the Texan who homesteaded this ranch. As I walk past, one of the boughs, shaped like an undulating dragon, splits off from the trunk and drops.

Space is an arena where the rowdy particles that are the building blocks of life perform their antics. All spring, things fall; the general law of increasing disorder is on the rise. What is it to be a cause without an effect, an effect without a cause, to abandon time-bound thinking, the use of tenses, the temporally related emotions of impatience, expectation, hope, and fear? But I can't. At the edge of the lake I watch ducks. Like them, my thinking rises and falls on the same water.

Another day. Feeling small-minded, I take a plane ride over Wyoming. As we take off, the plane resists accepting air under its wings. Is this how an eagle feels? Ernst Mach's principle tells me that an object's resistance against being accelerated is not the intrinsic property of matter but a measure of its interaction with the universe; that matter has inertia only because it exists in relation to other matter.

Airborne, we fly southeast from Heart Mountain across the Big Horn River, over the long red wall where Butch Cassidy trailed stolen horses, across the high plains to Laramie. Coming home, we hit clouds. Turbulence, like many forms of trouble, cannot always be seen. We bounce so hard my arms sail helplessly above my head. In evolution, wing bones became arms and hands; perhaps I'm de-evolving.

From ten thousand feet I can see that spring is only half here: the southern part of the state, being higher in altitude, is white; the northern half is green. Time is one of spring's greening forms, a clock whose hands are blades of grass moving vertically, up through the fringe of numbers, spreading across the middle of the face, sinking again as the sun moves from one horizon to the other. Time doesn't go anywhere; the shadow of the plane, my shadow, moves across it.

To sit on a plane is to sit on the edge of sleep, where the mind's forge brightens into incongruities. Down there I see disparate wholenesses strung together and the string dissolving. Mountains run like rivers; I fly through waves and waves of chiaroscuro light. The land looks bare but is articulate. The body of the plane is my body, pressing into spring, pressing matter into relation with matter. Is it even necessary to say the obvious? That spring brings on surges of desire? From this disinterested height I say out loud what Saint Augustine wrote: "My love is my weight. Because of it I move."

Directly below us now is the fine old Wyoming ranch where Joel, Mart, Dave, Hughy, and I have moved thousands of head of cattle. Joel's father, Smokey, was one of two brothers who put the outfit together. They worked hard, lived frugally, and even after his brother died, Smokey did not marry until his late fifties. As testimony to a long bachelorhood, there is no kitchen in the main house. The cookhouse stands separate from all the other buildings. In back is a bedroom and bath, which has housed a list of itinerant cooks ten pages long.

Over the years I've helped during roundup and branding. We'd rise at four. Smokey, then in his eighties, cooked flapjacks and boiled coffee on the wood cookstove. There was a long table. Joel and Smokey always sat at one end. They were look-alikes, both skin-and-bones tall, with tipped-up dark eyes set in narrow faces. Stern and vigilant, Smokey once threw a young hired hand out of the cookhouse because he hadn't grained his saddle horse after a long day's ride. "On this outfit we take care of our animals first," he said. "Then, if there's time, we eat."

Even in his early twenties, Joel had his father's dignity and razor-sharp wit. They both wore white Stetsons, identically shaped. Only their hands were different: Joel had eight fingers and one thumb—the other he lost while roping.

Ten summers ago my parents and I visited their ranch. We drank home-made whiskey left over from Prohibition days, ate steaks cut from an Angus bull, four kinds of vegetables, watermelon, ice cream and pie. Despite a thirteen-year difference in our ages, Smokey wanted Joel to marry me. As we rose from the meal, he shook my father's hand. "I guess you'll be my son's father-in-law," he said. That was news to all of us. Joel's face turned crimson. My father threw me an astonished look, cleared his throat, and thanked his host for the fine meal.

One night Joel *did* come to my house and asked if I would take him into my bed. It was a gentlemanly proposition—doffed hat, moist eyes, a smile grimacing with loneliness.

"You're an older woman. Think of all you could teach me," he said jauntily but with a blush. He stood ramrod straight, waiting for an answer. My silence turned him away like a rolling wave, and he drove to the home ranch, spread out across the Emblem Bench, thirty-five miles away.

The night Joel died, I was staying at a friend's farm in Missouri. I had fallen asleep early, then awakened suddenly, feeling claustrophobic. I jumped out of bed and stood in the dark. I wanted to get out of there, drive home to Wyoming, and I didn't know why. Finally, at seven in the morning, able to sleep, I dreamed about a bird landing on, then lifting out of a tree along a riverbank. That was the night Joel's pickup rolled. He wasn't found until daylight and died on the way to the hospital.

Now I'm sitting on a fin of Gypsum Springs rock, looking west. The sun is setting. What I see are three gray cloud towers letting rain down at the horizon. The sky behind these massifs is gilded gold, and long fingers of land— benches where Charolais cattle graze—are pink. Somewhere over Joel's grave, the sky is bright. The road where he died shines like a dash in a Paul Klee painting. But here it is still winter: snow, dry as Styrofoam when squeezed together, tumbles into my lap. I think about flying and falling. The place in the sky where the eagle fell is dark. Why does a wounded eagle get well and fly away? Why do the head wounds of a young man cut him down? Useless questions.

Sex and death are the riddles thrown into the hopper, thrown down on the planet like red and black hailstones. Where one hits the earth, makes a crater, and melts, perhaps a weed can germinate; perhaps not. If I dice life into atoms, the trajectories I find are so wild, so random, anything could happen: life or nonlife. But once we have a body, who can give it up easily? Our own or others'? We check our clocks and build our beautiful narratives, under which indeterminacy seethes.

Sometimes, lying in bed, I feel like a flounder with its two eyes on one side pointing upward into nothingness. The casings of thought rattle. Then I realize there are no casings at all. Is it possible that the mind, like space, is finite but, has no boundaries, no center or edge? I sit cross-legged on old blankets. My bare feet strain against the backs of my knees. Just as morning comes and the indigo lifts, the leaflessness of the old apple tree looks ornate. *Nothing in this world is plain.*

"Every atom in your body was once inside a star," another physicist says, trying to humor me. Not all atoms in all kinds of matter are shared. But who wouldn't find that idea appealing? Outside, shadows trade places with a sliver of sun, which trades places with shadow. A Pacific storm blows in from the south like a jib sail reaching far out, backhanding me with a tropical gust. It snows into my mouth, between my breasts, against my shins. Spring teaches me what space and time teach me: that I am a random multiple; that the many fit together; that my swell is a collision of particles. Spring is music, a seething minor, a twelve-tone scale. Odd harmonies amass and lift up only to dissolve.

Spring presses harder and harder and is feral. The first thunder cracks the sky into a larger domain. Sap rises in obdurateness. For the first time in seven months, rain slants down in a slow pavanne—sharp but soft, like desire. I drive the highway that crosses the wild-horse range. Near Emblem a lone black stud horse trots across the landscape. He travels north, then turns in my direction as if coming to me. Now, when I dream of Joel, he is riding that horse and he knows he is dead. One night he rides to my house, all smiles and shyness, and I let him in.

The Black Widow

Gordon Grice

I hunt black widow. When I find one, I capture it. I have found them in discarded wheels and tires and under railroad ties. I have found them in house foundations and cellars, in automotive shops and toolsheds, in water meters and rock gardens, against fences and in cinderblock walls. I have found them in a hospital and in the den of a rattlesnake, and once on the bottom of the chair I was sitting in.

Sometimes I raise a generation or two in captivity. The egg sacs produce a hundred or more pinpoint cannibals, each leaving a trail of gleaming light in the air, the group of them eventually producing a glimmering tangle in which most of them die, eaten by stronger sibs. Finally I separate the three or four survivors and feed them bigger game.

Once I let several egg sacs hatch out in a container about eighteen inches on a side, a tight wooden box with a sliding glass top. As I tried to move the box one day, the lid slid off and I fell, hands first, into the mass of young widows. Most were still translucent newborns, their bodies a swirl of brown and cream. A few of the females had eaten enough to molt; they had the beginnings of their blackness. Their tangle of broken web clung to my forearms. They felt like trickling water in my arm hairs.

I walked out into the open air and raised my arms into the stiff wind. The widows answered the wind with new strands of web and drifted away, their bodies gold in the late sun. In about ten minutes my arms carried nothing but old web and the husks of spiderlings eaten by their sibs.

I have never been bitten.

The black widow has the ugliest web of any spider. The orb weavers make those seemingly delicate nets that poets have traditionally used as symbols of imagination, order, and perfection. The sheet-web spiders weave crisp linens on the grass. But the widow makes messy-looking tangles in the corners and bends of things and under logs and debris. Often the web is littered with leaves. Beneath it lie the husks of insect prey, their antennae still as gargoyle horns, cut loose and dropped; on them and the surrounding ground are splashes of the spider's white urine, which looks like bird guano and smells of ammonia even at a distance of several feet. This fetid material draws scavengers—ants, sow bugs, crickets, roaches, and so on—which become tangled in vertical strands of silk reaching from the ground up into the web. The widow comes down and, with a bicycling of the hind pair of legs, throws gummy silk onto this new prey.

When the prey is seriously tangled but still struggling, the widow cautiously descends and bites the creature, usually on a leg joint. This is a killing bite; it pumps neurotoxin into the victim. The widow will deliver a series of bites as the creature dies, injecting substances that liquefy the organs. Finally it will settle down to suck the liquefied innards out of the prey, changing position two or three times to get it all.

Before the eating begins, and sometimes before the victim dies from the slow venom, the widow usually moves it higher into the web. It attaches some line to the prey with a leg-bicycling toss, moves up the vertical web strand that originally snagged the prey, crosses a diagonal strand upward to a higher point on a different vertical strand, and here secures the line. It has thus dragged the prey's body up off the ground. The whole operation is like that of a person moving a load with block and tackle. It occurs in three dimensions—as opposed to the essentially two-dimensional operations of orb weavers and sheet weavers.

You can't watch the widow in this activity very long without realizing that its web is not a mess at all but an efficient machine. It allows complicated uses of leverage and also, because of its complexity of connections, lets the spider feel a disturbance anywhere in the web—usually with enough accuracy to tell the difference at a distance between a raindrop or leaf and viable prey. The web is also constructed in a certain relationship to movements of air so that flying insects are drawn into it. This fact partly explains why widow webs are so often found in the face-down side of discarded car wheels—the wheel is essentially a vault of still air that protects the web, but the central hole at the top allows airborne insects to fall in. An insect that is clumsy and flies in random hops, such as a June beetle, is especially vulnerable to this trap. The widow often seems to choose her building sites according to indigenous smells rather than creating her own stinking waste pile from scratch. The webs turn up, for example, in piles of trash and rotting wood. A few decades ago, the widow was notorious for building its home inside the works of outdoor toilets. Scraping around with a stick before using the toilet was a common practice.

The architectural complexities of the widow web do not particularly impress the widows. They move around in these webs almost blind, yet they never misstep or get lost. In fact, a widow forcibly removed from its web and put back at a different point does not seem confused; it will quickly return to its habitual resting place. Furthermore, widows never snare themselves, even though every strand of the web is a potential trap. A widow will spend a few minutes every day coating the clawed tips of its legs with the oil that lets it walk the sticky strands. It secretes the oil from its mouth, coating its legs like a cat cleaning its paws.

The human mind cannot grasp the complex functions of the web but must infer them. The widow constructs it by instinct. A brain smaller than a pinhead contains the blueprints, precognitive memories the widow unfolds out of itself into actuality. I have never dissected with enough precision or delicacy to get a good specimen of the black widow brain, but I did glimpse one once. A widow was struggling to wrap a praying mantis when the insect's forelegs, like scalpels mounted on lightning, sliced away the spider's carapace and left exposed the clear droplet of bloody brain.

Widows reportedly eat mice, toads, tarantulas—anything that wanders into that remarkable web. I have never witnessed a widow performing a gustatory act of that magnitude, but I have seen them eat scarab beetles heavy as pecans; carabid beetles strong enough to prey on wolf spiders; cockroaches more than an inch long; and hundreds of other arthropods of various sizes. Widows begin life by eating their siblings. An adult female will fight any other female; the winner often eats the loser. A popular game among Mexican children is to stage such fights and bet on the outcome. The children put the widows on a stick and pass it around so that everyone can see. Sometimes one female ties another up and leaves without killing her. I have come across such black pearls wrapped in silk and, upon peeling off the skin, seen the pearls unfold their legs and rush away.

The widow gets her name by eating her lover, though this does not always happen. He distinguishes himself from ordinary prey by playing her web like a lyre. Sometimes she eats him without first copulating; sometimes she snags him as he withdraws his palp from her genital pore. Sometimes he leaves unharmed after mating; in this case, he soon withers and dies on his own. I have witnessed male and female living in platonic relationships in one web. The males' palps, still swollen with sperm, proved that these relationships had not been sexual.

Many widows will eat as much as opportunity gives. One aggressive female had an abdomen a little bigger than an English pea. She snared a huge cockroach and spent several hours subduing it, then three days consuming it. Her abdomen swelled to the size of a largish marble, its glossy black stretching to a tight red brown. With a different widow, I decided to see whether that appetite was really insatiable. I collected dozens of large crickets and grasshoppers and began to drop them into her web at a rate of one every three or four hours. After catching and consuming her tenth victim, this bloated widow fell from her web, landing on her back. She remained in this position for hours, making only feeble attempts to move. Then she died.

The first thing people ask when they hear about my fascination with the widow is why I am not afraid. The truth is that my fascination is rooted in fear.

I have childhood memories that partly account for my fear. When I was six my mother took my sister and me to the cellar of our farmhouse and told us to watch as she killed a widow. With great ceremony she produced a long stick (I am tempted to say a ten-foot pole) and, narrating her technique in exactly the hushed voice she used for discussing religion or sex, went to work. Her flashlight beam found a point halfway up the cement wall where two marbles hung together—one crisp white, the other a glossy black. My mother ran her stick through the dirty silver web around them, and as it tore it sounded like the crackling of paper in fire. This sound is unique to the widow's powerful web—anybody with a little experience can tell a widow's work from another spider's by ear. The black marble rose on thin legs to fight off the intruder. As the plump abdomen wobbled across the wall, it seemed to be constantly throwing those legs out of its path. The impression it gave was of speed and frantic anger, but actually a widow's movements outside the web are slow and inefficient. My mother smashed the widow onto the stick and carried it up into the light. It was still kicking its remaining legs. Mom scraped it against the sidewalk, grinding it to a paste. Then she returned for the white marble—the widow's egg sac. This, too, came to an abrasive end.

My mother's stated purpose was to teach us how to recognize and deal with a dangerous creature we would probably encounter on the farm. But of course we also took the understanding that widows were actively malevolent, that they waited in dark places to ambush us, that they were worthy of ritual disposition, like an enemy whose death is not sufficient but must be followed with the murder of his children and the salting of his land and whose unclean remains must not touch our hands.

The odd thing is that so many people, some of whom presumably did not first encounter the widow in such an atmosphere of mystic reverence, hold the widow in awe. Various friends have told me that the widow always devours her mate, or that her bite is always fatal to humans—in fact, it almost never is. I have heard told for truth that goods imported from the Orient are likely infested with widows and that women with bouffant hairdos have died of widow infestation. Any contradiction of such tales is received as if it were a proclamation of atheism.

The most startling contribution to the widow's mythical status I have ever encountered was *Black Widow: America's Most Poisonous Spider*, a book that appeared in 1945. Between genuine scientific observations, the authors present the widow as a lurking menace with a taste for human flesh. They describe the experiments of other investigators; one involved inducing a widow to bite a laboratory rat on the penis, after which event the rat "appeared to become dejected and depressed." Perhaps the most psychologically revealing passage is the authors' quotation from another writer, who said the "deadliest Communists are like the black widow spider; they conceal their *red* underneath."

We project our archetypal terrors onto the widow. It is black; it avoids the light; it is a voracious carnivore. Its red markings suggest blood. Its name, its sleek, rounded form invite a strangely sexual discomfort; the widow becomes an emblem for a man's fear of extending himself into the blood and darkness of a woman, something like the legendary Eskimo vampire that takes the form of a fanged vagina.

The widow's venom is, of course, a soundly pragmatic reason for fear. The venom contains a neurotoxin that can produce sweats, vomiting, swelling, convulsions, and dozens of other symptoms. The variation in symptoms from one person to the next is remarkable. The constant is pain. A useful question for a doctor trying to diagnose an uncertain case: "Is this the worst pain you've ever felt?" A "yes" suggests a diagnosis of black widow bite. Occasionally people die from widow bites. The very young and the very old are especially vulnerable. Some people seem to die not from the venom but from the infection that may follow; because of its habitat, the widow carries dangerous microbes.

Some researchers hypothesized that the virulence of the venom was necessary for killing beetles of the scarab family. This family contains thousands of species, including the June beetle and the famous dung beetle the Egyptians thought immortal. All the scarabs have thick, strong bodies and unusually tough exoskeletons, and many of them are common prey for the widow. The tough hide was supposed to require a particularly nasty venom. As it turns out, the venom is thousands of times more virulent than necessary for this purpose. The whole idea is full of the widow's glamour: an emblem of eternal life killed by a creature whose most distinctive blood-colored markings people invariably describe as an hour-glass.

No one has ever offered a sufficient explanation for the dangerous venom. It provides no evolutionary advantages: all of the widow's prey items would find lesser toxins fatal, and there is no particular benefit in killing or harming larger animals. A widow that bites a human being or other large animal is likely to be killed. Evolution does sometimes produce such flowers of natural evil—traits that are neither functional nor vestigial but utterly pointless. Natural selection favors the inheritance of useful characteristics that arise from random mutation and tends to extinguish disadvantageous traits. All other characteristics, the ones that neither help nor hinder survival, are preserved or extinguished at random as mutation links them with useful or harmful traits. Many people—even many scientists—assume that every animal is elegantly engineered for its ecological niche, that every bit of an animal's anatomy and behavior has a functional explanation. This assumption is false. Nothing in evolutionary theory sanctions it; fact refutes it.

We want the world to be an ordered room, but in a corner of that room there hangs an untidy web. Here the analytical minds find an irreducible mystery, a motiveless evil in nature, and the scientist's vision of evil comes to match the vision of a God-fearing country woman with a ten-foot pole. No idea of the cosmos as elegant design accounts for the widow. No idea of a benevolent God is comfortable in a world with the widow. She hangs in her web, that marvel of design, and defies teleology.

Sex in Trees

Bernd Heinrich

There is more of good nature than of good sense at the bottom of most marriages.

—Henry David Thoreau

One day in mid-April, the alders down by the brook unfurled their hard, tight, purple catkins. Overnight they were transformed into long, loose dangling tassels that trembled in the least bit of a breeze. Wisps of yellow pollen flew off like puffs of smoke. The brook, aptly named Alder Stream, roared full of tannin-stained yellow water collected in rivulets off the hill still under thick banks of snow. Slightly above the alder thickets under the bare poplars, the beaked hazelnuts were also unfurling their male catkins. As in the alders, the female hazelnut flowers are on the same twigs. But I see these tiny delicate purple wisps only when I look closely. Windblown pollen grains find them.

The alders, hazelnuts, poplars, willows, sugar and red maples, beeches, ashes, and oaks each shed their pollen in a few days. All are done blooming when the first leaf buds open from the beginning of May and on into June. The insect-pollinated trees, the basswoods and chestnuts, wait to flower until summer, weeks after they have leaves. Each species has a schedule, and that schedule is especially strict in matters pertaining to sex.

Flowers are sexual organs, and flowering is not sex but the preliminaries. A great deal of investment goes into sex, and the mechanisms that animals and plants have evolved to achieve sex are a source of wonder and beauty. Without sex there would be no flowers and no bees, nor would there be brightly colored birds and birdsong. There would be no alluring scents that female moths give off at night that attract males from a mile or more downwind. There would be no flashing of fireflies through the trees on hot July nights, nor would there be evening serenades of crickets and katydids in August. Scents, sounds, and colors often combined in fantastic forms have the purpose of attracting mates. But trees can't be attracted. They are rooted in place.

In order to achieve sex, each male tree (or the portion of it that is male) sends forth millions of tiny pollen grains. These structures contain sperm, but they are not sperm. Instead, they are analogous to whole male reproductive tracts. When one pollen grain lodges on the stigma of a flower—the receptive part of a compatible female reproductive tract of another tree —it sends forth a penislike tube that grows rapidly, thrusting into the plant's ovary. Only then do the sperm descend through this self-made tube into the ovary to fertilize the eggs. However, the female is not passive. She chemically recognizes the proper pollen and permits the growth of pollen tubes only for mates she chooses. The plants own pollen is usually rejected or accepted only when none other reaches her.

There are several ways whereby a tree's pollen grains may find appropriate ovaries. The forte of the angiosperm plants is their ability to harness intermediaries to carry the pollen. Apple trees, for example, have harnessed bees by tailoring the flowers' shapes, colors, scents, and food rewards to suit bees. Apple flowers are perfumed and colored bright pink. They stand out like billboards to bees and advertise to them from afar, inviting them to come sip sweet nectar and take pollen. As bees feed on the flowers' nectar they become dusted with pollen. They scrape most of this pollen from their bodies and collect it to feed their larvae back in their hive. However, some of the pollen remains on their body hairs, and it inadvertently gets deposited on other apple flowers on other trees that the bee also visits. The bee thus becomes a long-range mating agent for trees rooted in place. In some other plants, such as saguaro cactus trees, the much larger white flowers open only at night and provide much more nectar than apple flowers. They are shaped so that the fur of specific bats that are adapted to eat nectar and pollen gets dusted with pollen, and this pollen then gets deposited in flowers of the next plant the bat visits. Many other plants are tailored in shape, color, scent, and the food they offer to attract moths, butterflies, flies, beetles, or birds. In turn, the flower bats, hummingbirds, sphinx moths, and bees are highly dependent on the plants for their own livelihood and neither organism can now exist without the other. Through evolution, flowers made these animals what they are, and the animals in turn made flowers.

Almost all of the trees in my forest use wind, rather than bees or other animals, to transfer their pollen. Wind has drawbacks. It is unpredictable. It may be absent when the flowers bloom, or it could blow from the wrong direction. Insects, however, are there to be beckoned at any time, and they can come from any direction. In comparison to a bee flying directly from flower to flower, using the wind to send pollen or to receive it from a neighbor might seem like a big gamble for achieving sex. As in all gambles, however, there are ways of improving the odds. Trees improve their odds of fertilization by dispersing astronomical numbers of pollen grains. More than five million are released from a single birch flower or catkin, and each tree has hundreds of thousands of flowers. Female wind-pollinated flowers have enlarged sticky stigmatic surfaces that aid in catching pollen grains out of the air. In all of the deciduous wind-pollinated trees (ashes, elms, beeches, sugar and red maples, oaks, birches, willows, poplars, and aspens), the narrow window of time when sexual unions occur is very early in the spring before the leaf buds open. If flowers waited until after the leaves unfurled, then they would be partially shielded from the wind and there would be less chance for successful transfer of pollen between flowers.

Animals search out flowers even within foliage. After having been rewarded with food from one kind of flower, most animals search persistently for others of the same kind, identifying them by scent, color, and shape. Male and female flowers must be similar in appearance; otherwise the pollinator might fly to flowers of one sex and not the other. Having both sexes on the same flower, such as in the apple, is one common solution that helps solve the problem (so long as the plant also has means to prevent self-pollinating). The sexual system of an apple tree thus differs from that of an animal in that male and female roles are usually not mutually exclusive within one individual. Most plants have little or no sexual identity. An apple blossom is both male and female. It gives and receives pollen. Having both sexes on the same flower, apples have so-called perfect flowers, as opposed to "imperfect" ones (either male or female), as are found on alder, hazelnut, or maple, for example.

Wind-pollinated plants do not have showy flowers. In them the appearance of male and female flowers is irrelevant and the sexes are usually on separate flowers. Sometimes there are even whole trees that have either all male or all female flowers. In willows, for example, some individual trees have only male flowers and others have only female flowers. In American white ash trees and red maples there are (usually) separate male and female trees. Two of the three American chestnuts I have planted have so far produced both male and female flowers on the same tree. However, one produced primarily male flowers. Only the female flowers produce nuts. On hazelnut, alder, beech, and oak, separate male and female flowers are always on the same tree, and to achieve cross-pollination these trees must avoid self-fertilization and achieve cross-pollination in various complex ways. Given all the large investment, and all the complex and wonderful mechanisms that have gone into achieving sexual reproduction, one wonders: What is the point of it?

The point of *reproduction* is to pass on as many of the individual's genes as possible. If a tree's flowers were self-pollinated, then all of its seeds would contain only its own genes. One that must be cross-pollinated automatically halves the number of its genes that it packages into each seed, since the other half comes from an unrelated other parent. Cross-pollination from the perspective of reproduction is thus not a solution. It's an immense problem. What does sex do for the tree? Why bother with it? Why should a tree cross-pollinate when, by so doing, it reduces the number of genes it passes on relative to what could be achieved by self-pollination?

Sex is a mechanism that introduces genetic variety into offspring. Sex dissolves old genetic combinations, scrambles them, and randomly reassembles them into many new mosaics. It's a little bit like having two similar cars (originating from two factories), taking them apart piece by piece, putting all the pieces into one heap, duplicating the pieces many times, and then picking appropriate pieces of each kind randomly to reassemble them again into numerous new cars. Each of these cars will have different percentages of parts in different combinations from the two parent lines.

Every one of these new cars is apt to be slightly different. Some will perform better and some will perform worse in each varied situation. However, genetic variety increases the odds that one or another of these "offspring" will succeed in a changing or variable environment relative to that of the "parents." Of course the two original cars can't be too different—say a VW "bug" and a Mack truck—else the parts won't mesh and then none survives.

For trees and other plants as well as animals, diseases may be one of the greatest variables of the environment. Right now, for example, blister rust is devastating the white pines and Dutch elm disease the elms. Both of the fungi that cause these diseases are highly effective because they have fine-tuned their biochemistry to that of potential hosts. If they eventually specialize to attack a clone rather than a sexually reproducing tree, then *all* "individuals" of that clone would be equally vulnerable. Since each pine and elm tree is the product of a sexual union, however, there is more chance of individual immunity or resistance, offering them an evolutionary escape mechanism. Given sufficient isolation and time, potentially a whole new population could arise from a new variant. The rewards of sex in trees are not immediate. They are strictly long-term.

In the short term there are often situations when sex is disadvantageous to trees. Perhaps the greatest drawback is when potential mates are not within the trees' sexual reach. Since trees cannot travel, they face a problem. I could see it in my chestnut trees. In the fall of 1996 I examined my American chestnut trees and found that they had both male and female flowers. So far so good. The trees had even produced the typical round, spiny fruit of chestnut trees. However, inside the fruit were only the empty shells of typical-looking brown nuts. I suspect therefore that American chestnut trees don't self-pollinate. The flowers had probably not been cross-pollinated, so no embryos grew although receptacles for them did. Perhaps there were not sufficient numbers of suitable sexual partners nearby, or maybe the critical pollinating insect required by chestnuts was absent. Similarly, I found the ground strewn with sterile nuts under a lone black walnut tree (on a farm in Vermont). I eagerly picked up enough walnuts to fill a grocery bag. Unfortunately, each of thirty-five nuts I cracked was empty. The flowers from which they had grown probably had not been cross-pollinated for lack of a nearby partner.

I have often wondered why most of the trees in my forest use the wind to transfer their pollen and in many cases to disperse their seeds. In tropical forests, the trees hitch both their pollen and seed transfer almost exclusively onto animals, and the animals in turn come to depend on them. Especially in the tropical forests, trees can scarcely be thought of as separate organisms at all. They exist as parts of an unfathomable complex web where each species is linked to others in growth, reproduction, and sex.

Nobody has "the answer" to why northern trees are mostly wind-pollinated rather than animal-pollinated. There are probably many answers. Maybe there is not enough wind in tropical forests, or not enough animals in northern forests. Perhaps there are fewer animals in northern forests simply because the trees don't offer nectar rewards because they use the wind. Cause and effect often become blurred.

Tree distribution is undoubtedly important in determining the kind of pollination system that is needed to accomplish the job. A one-hectare plot (about two and a half acres) of Borneo rain forest selected at random contains about seven hundred species of trees, and the trees of any one species therefore tend to be *isolated* one from another. In contrast, in my forest, a one-hectare area selected at random would likely contain only one-hundredth the variety of trees, and many trees of a single species grow in dense crowds. Different sections of the southern slope down to Alder Stream are dominated respectively by quaking aspen, red maple, and sugar maple. The top of the ridge grows mainly red spruce, while on the western slope of the hill balsam fir and white birch predominate. The alders grow in patches along the side of the brook. In most cases, the individual trees of the same species touch or almost touch each other. I can hardly differentiate individuals. I doubt that pollinators do so. The trees are an *anonymous* crowd; they are not individually labeled by unique sign or location.

Looking at the pollinators' world in human terms, it is as if a street had many unlabelled, identical-looking, and identically scented restaurants all randomly intermingled. Some of them serve ample food of superior quality and some of them serve very poor food or none at all. To enter any one you have to pay at the door, and customers must visit several locales each evening to be satiated. As long as customers feel that on average they get suitable food they'll take chances and keep on coming to that group of anonymous restaurants. The restaurateurs, however, are individuals, and they are in intense competition with one another. In order to stay in business many of the more shrewd or dishonest slyly provide less food. Others must follow suit, with the end result that the customers eventually stop coming to eat on that particular street, because on average they keep paying the same and getting less. Substitute plants with nectar-rewarding flowers for restaurants, and bees for people, and we have the same situation. The plants get a payoff not from having the nectar eaten out of their flowers, but from having the insects enter their flowers, which pollinates them. When the customers no longer enter their flowers, plants need to devise a new mechanism of pollination. Could sex in the wind be the solution?

Passionate Science

Sue Hubbell

I went to three different colleges before I managed to snag an undergraduate degree, and considering how callow I was in those days, it is a wonder I learned anything at all. But looking back, I believe I learned three things. Two are irrelevant to our purposes here, but one has some bearing. A professor at the first of those colleges penetrated my attention sufficiently to impress upon me that there was no such thing as objective writing, that every inscription, every traveler's tale, every news account, every piece of technical writing, tells more about the author and his times than it does about the ostensible subject. The best that can be hoped is that the writer will lay out his bias up front.

I'm nearly half a century away from my college days, but everything I've ever read, including the scientific papers on biological subjects that I mine for my own writing, has convinced me that the professor was right. The writers of those papers, men and women I have interviewed and have come to know and admire, have selected their subjects because they have a passion for them. They have observed phenomena with an eye shaped by their experiences in particular places and times and have found interest and significance according to their own gifts, limitations, sadnesses, and sociabilities; their understandings have been shaped by their own peculiar and quirky worlds.

One of the better achievements of Western thought is the scientific method, which, when it works well, makes allowances for all those passions, limitations, and quirks. A good field biologist goes out and looks at the real world, sees something no one else has noticed, writes it down as accurately as he can, and reports it to others through publication. On the basis of his observation, he or someone else may spin a theory that explains it. Other observers with other passions, later observers with other biases, check it out, supplement, amplify, disagree, revise. Science is a process, not a body of received wisdom.

My own interests run to small animals that creep and jump and slither and flutter, the invertebrates—"the little things that run the world," as E. O. Wilson has said. What I hope to do when I write, keeping my old professor in mind, is to tell about the world of invertebrates, which appears to me an interesting and engaging one. I try to lay out my biases up front. I am grateful but astonished that over my writing life—one of the several lives I've had—sober, serious, responsible grownup editors have let me loose in that particular world to satisfy my own curiosity and amuse myself, in return for bringing back reports of what I see. There is a lot of news.

Because we have backbones—vertebrae—we think they are important, so in one of those smug Aristotelian bifurcations, we have divided up the animals into vertebrates and invertebrates. Actually, it was Lamarck, the eighteenth-century French naturalist, inventor of the notion that acquired characteristics could be inherited, who dreamed up the word "invertebrates." But the idea goes back to Aristotle, the original digital thinker, a man who always divided things into two categories. His basic division of animals was into those that had blood and those that lacked it. By blood he meant good, rich, red blood, not the pale ichor that oozes from a bug when you squash it, and in the blooded category he included mammals, birds, reptiles, and fishes—in short, vertebrates, animals with backbones. The bloodless were crustaceans, cephalopods, insects, and snails—in short, invertebrates, or at least the ones he knew about. His scheme made further divisions of the Twenty Questions sort. Does the blooded animal have hair or is it hairless? Legged or legless? If it has legs, are there four or two? This digital, yes or no, approach is familiar to anyone who has used a botanical key. Leaves alternate or opposite? Stems fuzzy or smooth?

Today, however, the basic principle of taxonomy is that living things should be defined by what they have, not what they lack, so taxonomic divisions come in varying numbers, not just in twos. The biological reference text I use divides all animals into thirty-two phylum units, of which animals with backbones are only one. But the Aristotelian way of thinking is powerful and still dominates our view of the world. College courses are taught and textbooks written on "Invertebrate Zoology." The premier zoological research institutions of the world, such as the Smithsonian, have departments of vertebrate and of invertebrate zoology.

Thoughtful taxonomists and zoologists grumble about this backbone fixation. One of them, Robert O'Hara, part philosopher, part zoologist, wondered how humans might be classified if an arthropod were making up the scheme. Arthropoda, meaning "joint-footed," is the biggest phylum of animals, those that by numerical rights, at least, should do the classifying if they were so inclined. The phylum includes spiders, insects, crabs, and lobsters. An arthropod might, according to O'Hara, describe us and our near relatives this way: "The anarthropods are a primitive group with few species and a limited diversity of form. Their reproductive rates prevent them from adapting to their environments closely, and the giantism exhibited by many anarthropods has kept their numbers very low and is no doubt the cause of their general sluggishness."

The invertebrates could get along without us quite nicely, and did for hundreds of millions of years, but we could not get along without them, so dependent are we on the life processes they have initiated and keep going. We humans are a minority of giants stumbling around in the world of little things, often not noticing our neighbors, not even being able to see many of them because they are *very* small. Yet each and every species, constituted from the same basic handful of chemicals as we are, has a complicated and special way of getting on in the world, different from ours and different one from another.

When we learn something about the way invertebrates live, they become familiar to us and we develop some charity and friendliness toward them. I am pleased to know that the woman who lives next door to Arne and me in Washington, D.C., has a home business that is thriving and that her children are doing well in school. I am pleased, also, to know that the bumblebee I see in early spring time, working the azaleas in our front yard, is a solitary mother queen hustling up enough provisions to raise daughters who will help her work during the months ahead. I find it satisfying and enjoyable to watch a periwinkle snuffling through the algae on a seaside rock near our new home in Maine and know that it is having a good feed.

Although we don't know everything about vertebrates, we know quite a lot: occasionally a new bird or fish or mammal or reptile is discovered, but those discoveries are rare, so we know pretty well how many tens of thousands of vertebrate species there are, and we know a good deal about their biology and behavior. But more than 95 percent of the animal species are invertebrates, and we have discovered only a fraction of the suspected tens of millions of them. We know next to nothing about how they get on in their lives or what happens when we lurch through their communities. We don't even have a fix on the number of invertebrate species already known and described, which is surprising in these days of computer technology and catalogs. Nowhere in the world is there any tidy master list of all discovered species with their names neatly registered and affixed. Specialists in a particular group—the fireflies, for instance—usually have a fair notion of how many species there are in that group, but even those are educated estimates, and the numbers within bigger groupings, such as insects or sponges, are guesses. So we don't even know what we know. Anyone venturing among invertebrates is sure to have the pleasure of discovery. And nearly every observation becomes a piece of news from an uncharted world.

That sort of pleasure is certainly one of the reasons zoologists go out into the field . . . and why I follow them there. In working with them I have been struck, as a writer, with the similarity of our occupations. Both journalism and field biology require standing aside a little, playing observer, not participant, taking a look at the real world, interviewing its inhabitants one way or another, watching the manner in which they get along, and reporting what we have seen or heard. But more than that, both writers and biologists share a compulsion to describe to others how we see that world. We keep at it, publishing this bit now, another later, piling up reports of our own realities.

A couple of books ago, I learned just how heady the pleasure of discovery could be and what a compulsion its pursuit becomes. In that book, *Broadsides from the Other Orders*, I was writing on several themes and using the biology and behavior of a particular bug to explore each one. I selected my bug examples in direct proportion to my own curiosity, which is to say ignorance, about them: silverfish, katydids, water striders, daddy longlegs, and so on. For twenty years I had been living, on my farm in Missouri, in close company with camel crickets—pale, silent, humpbacked crickets with stripy brown jumping legs. When I looked them up in guidebooks I found the same three or four tired facts about them, but nothing that satisfied, so I put camel crickets on my list for the book. My procedure, as chapter added to chapter, was to head down to the Library of Congress and spend several weeks reading everything I could find on the new chapter's bug. Usually, by the end of that time I had found the one person who was doing interesting work on it. I would telephone him or her and ask if I could come talk. Entomologists are generous people, and they invariably said yes. But with camel crickets the situation was different. Very little was known about them, and nearly all of it had been discovered by one man who had died by the time I started my reading. A student of his, on the verge of retirement himself, had continued some of the taxonomic work, and he kindly identified the species I had on my farm. He also informed me that my species was a special kind that had piqued his mentor's interest. In fact, he gave me a paper written by that man near the end of his life, in which he described the species as a piece of "unfinished business and a beckoning problem."

Briefly, the paper explained that my camel crickets existed in a small area in and around my farm as an isolated group within a larger population that were thought to be the same species. When the males of this group matured sexually, they became puzzlingly different from the males outside, whom they otherwise resembled. They grew a bright orange bump on the back of what we would like to call their necks but mustn't, because bugs don't have necks. And, the taxonomist told me, no one knew anything about how camel crickets mated, for that act had never been seen: perhaps the orange bump contained a food gift that males allowed the females to bite into during courtship. The contribution of a body part is a part of some insect wooings. Camel crickets of other species are common across the United States. They are nocturnal and live in basements, under piles of stacked lumber, in corners of garages, in country well houses, but none besides mine flaunted an orange bump.

I learned to sex even immatures, captured a few males and females, and began keeping them in a terrarium. I figured out what they liked to eat, gave them water in bottle caps, learned that they were virtually blind and deaf but received a startling array of information through their more-than-body-length antennae. I watched them molt and grow, and took notes on all this as much for myself as for the chapter I was to write for the book. And, yes, I became the first person to see them mate and lay eggs. They mated in a contorted position, but the female never nibbled at the male's orange bump.

For comparison, I began raising, in separate terraria, populations of camel crickets from twenty miles south of my farm, outside the range of my group. I discovered, to my surprise, that those males and females matured more slowly than did the ones from my farm and therefore mated much later in the season. This meant that in the wild the two populations would never interbreed. Could they? I isolated immature males and females from both populations and kept them cloistered in single-gender terraria until the ones lacking the orange bump were ready to breed and then mixed them, pair by pair, in still other terraria.

By this time my chapter on camel crickets had long since been written and the book published, but I was still fired with the delight of investigation. In those days I was regularly commuting the 1,010 miles between my Missouri farm and the house in Washington in a van loaded with manuscripts, source books, two dogs, a cat, the unabridged dictionary, and the eleventh edition of the *Encyclopedia Britannica*. To that pile I added a good many terraria of camel crickets.

In the end I found that the two populations could be induced, in this artificial way, to interbreed and that their offspring were fertile, so that by the common definition they did indeed belong to the same species. That definition holds that a species is made up of individuals that interbreed and produce fertile offspring. But the offspring of these forced matches were frequently deformed; some could not molt successfully and often died before their time. Does the orange bump of the speedily maturing group contain a hormone that hastens development? Are the two groups genetically distinct? Is the orange-bump group a species in formation or, alternatively, a primitive group? My farm bordered a geologically unusual area that contains plants relict from the Ice Age. Might my camel crickets be relict, too, from a time when the season was shorter?

I haven't the equipment, skills, or training to answer those questions, but they spurred me, when I finally admitted that I had to give up the farm, to place it with an organization that will keep it and the camel crickets forever wild and safe. There were, to be sure, additional reasons for that decision, but the presence of the unusual camel crickets contributed to it. It is my hope that someday a young entomologist will stumble across something I've written and go looking for camel crickets with bright orange bumps one springtime. He may answer those questions, but he will ask others. That's the way the process goes.

There will always be people who believe that watching camel crickets is an unsuitable way for a grownup to spend her time and energies. One reason for the lack of information about camel crickets was that although they are an extremely common insect, big and easy to observe; they have little relevance to humans; they neither help nor harm us. Most research is driven by the availability of funding, and funding agencies need to see a payback. Will research on this particular oddly named animal we have never heard of improve human life in some demonstrable way? If we fund the research, will we find a better way to kill the animal if we believe it to be harmful or to encourage it if we find it beneficial? Camel crickets, in that sense, are neither "good" nor "bad" bugs. In this they resemble most of the life on the planet. In the very short run, the one in which research funding takes place, it is hard to show that much of what lives and grows in the world relates to us. We eat salmon but not sea mice, the elusive *Aphrodite,* a genus of worms that live in the ocean deeps, where, some scientists say, there may be as many as ten million other species as unconcerned with our existence as we are ignorant of theirs. Certain black flies cause a terrible tropical disease in humans, river blindness, but camel crickets do not make us sick, nor do most of the more than one million other species of insects. Sensible, practical concerns should and do make salmon and black flies of more importance and interest in the funding of research and the formation of public environmental policy than camel crickets or *Aphrodite* or those other nameless millions. That is the way of the world, or at least of our time in the world.

I must confess, however, that I've never been convinced that to be interesting and important an animal needs to have a relationship to, or use for, human beings. As a matter of fact, otherness, remoteness, and independence engage my curiosity and intellect more than do similarity and utility. And I think there are a number of good long-term reasons why we should persist in our interest in camel crickets and sea mice and all those millions of invertebrates awaiting discovery. Some of those reasons will turn up in the pages that follow. But here, initially, I want to return to this compulsion that we have, writers and naturalists, to become tellers of tales about the world we have traveled in.

My brother, Bil Gilbert, a writer whose preoccupations run to animals with backbones, most especially crows, has often written of our "fascination with other bloods" as the basis of our yearning to understand the ways of others, as an escape from mere human perspective. But it is my son, Brian Hubbell, also a writer, a poet, who has said it best of all. Poets often do. He wrote, in a 1996 issue of the *Beloit Poetry Journal*:

The Message

Dry September weekday morning,
time indolence equates to sin,
I was outside, eyes closed over coffee
thinking some things I think when
a grasshopper flew in a certain fury
arcing off the desiccating asters
and affixed itself sharply to my upper lip,
returning startle with a compound stare
a ceaseless green on green.

Buttoned in its urgent grip
words came as plain as under
a falconed pigeon's ring.
or in a half-corked bottle;
surely the heart of sadness is this knowing:
each embarks a gulf alone, each with
his fractured bit of seeing and a need
but not the tools to tell.

"Thinking Like a Mountain"
An Excerpt from *A Sand Country*

Aldo Leopold

A deep chesty bawl echoes from rimrock to rimrock, rolls down the mountain, and fades into the far blackness of the night. It is an outburst of wild defiant sorrow, and of contempt for all the adversities of the world.

Every living thing (and perhaps many a dead one as well) pays heed to that call. To the deer it is a reminder of the way of all flesh, to the pine a forecast of midnight scuffles and of blood upon the snow, to the coyote a promise of gleanings to come, to the cowman a threat of red ink at the bank, to the hunter a challenge of fang against bullet. Yet behind these obvious and immediate hopes and fears there lies a deeper meaning, known only to the mountain itself. Only the mountain has lived long enough to listen objectively to the howl of a wolf.

Those unable to decipher the hidden meaning know nevertheless that it is there, for it is felt in all wolf country, and distinguishes that country from all other land. It tingles in the spine of all who hear wolves by night, or who scan their tracks by day. Even without sight or sound of wolf, it is implicit in a hundred small events: the midnight whinny of a pack horse, the rattle of rolling rocks, the bound of a fleeing deer, the way shadows lie under the spruces. Only the ineducable tyro can fail to sense the presence or absence of wolves, or the fact that mountains have a secret opinion about them.

My own conviction on this score dates from the day I saw a wolf die. We were eating lunch on a high rimrock, at the foot of which a turbulent river elbowed its way. We saw what we thought was a doe fording the torrent, her breast awash in white water. When she climbed the bank toward us and shook out her tail, we realized our error: it was a wolf. A half-dozen others, evidently grown pups, sprang from the willows and all joined in a welcoming mêlée of wagging tails and playful maulings. What was literally a pile of wolves writhed and tumbled in the center of an open flat at the foot of our rimrock.

In those days we had never heard of passing up a chance to kill a wolf. In a second we were pumping lead into the pack, but with more excitement than accuracy: how to aim a steep downhill shot is always confusing. When our rifles were empty, the old wolf was down, and a pup was dragging a leg into impassable slide-rocks.

We reached the old wolf in time to watch a fierce green fire dying in her eyes. I realized then, and have known ever since, that there was something new to me in those eyes—something known only to her and to the mountain. I was young then, and full of trigger-itch; I thought that because fewer wolves meant more deer, that no wolves would mean hunters' paradise. But after seeing the green fire die, I sensed that neither the wolf nor the mountain agreed with such a view.

Since then I have lived to see state after state extirpate its wolves. I have watched the face of many a newly wolfless mountain, and seen the south-facing slopes wrinkle with a maze of new deer trails. I have seen every edible bush and seedling browsed, first to anaemic desuetude, and then to death. I have seen every edible tree defoliated to the height of a saddlehorn. Such a mountain looks as if someone had given God a new pruning shears, and forbidden Him all other exercise. In the end the starved bones of the hoped-for deer herd, dead of its own too-much, bleach with the bones of the dead sage, or molder under the high-lined junipers.

I now suspect that just as a deer herd lives in mortal fear of its wolves, so does a mountain live in mortal fear of its deer. And perhaps with better cause, for while a buck pulled down by wolves can be replaced in two or three years, a range pulled down by too many deer may fail of replacement in as many decades.

So also with cows. The cowman who cleans his range of wolves does not realize that he is taking over the wolf's job of trimming the herd to fit the range. He has not learned to think like a mountain. Hence we have dust-bowls, and rivers washing the future into the sea.

We all strive for safety, prosperity, comfort, long life, and dullness. The deer strives with his supple legs, the cowman with trap and poison, the states-man with pen, the most of us with machines, votes, and dollars, but it all comes to the same thing: peace in our time. A measure of success in this is all well enough, and perhaps is a requisite to objective thinking, but too much safety seems to yield only danger in the long run. Perhaps this is behind Thoreau's dictum: In wildness is the salvation of the world. Perhaps this is the hidden meaning in the howl of the wolf, long known among mountains, but seldom perceived among men.

The Loss of the Creature

Walker Percy

Every explorer names his island Formosa, beautiful. To him it is beautiful because, being first, he has access to it and can see it for what it is. But to no one else is it ever as beautiful—except the rare man who manages to recover it, who knows that it has to be recovered.

Garcia López de Cárdenas discovered the Grand Canyon and was amazed at the sight. It can be imagined: One crosses miles of desert, breaks through the mesquite, and there it is at one's feet. Later the government set the place aside as a national park, hoping to pass along to millions the experience of Cárdenas. Does not one see the same sight from the Bright Angel Lodge that Cárdenas saw?

The assumption is that the Grand Canyon is a remarkably interesting and beautiful place and that if it had a certain value P for Cárdenas, the same value P may be transmitted to any number of sightseers—just as Banting's discovery of insulin can be transmitted to any number of diabetics. A counter-influence is at work, however, and it would be nearer the truth to say that if the place is seen by a million sightseers, a single sightseer does not receive the value P but a millionth part of value I.

It is assumed that since the Grand Canyon has the fixed interest value P, tours can be organized for any number of people. A man in Boston decides to spend his vacation at the Grand Canyon. He visits his travel bureau, looks at the folder, signs up for a two-week tour. He and his family take the tour, see the Grand Canyon, and return to Boston. May we say that this man has seen the Grand Canyon? Possibly he has. But it is more likely that what he has done is the one sure way not to see the canyon.

Why is it almost impossible to gaze directly at the Grand Canyon under these circumstances and see it for what it is—as one picks up a strange object from one's back yard and gazes directly at it? It is almost impossible because the Grand Canyon, the thing as it is, has been appropriated by the symbolic complex which has already been formed in the sightseer's mind. Seeing the canyon under approved circumstances is seeing the symbolic complex head on. The thing is no longer the thing as it confronted the Spaniard; it is rather that which has already been formulated—by picture postcard, geog-

69

raphy book, tourist folders, and the words *Grand Canyon*. As a result of this preformulation, the source of the sightseer's pleasure undergoes a shift. Where the wonder and delight of the Spaniard arose from his penetration of the thing itself, from a progressive discovery of depths, patterns, colors, shadows, etc., now the sightseer measures his satisfaction *by the degree to which the canyon conforms to the preformed complex.* If it does so, if it looks just like the postcard, he is pleased; he might even say, "Why it is every bit as beautiful as a picture postcard!" He feels he has not been cheated. But if it does not conform, if the colors are somber, he will not be able to see it directly; he will only be conscious of the disparity between what it is and what it is supposed to be. He will say later that he was unlucky in not being there at the right time. The highest point, the term of the sightseer's satisfaction, is not the sovereign discovery of the thing before him; it is rather the measuring up of the thing to the criterion of the preformed symbolic complex.

Seeing the canyon is made even more difficult by what the sightseer does when the moment arrives, when sovereign knower confronts the thing to be known. Instead of looking at it, he photographs it. There is no confrontation at all. At the end of forty years of preformulation and with the Grand Canyon yawning at his feet, what does he do? He waives his right of seeing and knowing and records symbols for the next forty years. For him there is no present; there is only the past of what has been formulated and seen and the future of what has been formulated and not seen. The present is surrendered to the past and the future.

The sightseer may be aware that something is wrong. He may simply be bored; or he may be conscious of the difficulty: that the great thing yawning at his feet somehow eludes him. The harder he looks at it, the less he can see. It eludes everybody. The tourist cannot see it; the bellboy at the Bright Angel Lodge cannot see it: for him it is only one side of the space he lives in, like one wall of a room; to the ranger it is a tissue of everyday signs relevant to his own prospects— the blue haze down there means that he will probably get rained on during the donkey ride.

How can the sightseer recover the Grand Canyon? He can recover it in any number of ways, all sharing in common the strategem of avoiding the approved confrontation of the tour and the Park Service.

It may be recovered by leaving the beaten track. The tourist leaves the tour, camps in the back country. He arises before dawn and approaches the South Rim through a wild terrain where there are no trails and no railed-in lookout points. In other words, he sees the canyon by avoiding all the facilities for seeing the canyon. If the benevolent Park Service hears about this fellow and thinks he has a good idea and places the following notice in the Bright Angel Lodge:

Consult ranger for information on getting off the beaten track—the end result will only be the closing of another access to the canyon.

It may be recovered by a dialectical movement which brings one back to the beaten track but at a level above it. For example, after a lifetime of avoiding the beaten track and guided tours, a man may deliberately seek out the most beaten track of all, the most commonplace tour imaginable: he may visit the canyon by a Greyhound tour in the company of a party from Terre Haute—just as a man who has lived in New York all his life may visit the Statue of Liberty. (Such dialectical savorings of the familiar as the familiar are, of course, a favorite strategem of the *The New Yorker* magazine.) The thing is recovered from familiarity by means of an exercise in familiarity. Our complex friend stands behind his fellow tourists at the Bright Angel Lodge and sees the canyon through them and their predicament, their picture taking and busy disregard. In a sense, he exploits his fellow tourists; he stands on their shoulders to see the canyon.

Such a man is far more advanced in the dialectic than the sightseer who is trying to get off the beaten track—getting up at dawn and approaching the canyon through the mesquite. This strategem is, in fact, for our complex man the weariest, most beaten track of all.

It may be recovered as a consequence of a breakdown of the symbolic machinery by which the experts present the experience to the consumer. A family visits the canyon in the usual way. But shortly after their arrival, the park is closed by an outbreak of typhus in the south. They have the canyon to themselves. What do they mean when they tell the home folks of their good luck: "We had the whole place to ourselves"? How does one see the thing better when the others are absent? Is looking like sucking: the more lookers, the less there is to see? They could hardly answer, but by saying this they testify to a state of affairs which is considerably more complex than the simple statement of the schoolbook about the Spaniard and the millions who followed him. It is a state in which there is a complex distribution of sovereignty, of zoning.

It may be recovered in a time of national disaster. The Bright Angel Lodge is converted into a rest home, a function that has nothing to do with the canyon a few yards away. A wounded man is brought in. He regains consciousness; there outside his window is the canyon.

The most extreme case of access by privilege conferred by disaster is the Huxleyan novel of the adventures of the surviving remnant after the great wars of the twentieth century. An expedition from Australia lands in Southern California and heads east. They stumble across the Bright Angel Lodge, now fallen into ruins. The trails are grown over, the guard rails fallen away, the dime telescope at Battleship Point rusted. But there is the canyon, exposed at last. Exposed by what? By the decay of those facilities which were designed to help the sightseer.

This dialectic of sightseeing cannot be taken into account by planners, for the object of the dialectic is nothing other than the subversion of the efforts of the planners.

The dialectic is not known to objective theorists, psychologists, and the like. Yet it is quite well known in the fantasy-consciousness of the popular arts. The devices by which the museum exhibit, the Grand Canyon, the ordinary thing, is recovered have long since been stumbled upon. A movie shows a man visiting the Grand Canyon. But the movie maker knows something the planner does not know. He knows that one cannot take the sight frontally. The canyon must be approached by the strategems we have mentioned: the Inside Track, the Familiar Revisited, the Accidental Encounter. Who is the stranger at the Bright Angel Lodge? Is he the ordinary tourist from Terre Haute that he makes himself out to be? He is not. He has another objective in mind, to revenge his wronged brother, counterespionage, etc. By virtue of the fact that he has other fish to fry, he may take a stroll along the rim after supper and then we can see the canyon through him. The movie accomplishes its purpose by concealing it. Overtly the characters (the American family marooned by typhus) and we the onlookers experience pity for the sufferers, and the family experience anxiety for themselves; covertly and in truth they are the happiest of people and we are happy for them through them, for we have the canyon to ourselves. The movie cashes in on the recovery of sovereignty through disaster. Not only is the canyon now accessible to the remnant: the members of the remnant are now accessible to each other, a whole new ensemble of relations becomes possible—friendship, love, hatred, clandestine sexual adventures. In a movie when a man sits next to a woman on a bus, it is necessary either the bus break down or that the woman lose her memory. (The question occurs to one: Do you imagine that there are sightseers who see sights just as they are supposed to? A family who live in Terre Haute, who decide to take the canyon tour, who go there, see it, enjoy it immensely, and go home content? A family who are entirely innocent of all the barriers, zones, losses of sovereignty I have been talking about? Wouldn't most people be sorry if Battleship Point fell into the canyon, carrying all one's fellow passengers to their death, leaving one alone on the South Rim? I cannot answer this. Perhaps there are such people. Certainly a great many American families would swear they had no such problems, that they came, saw, and went away happy. Yet it is just these families who would be happiest if they had gotten the Inside Track and been among the surviving remnant.)

It is now apparent that as between the many measures which may be taken to overcome the opacity, the boredom, of the direct confrontation of the thing or creature in its citadel of symbolic investiture, some are less authentic than others. That is to say, some strategems obviously serve other purposes than that of providing access to being—for example, various unconscious motivations which it is not necessary to go into here.

Let us take an example in which the recovery of being is ambiguous, where it may under the same circumstances contain both authentic and unauthentic components. An American couple, we will say, drives down into Mexico. They see the usual sights and have a fair time of it. Yet they are never without the sense of missing something. Although Taxco and Cuernavaca are interesting and picturesque as advertised, they fall short of "it." What do the couple have in mind by "it"? What do they really hope for? What sort of experience could they have in Mexico so that upon their return, they would feel that "it" had happened? We have a clue: Their hope has something to do with their own role as tourists in a foreign country and the way in which they conceive this role. It has something to do with other American tourists. Certainly they feel that they are very far from "it" when, after traveling five thousand miles, they arrive at the plaza in Guanajuato only to find themselves surrounded by a dozen other couples from the Midwest.

Already we may distinguish authentic and unauthentic elements. First, we see the problem the couple faces and we understand their efforts to surmount it. The problem is to find an "unspoiled" place. "Unspoiled" does not mean only that a place is left physically intact; it means also that it is not encrusted by renown and by the familiar (as in Taxco), that it has not been discovered by others. We understand that the couple really want to get at the place and enjoy it. Yet at the same time we wonder if there is not something wrong in their dislike of their compatriots. Does access to the place require the exclusion of others?

Let us see what happens.

The couple decide to drive from Guanajuato to Mexico City. On the way they get lost. After hours on a rocky mountain road, they find themselves in a tiny valley not even marked on the map. There they discover an Indian village. Some sort of religious festival is going on. It is apparently a corn dance in supplication of the rain god.

The couple know at once that this is "it." They are entranced. They spend several days in the village, observing the Indians and being themselves observed with friendly curiosity.

Now may we not say that the sightseers have at last come face to face with an authentic sight, a sight which is charming, quaint, picturesque, unspoiled, and that they see the sight and come away rewarded? Possibly this may occur. Yet it is more likely that what happens is a far cry indeed from an immediate encounter with being, that the experience, while masquerading as such, is in truth a rather desperate impersonation. I use the word *desperate* advisedly to signify an actual loss of hope.

The clue to the spuriousness of their enjoyment of the village and the festival is a certain restiveness in the sightseers themselves. It is given expression by their repeated exclamations that "this is too good to be true," and by their anxiety that it may not prove to be so perfect, and finally by their downright relief at leaving the valley and having the experience in the bag, so to speak—that is, safely embalmed in memory and movie film.

What is the source of their anxiety during the visit? Does it not mean that the couple are looking at the place with a certain standard of performance in mind? Are they like Fabre, who gazed at the world about him with wonder, letting it be what it is; or are they not like the overanxious mother who sees her child as one performing, now doing badly, now doing well? The village is their child and their love for it is an anxious love because they are afraid that at any moment it might fail them.

We have another clue in their subsequent remark to an ethnologist friend. "How we wished you had been there with us! What a perfect goldmine of folkways! Every minute we would say to each other, if only you were here! You must return with us." This surely testifies to a generosity of spirit, a willingness to share their experience with others, not at all like their feelings toward their fellow Iowans on the plaza at Guanajuato!

I am afraid this is not the case at all. It is true that they longed for their ethnologist friend, but it was for an entirely different reason. They wanted him, not to share the experience, but to certify their experience as genuine.

"This is it" and "Now we are really living" do not necessarily refer to the sovereign encounter of the person with the sight that enlivens the mind and gladdens the heart. It means that now at last we are having the acceptable experience. The present experience is always measured by a prototype, the "it" of their dreams. "Now I am really living" means that now I am filling the role of sightseer and the sight is living up to the prototype of sights. The quaint and picturesque village is measured by a Platonic ideal of the Quaint and Picturesque.

Hence their anxiety during the encounter. For at any minute something could go wrong. A fellow Iowan might emerge from a 'dobe hut; the chief might show them his Sears catalog. (If the failures are "wrong" enough, as these are, they might still be turned to account as rueful conversation pieces. "There we were expecting the chief to bring us a churinga and he shows up with a Sears catalog!") They have snatched victory from disaster, but their experience always runs the danger of failure.

They need the ethnologist to certify their experience as genuine. This is borne out of their behavior when the three of them return for the next corn dance. During the dance, the couple do not watch the goings-on; instead they watch the ethnologist! Their highest hope is that their friend should find the dance interesting. And if he should show signs of true absorption, an interest in the goings-on so powerful that he becomes oblivious to his friends—then their cup is full. "Didn't we tell you?" they say at last. What they want from him is not ethnological explanations; all they want is his approval.

What has taken place is a radical loss of sovereignty over that which is as much theirs as it is the ethnologist's. The fault does not lie with the ethnologist. He has no wish to stake a claim to the village; in fact, he desires the opposite: he will bore his friends to death by telling them about the village and the meaning of the folkways. A degree of sovereignty has been surrendered by the couple. It is the nature of the loss, moreover, that they are not aware of the loss, beyond a certain uneasiness. (Even if they read this and admitted it, it would be very difficult for them to bridge the gap in their confrontation of the world. Their consciousness, so that with the onset of their first direct enjoyment, their higher consciousness pounces and certifies: "Now you are doing it! Now you are really living!" and, in certifying the experience, sets it at nought.)

Their basic placement in the world is such that they recognize a priority of title of the expert over this particular department of being. The whole horizon of being staked out by "them," the experts. The highest satisfaction of the sightseer (not merely the tourist but any layman seer of sights) is that this sight should be certified as genuine. The worse of this impoverishment is that there is no sense of impoverishment. The surrender of title is so complete that it never even occurs to one to reassert title. A poor man may envy the rich man, but the sightseer does not envy the expert. It is due altogether to the eager surrender of sovereignty by the layman so that the may take up the role not of the person but of the consumer.

I do not refer only to the special relation of layman to theorist. I refer to the general situation in which sovereignty is surrendered to a class of privileged knowers, whether these be theorists or artists. A reader may surrender sovereignty over that which has been written about, just as a consumer may surrender sovereignty over a thing which has been written about, just as a consumer may surrender sovereignty over a thing which has been theorized about. The consumer is content to receive an experience just as it has been presented to him by theorists and planners. The reader may also be content to judge life by whether it has or has not been formulated by those who know and write about life. A young man goes to France. He too has a fair time of it, sees the sights, enjoys the food. On his last day, in fact as he sits in a restaurant in Le Havre waiting for his boat, something happens. A group of French students in the restaurant get into an impassioned argument over a recent play. A riot takes place. Madame le concierge joins in, swinging her mop at the rioters. Our young American is transported. This is "it." And he had almost left France without seeing "it"!

But the young man's delight is ambiguous. On the one hand, it is a pleasure for him to encounter the same Gallic temperament he had heard about from

Puccini and Rolland. But on the other hand, the source of his pleasure testifies to a certain alienation. For the young man is actually barred from a direct encounter with anything French excepting only that which has been set forth, authenticated by Puccini and Rolland—those who know. If he had encountered the restaurant scene without reading Hemingway, without knowing that the performance was so typically, charmingly French, he would not have been delighted. He would only have been anxious at seeing those things get so out of hand. The source of his delight is the sanction of those who know.

This loss of sovereignty is not a marginal process, as might appear from my example of estranged sightseers. It is a generalized surrender of the horizon to those experts within whose competence a particular segment of the horizon is thought to lie. Kwakuitls are surrendered to Franz Boas; decaying Southern mansions are surrendered to Faulkner and Tennessee Williams. So that, although it is by no means the intention of the expert to expropriate sovereignty—in fact he would not even know what sovereignty meant in this context—the danger of theory and consumption is a seduction and deprivation of the consumer.

In the New Mexico desert, natives occasionally come across strange-looking artifacts which have fallen from the skies and which are stenciled: *Return to U.S. Experimental Project, Alamogordo. Reward.* The finder returns the object and is rewarded. He knows nothing of the nature of the object he has found and does not care to know. The sole role of the native, the highest role he can play, is that of finder and returner of the mysterious equipment.

The same is true of the laymen's relation to *natural* objects in the modern technical society. No matter what the object or event is, whether it is a star, a swallow, a Kwakuitl, a "psychological phenomenon," the layman who confronts it does not confront it as a sovereign person, as Crusoe confronts a seashell he finds on the beach. The highest role he can conceive himself as playing is to be able to recognize the title of the object, to return it to the appropriate expert and have it certified as a genuine find. He does not even permit himself to see the thing—as Gerard Hopkins could see a rock or a cloud or a field. If anyone asks him why he doesn't look, he may reply that he didn't take that subject in college (or he hasn't read Faulkner).

This loss of sovereignty extends even to oneself. There is the neurotic who asks nothing more of his doctor than that his symptoms should prove interesting. When all else fails, the poor fellow has nothing to offer but his own neurosis. But even this is sufficient if only the doctor will show interest when he says, "Last night I had a curious sort of dream; perhaps it will be significant to one who knows about such things. It seems I was standing in a sort of alley—" (I have nothing else to offer you but my own unhappiness. Please say that it, at least, measures up, that it is a *proper* sort of unhappiness.)

II

A young Falkland Islander walking along a beach and spying a dead dogfish and going to work on it with his jackknife has, in a fashion wholly unprovided in modern educational theory, a great advantage over the Scarsdale high-school pupil who finds the dogfish on this laboratory desk. Similarly the citizen of Huxley's *Brave New World* who stumbles across a volume of Shakespeare in some vine-grown ruins and squats on a potsherd to read it is in a fairer way of getting at the sonnet than the Harvard sophomore taking English Poetry II.

The educator whose business it is to teach students biology or poetry is unaware of a whole ensemble of relations which exist between the student and the dog-fish and between the student and the Shakespeare sonnet. To put it bluntly: A student who has the desire to get at a dogfish or a Shakespeare sonnet may have the greatest difficulty in salvaging the creature itself from the educational package in which it is presented. The great difficulty is that he is not aware that there is a difficulty; surely, he thinks, in such a fine classroom, with such a fine textbook, the sonnet must come across! What's wrong with me?

The sonnet and the dogfish are obscured by the two different processes. The sonnet is obscured by the symbolic package which is formulated not by the sonnet itself but by the media through which the sonnet is transmitted, the media which the educators believe for some reason to be transparent. The new text-book, the type, the smell of the page, the classroom, the aluminum windows and the winter sky, the personality of Miss Hawkins—these media which are supposed to transmit the sonnet may only succeed in transmitting themselves. It is only the hardiest and cleverest of students who can salvage the sonnet from this many-tissued package. It is only the rarest student who knows that the sonnet must be salvaged from the package. (The educator is well aware that something is wrong, that there is a fatal gap between the student's learning and the student's life: the student reads the poem, appears to understand it, and gives all the answers. But what does he recall if he should happen to read a Shakespeare sonnet twenty years later? Does he recall the poem or does he recall the smell of the page and the smell of Miss Hawkins?)

One might object, pointing out that Huxley's citizen reading his sonnet in the ruins and the Falkland Islander looking at his dogfish on the beach also receive them in a certain package. Yes, but the difference lies in the funda-mental placement of the student in the world, a placement which makes it possible to extract the thing from the package. The pupil at Scarsdale High sees himself placed as a consumer receiving an experience-package; but the Falkland Islander exploring his dogfish is a person exercising the sovereign right of a person in his lordship and mastery of creation. He too could use an instructor and a book and a technique, but he would use them as his subordinates, just as he uses his jackknife. The biology student does not use his scalpel as an instrument, he uses it as a magic wand! Since it is a "scientific instrument," it should do "scientific things."

The dogfish is concealed in the same symbolic package as the sonnet. But the dogfish suffers an additional loss. As a consequence of this double deprivation, the Sarah Lawrence student who scores A in zoology is apt to know very little about a dogfish. She is twice removed from the dogfish, once by the symbolic complex by which the dogfish is concealed, once again by the spoliation of the dogfish by theory which renders it invisible. Through no fault of zoology instructors, it is nevertheless a fact that the zoology laboratory at Sarah Lawrence College is one of the few places in the world where it is all but impossible to see a dogfish.

The dogfish, the tree, the seashell, the American Negro, the dream, are rendered invisible by a shift of reality from concrete thing to theory which Whitehead has called the fallacy of misplaced concreteness. It is the mistaking of an idea, a principle, an abstraction, for the real. As a consequence of the shift, the "specimen" is seen as less real than the theory of the specimen. As Kierkegaard said, once a person is seen as a specimen of a race or a species, at that very moment he ceases to be an individual. Then there are no more individuals but only specimens.

To illustrate: A student enters a laboratory which, in the pragmatic view, offers the students the optimum conditions under which an educational experience may be had. In the existential view, however—that view of the student in which he is regarded not as a receptacle of experience but as a knowing being whose peculiar property it is to see himself as being in a certain situation—the modern laboratory could not have been more effectively designed to conceal the dogfish forever.

The student comes to his desk. On it, neatly arranged by his instructor, he finds his laboratory manual, a dissecting board, instruments, and a mimeographed list:

Exercise 22: Materials
1 dissecting board
1 scalpel
1 forceps
1 probe
1 bottle india ink and syringe
I specimen of *Squalus acanthias*

The clue of the situation in which the student finds himself is to be found in the last item: 1 specimen of *Squalus acanthias*.

The phrase *specimen of* expresses in the most succinct way imaginable the radical character of the loss of being which has occurred under his very nose. To refer to the dogfish, the unique concrete existence before him, as a "specimen of *Squalus acanthias*" reveals by its grammar the spoliation of the dogfish by the theoretical method. This phrase, *specimen of*, example of, instance of, indicates the ontological status of the individual creature in the eyes of the theorist. The dogfish itself is seen as a rather shabby expression on an ideal reality, the species *Squalus acanthias*. The result is the radical devaluation of the individual dogfish. (The *reductio ad absurdum* of Whitehead's shift is Toynbee's employment of it in his historical method. If a gram of NaCl is referred to by the chemist as a "sample of" NaCl, one may think of it as such and not much is missed by the oversight of the act of being of this particular pinch of salt, but when the Jews and the Jewish religion are understood as—in Toynbee's favorite phrase—a "classical example of" such and such a kind of *Voelkerwunderung*, we begin to suspect that something is being left out.)

If we look into the ways in which the student can recover the dogfish (or the sonnet), we will see that they have in common the strategem of avoiding the educator's direct presentation of the object as a lesson to be learned and restoring access to sonnet and dogfish as being to be known, reasserting the sovereignty of knower over known.

In truth, the biography of scientists and poets is usually the story of the discovery of the indirect approach, the circumvention of the educator's presentation—the young man who was sent to the *Technikum* and on his way fall into the habit of loitering in book stores and reading poetry; or the young man dutifully attending law school who on the way became curious about the comings and goings of ants. One remembers the scene in *The Heart Is a Lonely Hunter* where the girl hides in the bushes to hear the Capehart in the big house play Beethoven. Perhaps she was the lucky one after all. Think of the unhappy souls inside, who see the record, worry about scratches, and most of all worry about whether they are *getting it*, whether they are bona fide music lovers. What is the best way to hear Beethoven: sitting in a proper silence around the Capehart or eavesdropping from an azalea bush?

However it may come about, we notice two traits of the second situation: (1) an openness of the thing before one—instead of being an exercise to be learned according to an approved mode, it is a garden of delights which beckons to one; (2) a sovereignty of the knower—instead of being a consumer of a prepared experience, I am a sovereign wayfarer, a wanderer in the neighborhood of being who stumbles into the garden.

One can think of two sorts of circumstances through which the thing may be restored to the person. (There is always, of course, the direct recovery: A student may simply be strong enough, brave enough, clever enough to take the dogfish and the sonnet by storm, to wrest control of it from the educators and the educational packages.) First by ordeal: The Bomb falls; when the young man recovers consciousness in the shambles of the biology laboratory, there not ten inches from his nose lies the dogfish. Now all at once he can see it directly without let, just as the exile or the prisoner or the sick man sees the sparrow at his window in all its inexhaustibility; just as the commuter who has had a heart attack sees his own hand for the first time. In these cases, the simulacrum of everydayness and of consumption has been destroyed by disaster; in the case of the bomb, literally destroyed. Secondly, by apprenticeship to a great man: one day a great biologist walks into the laboratory; he stops in front of our student's desk; he leans over, picks up the dogfish, and ignoring instruments and procedure, probes with a broken fingernail into the little carcass. "Now here is a curious business," he says, ignoring also the proper jargon of the speciality. "Look here how this little duct reverses its direction and drops into the pelvis. Now if you would look into a coelacanth, you would see that it—" And all at once the student can see. The technician and the sophomore who loves his textbooks are always offended by the genuine research man because the latter is usually a little vague and always humble before the thing; he doesn't have much use for the equipment or the jargon. Whereas the technician is never vague and never humble before the thing; he holds the thing disposed of by the principle, the formula, the textbook outline; and he thinks a great deal of equipment and jargon.

But since neither of these methods of recovering the dogfish is pedagogically feasible—perhaps the great man even less so than the Bomb—I wish to propose the following educational technique which should prove equally effective for Harvard and Shreveport High School. I propose that English poetry and biology should be taught as usual, but that at irregular intervals, poetry students should find dogfishes on their desks and biology students should find Shakespeare sonnets on their dissection boards. I am serious in declaring that a Sarah Lawrence English major who began poking about in a dogfish with a bobby pin would learn more in thirty minutes than a biology major in a whole semester; and that the latter upon reading on her dissecting board

> That time of year Thou may'st in me behold
> When yellow leaves, or none, or few, do hang
> Upon those boughs which shake against the cold—
> Bare ruin'd choirs where late the sweet birds sang

might catch fire at the beauty of it.

The situation of the tourist at the Grand Canyon and the biology student are special cases of a predicament in which everyone finds himself in a modern technical society—a society, that is, in which there is a division between expert and layman, planner and consumer, in which experts and planners take special measures to teach and edify the consumer. The measures taken are measures appropriate to the consumer: the expert and the planner *know* and *plan*, but the consumer *needs* and *experiences*.

There is a double deprivation. First, the thing is lost through its packaging. The very means by which the thing is presented for consumption, the very techniques by which the thing is made available as an item of need-satisfaction, these very means operate to remove the thing from the sovereignty of the knower. A loss of title occurs. The measures which the museum curator takes to present the thing to the public are self-liquidating. The upshot of the curator's efforts are not that everyone can see the exhibit but that no one can see it. The curator protests: why are they so different? Why do they even deface the exhibit? Don't they know it is theirs? But it is not theirs. It is his, the curator's. By the most exclusive sort of zoning, the museum exhibit, the park oak tree, is part of an ensemble, a package, which is almost impenetrable to them. The archaeologist who puts his find in a museum so that everyone can see it accomplishes the reverse of his expectations. The result of his action is that no one can see it now but the archaeologist. He would have done better to keep it in his pocket and show it now and then to strangers.

The tourist who carves his initials in a public place, which is theoretically "his" in the first place, has good reasons for doing so, reasons which the exhibitor and planner know nothing about. He does so because in his role of consumer of an experience (a "recreational experience" to satisfy a "recreational need") he knows that he is disinherited. He is deprived of his title over being. He knows very well that he is in a very special sort of zone in which his only rights are the rights of a consumer. He moves like a ghost through schoolroom, city streets, trains, parks, movies. He carves his initials as a last desperate measure to escape his ghostly role of consumer. He is saying in effect: I am not a ghost after all; I am a sovereign person. And he establishes title the only way remaining to him, by staking his claim over one square inch of wood or stone.

Does this mean that we should get rid of museums? No, but it means that the sightseer should be prepared to enter into a struggle to recover sight from a museum.

The second loss is the spoliation of the thing, the tree, the rock, the swallow, by the layman's misunderstanding of scientific theory. He believes that the thing is *disposed of* by theory, that it stands in the Platonic relation of being a *specimen* of such and such an underlying principle. In the transmission of scientific theory from theorist to layman, the expectation of the theorist is reversed. Instead of marvels of the universe being made available to the public, the universe is disposed of by theory. The loss of sovereignty takes this form: as a result of the science of botany, trees are not made available to every man. On the contrary, the tree loses its proper density and

81

mystery as a concrete existent and, as merely another *specimen* of a species, becomes itself nugatory.

Does this mean that there is no use in taking biology at Harvard and Shreveport High? No, but it means that the student should know what a fight he has on his hands to rescue the specimen from the educational package. The educator is only partly to blame. For there is nothing the educator can do to provide for this need of the student. Everything the educator does only succeeds in becoming, for the student, part of the educational package. The highest role of the educator is the maieutic role of Socrates: to help the student come to himself not as a consumer of experience but as a sovereign individual.

The thing is twice lost to the consumer. First, sovereignty is lost: it is theirs, not his. Second, it is radically devalued by theory. This is a loss which has been brought about by science but through no fault of the scientist and through no fault of scientific theory. The loss has come about as a consequence of the seduction of the layman by science. The layman will be seduced as long as he regards beings as consumer items to be experienced rather than prizes to be won, and as long as he waives his sovereign rights as a person and accepts his role of consumer as the highest estate to which the layman can aspire.

As Mounier said, the person is not something one can study and provide for; he is something one struggles for. But unless he also struggles for himself, unless he knows that there is a struggle, he is going to be just what the planners think he is.

The Corner of the Eye

Lewis Thomas

There are some things that human beings can see only out of the corner of the eye. The niftiest examples of this gift, familiar to all children, are small, faint stars. When you look straight at one such star, it vanishes; when you move your eyes to stare into the space nearby, it reappears. If you pick two faint stars, side by side, and focus on one of the pair, it disappears and now you can see the other in the corner of your eye, and you can move your eyes back and forth, turning off the star in the center of your retina and switching the other one on. There is a physiological explanation for the phenomenon: we have more rods, the cells we use for light perception, at the periphery of our retinas, more cones, for perceiving color, at the center.

Something like this happens in music. You cannot really hear certain sequences of notes in a Bach fugue unless at the same time there are other notes being sounded, dominating the field. The real meaning in music comes from tones only audible in the corner of the mind.

I used to worry that computers would become so powerful and sophisticated as to take the place of human minds. The notion of Artificial Intelligence used to scare me half to death. Already, a large enough machine can do all sorts of intelligent things beyond our capacities: calculate in a split second the answers to mathematical problems requiring years for a human brain, draw accurate pictures from memory, even manufacture successions of sounds with a disarming resemblance to real music. Computers can translate textbooks, write dissertations of their own for doctorates, even speak in machine-tooled, inhuman phonemes any words read off from a printed page. They can communicate with one another, holding consultations and committee meetings of their own in networks around the earth.

Computers can make errors, of course, and do so all the time in small, irritating ways, but the mistakes can be fixed and nearly always are. In this respect they are fundamentally inhuman, and here is the relaxing thought: computers will not take over the world, they cannot replace us, because they are not designed, as we are, for ambiguity.

Imagine the predicament faced by a computer programmed to make language, not the interesting communication in sounds made by vervets or in symbols by brilliant chimpanzee prodigies, but real human talk. The grammar would not be too difficult, and there would be no problem in constructing a vocabulary of etymons, the original, pure, unambiguous words used to name real things. The impossibility would come in making the necessary mistakes we humans make with words instinctively, intuitively, as we build our kinds of language, changing the meanings to imply quite different things, constructing and elaborating the varieties of ambiguity without which speech can never become human speech.

Look at the record of language if you want to glimpse the special qualities of the human mind that lie beyond the reach of any machine. Take, for example, the metaphors we use in everyday speech to tell ourselves who we are, where we live, and where we come from.

The earth is a good place to begin. The word "earth" is used to name the ground we walk on, the soil in which we grow plants or dig clams, and the planet itself; we also use it to describe all of humanity ("the whole earth responds to the beauty of a child," we say to each other).

The earliest word for earth in our language was the Indo-European root *dhghem*, and look what we did with it. We turned it, by adding suffixes, into *humus* in Latin; today we call the complex polymers that hold fertile soil together "humic" acids, and somehow or other the same root became "humility." With another suffix the word became "human." Did the earth become human, or did the human emerge from the earth? One answer may lie in that nice cognate word "humble." "Humane" was built on, extending the meaning of both the earth and ourselves. In ancient Hebrew, *adamha* was the word for earth, *adam* for man. What computer could run itself through such manipulations as those?

We came at the same system of defining ourselves from the other direction. The word *wiros* was the first root for man; it took us in our vanity on to "virile" and "virtue," but also turned itself into the Germanic word *weraldh*, meaning the life of man, and thence in English to our word "world."

There is a deep hunch in this kind of etymology. The world of man derives from this planet, shares origin with the life of the soil, lives in humility with all the rest of life. I cannot imagine programming a computer to think up an idea like that, not a twentieth-century computer, anyway.

The world began with what it is now the fashion to call the "Big Bang." Characteristically, we have assigned the wrong words for the very beginning of the earth and ourselves, in order to evade another term that would cause this century embarrassment. It could not, of course, have been a bang of any sort, with no atmosphere to conduct the waves of sound, and no ears. It was something else, occurring in the most absolute silence we can imagine. It was the Great Light.

We say it had been chaos before, but it was not the kind of place we use the word "chaos" for today, things tumbling over each other and bumping around. Chaos did not have that meaning in Greek; it simply meant empty.

We took it, in our words, from chaos to cosmos, a word that simply meant order, cosmetic. We perceived the order in surprise, and our cosmologists and physicists continue to find new and astonishing aspects of the order. We made up the word "universe" from the whole affair, meaning literally turning everything into one thing. We used to say it was a miracle, and we still permit ourselves to refer to the whole universe as a marvel, holding in our unconscious minds the original root meaning of these two words, miracle and marvel—from the ancient root word *smei,* signifying a smile. It immensely pleases a human being to see something never seen before, even more to learn something never known before, most of all to think something never thought before. The rings of Saturn are the latest surprise. All my physicist friends are enchanted by this phenomenon, marveling at the small violations of the laws of planetary mechanics, shocked by the unaccountable braids and spokes stuck there among the rings like graffiti. It is nice for physicists to see something new and inexplicable; it means that the laws of nature are once again about to be amended by a new footnote.

The greatest surprise of all lies within our own local, suburban solar system. It is not Mars; Mars was surprising in its way but not flabbergasting; it was a disappointment not to find evidences of life, and there was some sadness in the pictures sent back to earth from the Mars Lander, that lonely long-legged apparatus poking about with its jointed arm, picking up sample after sample of the barren Mars soil, looking for any flicker of life and finding none; the only sign of life on Mars was the Lander itself, an extension of the human mind all the way from earth to Mars, totally alone.

Nor is Saturn the great surprise, nor Jupiter, nor Venus, nor Mercury, nor any of the glimpses of the others.

The overwhelming astonishment, the queerest structure we know about so far in the whole universe, the greatest of all cosmological scientific puzzles, confounding all our efforts to comprehend it, is the earth. We are only now beginning to appreciate how strange and splendid it is, how it catches the breath, the loveliest object afloat around the sun, enclosed in its own blue bubble of atmosphere, manufacturing and breathing its own oxygen, fixing its own nitrogen from the air into its own soil, generating its own weather at the surface of its rain forests, constructing its own carapace from living parts: chalk cliffs, coral reefs, old fossils from earlier forms of life now covered by layers of new life meshed together around the globe, Troy upon Troy.

Seen from the right distance, from the corner of the eye of an extraterrestrial visitor, it must surely seem a single creature, clinging to the round warm stone, turning in the sun.

The Attic of the Brain

Lewis Thomas

My parents' house had an attic, the darkest and strangest part of the building, reachable only by placing a stepladder beneath the trapdoor and filled with unidentifiable articles too important to be thrown out with the trash but no longer suitable to have at hand. This mysterious space was the memory of the place. After many years all the things deposited in it became, one by one, lost to consciousness. But they were still there, we knew, safely and comfortably stored in the tissues of the house.

These days most of us live in smaller, more modern houses or in apartments, and attics have vanished. Even the deep closets in which we used to pile things up for temporary forgetting are rarely designed into new homes.

Everything now is out in the open, openly acknowledged and displayed, and whenever we grow tired of a memory, an old chair, a trunkful of old letters, they are carted off to the dump for burning.

This has seemed a healthier way to live, except maybe for the smoke—everything out to be looked at, nothing strange hidden under the roof, nothing forgotten because of no place left in impenetrable darkness to forget. Openness is the new life-style, no undisclosed belongings, no private secrets. Candor is the rule in architecture. The house is a machine for living, and what kind of a machine would hide away its worn-out, obsolescent parts?

But it is in our nature as human beings to clutter, and we hanker for places set aside, reserved for storage. We tend to accumulate and outgrow possessions at the same time, and it is an endlessly discomforting mental task to keep sorting out the ones to get rid of. We might, we think, remember them later and find a use for them, and if they are gone for good, off to the dump, this is a source of nervousness. I think it may be one of the reasons we drum our fingers so much these days.

We might take a lesson here from what has been learned about our brains in this century. We thought we discovered, first off, the attic, although its existence has been mentioned from time to time by all the people we used to call great writers. What we really found was the trapdoor and a stepladder, and off we clambered, shining flashlights into the corners, vacuuming the dust out of bureau drawers, puzzling over the names of objects, tossing them down to the floor below, and finally paying around fifty dollars an hour to have them carted off for burning.

After several generations of this new way of doing things we took up openness and candor with the febrile intensity of a new religion, everything laid out in full view, and as in the design of our new houses it seemed a healthier way to live, except maybe again for smoke.

And now, I think, we have a new kind of worry. There is no place for functionless, untidy, inexplicable notions, no dark comfortable parts of the mind to hide away the things we'd like to keep but at the same time forget. The attic is still there, but with the trapdoor always open and the stepladder in place we are always in and out of it, flashing lights around, naming everything, unmystified.

I have an earnest proposal for psychiatry, a novel set of therapeutic rules, although I know it means waiting in line.

Bring back the old attic. Give new instructions to the patients who are made nervous by our times, including me, to make a conscious effort to hide a reasonable proportion of thought. It would have to be a gradual process, considering how far we have come in the other direction talking, talking all the way. Perhaps only one or two thoughts should be repressed each day, at the outset. The easiest, gentlest way might be to start with dreams, first by forbidding the patient to mention any dream, much less to recount its details, then encouraging the outright forgetting that there was a dream at all, remembering nothing beyond the vague sense that during sleep there had been the familiar sound of something shifting and sliding, up under the roof.

We might, in this way, regain the kind of spontaneity and zest for ideas, things popping into the mind, uncontrollable and ungovernable thoughts, the feel that this notion is somehow connected unaccountably with that one. We could come again into possession of real memory, the kind of memory that can come only from jumbled forgotten furniture, old photographs, fragments of music.

It has been one of the great errors of our time to think that by thinking about thinking, and then talking about it, we could possibly straighten out and tidy up our minds. There is no delusion more damaging than to get the idea in your head that you understand the functioning of your own brain. Once you acquire such a notion, you run the danger of moving in to take charge, guiding your thoughts, shepherding your mind from place to place, *controlling* it, making lists of regulations. The human mind is not meant to be governed, certainly not by any book of rules yet written; it is supposed to run itself, and we are obliged to follow it along, trying to keep up with it as best we can. It is all very well to be aware of your awareness, even proud of it, but never try to operate it. You are not up to the job.

I leave it to the analysts to work out the techniques for doing what now needs doing. They are presumably the professionals most familiar with the route, and all they have to do is turn back and go the other way, session by session, step by step. It takes a certain amount of hard swallowing and a lot of revised jargon, and I have great sympathy for their plight, but it is time to reverse course.

If after all, as seems to be true, we are endowed with unconscious minds in our brains, these should be regarded as normal structures, installed wherever they are for a purpose. I am not sure what they are built to contain, but as a biologist, impressed by the usefulness of everything alive, I would take it for granted that they are useful, probably indispensable organs of thought. It cannot be a bad thing to own one, but I would no more think of meddling with it than trying to exorcise my liver, an equally mysterious apparatus. Until we know a lot more, it would be wise, as we have learned from other fields in medicine, to let them be, above all not to interfere. Maybe, even—and this is the notion I wish to suggest to my psychiatric friends—to stock them up, put more things into them, make *use* of them. Forget whatever you feel like forgetting. From time to time, practice *not* being open, discover new things *not* to talk about, learn reserve, hold the tongue. But above all, develop the human talent for forgetting words, phrases, whole unwelcome sentences, all experiences involving wincing. If we should ever lose the loss of memory, we might lose as well that most attractive of signals ever flashed from the human face, the blush. If we should give away the capacity for embarrassment, the touch of fingertips might be the next to go, and then the suddenness of laughter, the unaccountable sure sense of something gone wrong, and, finally, the marvelous conviction that being human is the best thing to be.

Attempting to operate one's own mind, powered by such a magical instrument as the human brain, strikes me as rather like using the world's biggest computer to add columns of figures, or towing a Rolls-Royce with a nylon rope.

I have tried to think of a name for the new professional activity, but each time I think of a good one I forget it before I can get it written down. Psychorepression is the only one I've hung on to, but I can't guess at the fee schedule.

The Bird of Paradise:
The Hunter and the Poet

E. O. Wilson

[handwritten marginalia: Presents idea that science and art should work together to give bigger picture]

[handwritten marginalia: I]

The role of science, like that of art, is to blend proximate imagery with more distant meaning, the parts we already understand with those given as new into larger patterns that are coherent enough to be acceptable as truth. Biologists know this relation by intuition during the course of fieldwork, as they struggle to make order out of the infinitely varying patterns of nature.

[handwritten marginalia: II — about to take trek]

Picture the Huon Peninsula of New Guinea, about the size and shape of Rhode Island, a weathered horn projecting from the northeastern coast of the main island. When I was twenty-five, with a fresh Ph.D. from Harvard and dreams of physical adventure in far-off places with unpronounceable names, I gathered all the courage I had and made a difficult and uncertain trek directly across the peninsular base. My aim was to collect a sample of ants and a few other kinds of small animals up from the lowlands to the highest part of the mountains. To the best of my knowledge I was the first biologist to take this particular route. I knew that almost everything I found would be worth recording, and all the specimens collected would be welcomed into museums.

[handwritten marginalia: III]

Three days' walk from a mission station near the southern Lae coast brought me to the spine of the Sarawaget range, 12,000 feet above sea level. I was above treeline, in a grassland sprinkled with cycads, squat gymnospermous plants that resemble stunted palm trees and date from the Mesozoic era; closely similar ancestral forms might have been browsed by dinosaurs 80 million years before. On a chill morning when the clouds lifted and the sun shone brightly, my Papuan guides stopped hunting alpine wallabies with dogs and arrows, I stopped putting beetles and frogs into bottles of alcohol, and together we scanned the rare panoramic view. To the north we could make out the Bismarck Sea, to the south the Markham Valley and the more distant Herzog Mountains. The primary forest covering most of this mountainous country was broken into bands of different vegetation according to elevation. The zone just below us was the cloud forest, a labyrinth of interlocking trunks and branches blanketed by a thick layer of moss, orchids, and other epiphytes that ran unbroken off the tree trunks and across the ground. To follow game

91

trails across this high country was like crawling through a dimly illuminated cave lined with a spongy green carpet.

A thousand feet below, the vegetation opened up a bit and assumed the appearance of typical lowland rain forest, except that the trees were denser and smaller and only a few flared out into a circle of blade-thin buttresses at the base. This is the zone botanists call the mid-mountain forest. It is an enchanted world of thousands of species of birds, frogs, insects, flowering plants, and other organisms, many found nowhere else. Together they form one of the richest and most nearly pure segments of the Papuan flora and fauna. To visit the mid-mountain forest is to see life as it existed before the coming of man thousands of years ago.

The jewel of the setting is the male Emperor of Germany bird of paradise (*Paradisaea guilielmi*), arguably the most beautiful bird in the world, certainly one of the twenty or so most striking in appearance. By moving quietly along secondary trails you might glimpse one on a lichen-encrusted branch near the treetops. Its head is shaped like that of a crow—no surprise, since the birds of paradise and crows have a close common lineage—but there the outward resemblance to any ordinary bird ends. The crown and upper breast of the bird are metallic oil-green and shine in the sunlight. The back is glossy yellow, the wings and tail deep maroon. Tufts of ivory-white plumes sprout from the flanks and sides of the breast, turning lacy in texture toward the tips. The plume rectrices continue on as wirelike appendages past the breast and tail for a distance equal to the full length of the bird. The bill is blue-gray, the eyes clear amber, the claws brown and black.

In the mating season the male joins others in leks, common courtship arenas in the upper tree branches, where they display their dazzling ornaments to the more somberly caparisoned females. The male spreads his wings and vibrates them while lifting the gossamer flank plumes. He calls loudly with bubbling and flutelike notes and turns upside down on the perch, spreading wings and tail and pointing his rectrices skyward. The dance reaches a climax as he fluffs up the green breast feathers and opens out the flank plumes until they form a brilliant white circle around his body, with only the head, tail, and wings projecting beyond. The male sways gently from side to side, causing the plumes to wave gracefully as if caught in an errant breeze. Seen from a distance, his body now resembles a spinning and slightly out-of-focus white disk.

This improbable spectacle in the Huon forest has been fashioned by thousands of generations of natural selection in which males competed and females made choices, and the accouterments of display were driven to a visual extreme. But this is only one trait, seen in physiological time and thought about at a single level of causation. Beneath its plumed surface, the Emperor

92

of Germany bird of paradise possesses an architecture marking the culmination of an equally ancient history, with details exceeding those that can be imagined from the elaborate visible display of color and dance.

Consider one such bird analytically, as an object of biological research. Encoded within its chromosomes is the developmental program that has led to a male *Paradisaea guilielmi*. Its nervous system is a structure of fiber tracts more complex than that of any existing computer, and as challenging as all the rain forests of New Guinea surveyed on foot. Someday microscopic studies will permit us to trace the events culminating in the electric commands carried by the efferent neurons to the skeletal-muscular system and to reproduce, in part, the dance of the courting male. We will be able to dissect and understand this machinery at the level of the cell through enzymatic catalysis, microfilament configuration, and active sodium transport during electric discharge. Because biology sweeps the full range of space and time, more and more discoveries will renew our sense of wonder at each step of research. Altering the scale of perception to the micrometer and millisecond, the cellular biologist's trek parallels that of the naturalist across the land. He looks out from his own version of the mountain crest. His spirit of adventure, as well as personal history of hardship, misdirection, and triumph, is fundamentally the same.

Described this way, the bird of paradise may seem to have been turned into a metaphor of what humanists dislike most about science; that it reduces nature and is insensitive to art, that scientists are conquistadors who melt down the Inca gold. But science is not just analytic; it is also synthetic. It uses artlike intuition and imagery. True, in the early analytic stages, individual behavior can be mechanically reduced to the level of genes and neurosensory cells. But in the synthetic phase even the most elementary activity of these biological units is seen to create rich and subtle patterns at the levels of organism and society. The outer qualities of *Paradisaea guilielmi*, its plumes, dance, and daily life, are functional traits open to a deeper understanding through the exact description of their constituent parts. They can be redefined as holistic properties that alter our perception and emotion in surprising ways.

There will come a time when a bird of paradise is reconstituted through a synthesis of all the hard-won analytic information. The mind, exercising a newfound power, will journey back to the familiar world of seconds and centimeters, where once again the glittering plumage takes form and is viewed at a distance through a network of leaves and mist. Once again we see the bright eye open, the head swivel, the wings extend. But the familiar motions are now viewed across a far greater range of cause and effect. The species is understood more completely; misleading illusions have given way to more

93

comprehensive light and wisdom. With the completion of one full cycle of intellect, the scientist's search for the true material nature of the species is partially replaced by the more enduring responses of the hunter and poet.

XI   What are these ancient responses? The full answer is available only through a combined idiom of science and the humanities, whereby the investigation turns back into itself. The human being, like the bird of paradise, awaits our examination in the analytic-synthetic manner. Feeling and myth can be viewed at a distance through physiological time, idiosyncratically, in the manner of traditional art. But they can also be penetrated more deeply than was ever possible in the prescientific age, to their physical basis in the processes of mental development, the brain structure, and indeed the genes themselves. It may even be possible to trace them back beyond the formation of cultures to the evolutionary origins of human nature. As each new phase of synthesis emerges from biological inquiry, the humanities will expand their reach and capability. In symmetric fashion, with each redirection of the humanities, science will add dimensions to human biology.

Science and the Humanities

Stranger in the Village

James Baldwin

From all available evidence no black man had ever set foot in this tiny Swiss village before I came. I was told before arriving that I would probably be a "sight" for the village; I took this to mean that people of my complexion were rarely seen in Switzerland, and also that city people are always something of a "sight" outside of the city. It did not occur to me—possibly because I am an American—that there would be people anywhere who had never seen a Negro.

It is a fact that cannot be explained on the basis of the inaccessibility of the village. The village is very high, but it is only four hours from Milan and three hours from Lausanne. It is true that it is virtually unknown. Few people making plans for a holiday would elect to come here. On the other hand, the villagers are able, presumably, to come and go as they please—which they do: to another town at the foot of the mountain, with a population of approximately five thousand, the nearest place to see a movie or go to the bank. In the village there is no movie house, no bank, no library, no theater; very few radios, one jeep, one station wagon; and, at the moment, one typewriter, mine, an invention which the woman next door to me here had never seen. There are about six hundred people living here, all Catholic—I conclude this from the fact that the Catholic church is open all year round, whereas the Protestant chapel, set off on a hill a little removed from the village, is open only in the summertime when the tourists arrive. There are four or five hotels, all closed now, and four or five *bistros*, of which, however, only two do any business during the winter. These two do not do a great deal, for life in the village seems to end around nine or ten o'clock. There are a few stores, butcher, baker, *épicerie*, a hardware store, and a money-changer—who cannot change travelers' checks, but must send them down to the bank, an operation which takes two or three days. There is something called the *Ballet Haus*, closed in the winter and used for God knows what, certainly not ballet, during the summer. There seems to be only one schoolhouse in the village, and this for the quite young children; I suppose this to mean that their older brothers and sisters at some point descend from these mountains in order to complete their education—possibly, again, to the town just below. The landscape is absolutely

97

forbidding, mountains towering on all four sides, ice and snow as far as the eye can reach. In this white wilderness, men and women and children move all day, carrying washing, wood, buckets of milk or water, sometimes skiing on Sunday afternoons. All week long boys and young men are to be seen shoveling snow off the rooftops, or dragging wood down from the forest in sleds.

The village's only real attraction, which explains the tourist season, is the hot spring water. A disquietingly high proportion of these tourists are cripples, or semicripples, who come year after year—from other parts of Switzerland, usually—to take the waters. This lends the village, at the height of the season, a rather terrifying air of sanctity, as though it were a lesser Lourdes. There is often something beautiful, there is always something awful, in the spectacle of a person who has lost one of his faculties, a faculty he never questioned until it was gone, and who struggles to recover it. Yet people remain people, on crutches or indeed on deathbeds; and whenever I passed, the first summer I was here, among the native villagers or among the lame, a wind passed with me—of astonishment, curiosity, amusement, and outrage. That first summer I stayed two weeks and never intended to return. But I did return in the winter, to work; the village offers, obviously, no distractions whatever and has the further advantage of being extremely cheap. Now it is winter again, a year later, and I am here again. Everyone in the village knows my name, though they scarcely ever use it, knows that I come from America—though, this, apparently, they will never really believe: black men come from Africa—and everyone knows that I am the friend of the son of a woman who was born here, and that I am staying in their chalet. But I remain as much a stranger today as I was the first day I arrived, and the children shout *Neger! Neger!* as I walk along the streets.

It must be admitted that in the beginning I was far too shocked to have any real reaction. In so far as I reacted at all, I reacted by trying to be pleasant—it being a great part of the American Negro's education (long before he goes to school) that he must make people "like" him. This smile-and-the-world-smiles-with-you routine worked about as well in this situation as it had in the situation for which it was designed, which is to say that it did not work at all. No one, after all, can be liked whose human weight and complexity cannot be, or has not been, admitted. My smile was simply another unheard-of phenomenon which allowed them to see my teeth—they did not, really, see my smile and I began to think that, should I take to snarling, no one would notice any difference. All of the physical characteristics of the Negro which had caused me, in America, a very different and almost forgotten pain were nothing less than miraculous—or infernal—in the eyes of the village people. Some thought my hair was the color of tar, that it had the texture of wire, or the texture of cotton. It was jocularly suggested that I might let it all grow long and make myself a winter coat. If I sat in the sun for more than five minutes some daring creature was certain to come along and gingerly put his fingers on my hair, as though he were afraid of an electric shock, or put his hand on my hand, astonished that the color did not rub off. In all of this, in which it must be conceded there was the charm of genuine wonder and in which there was certainly no element of intentional unkindness, there was yet no suggestion that I was human: I was simply a living wonder.

I knew that they did not mean to be unkind, and I know it now; it is necessary, nevertheless, for me to repeat this to myself each time that I walk out of the chalet. The children who shout *Neger!* have no way of knowing the echoes this sound raises in me. They are brimming with good humor and the more daring swell with pride when I stop to speak with them. Just the same, there are days when I cannot pause and smile, when I have no heart to play with them; when, indeed, I mutter sourly to myself, exactly as I muttered on the streets of a city these children have never seen, when I was no bigger than these children are now: *Your* mother *was a nigger.* Joyce is right about history being a nightmare—but it may be the nightmare from which no one *can* awaken. People are trapped in history and history is trapped in them.

There is a custom in the village—I am told it is repeated in many villages—of "buying" African natives for the purpose of converting them to Christianity. There stands in the church all year round a small box with a slot for money, decorated with a black figurine, and into this box the villagers drop their francs. During the *carnaval* which precedes Lent, two village children have their faces blackened—out of which bloodless darkness their blue eyes shine like ice—and fantastic horsehair wigs are placed on their blond heads; thus disguised, they solicit among the villagers for money for the missionaries in Africa. Between the box in the church and the blackened children, the village "bought" last year six or eight African natives. This was reported to me with pride by the wife of one of the *bistro* owners and I was careful to express astonishment and pleasure at the solicitude shown by the village for the souls of black folk. The *bistro* owner's wife beamed with a pleasure far more genuine than my own and seemed to feel that I might now breathe more easily concerning the souls of at least six of my kinsmen.

I tried not to think of these so lately baptized kinsmen, of the price paid for them, or the peculiar price they themselves would pay, and said nothing about my father, who having taken his own conversion too literally never, at bottom, forgave the white world (which he described as heathen) for having saddled him with a Christ in whom, to judge at least from their treatment of him, they themselves no longer believed. I thought of white men arriving for the first time in an African village, strangers there, as I am a stranger here, and tried to imagine the astounded populace touching their hair and marveling at the color of their skin. But there is a great difference between being the first white man to be seen by Africans and being the first black man to be seen by whites. The white man takes the astonishment as tribute, for he arrives to conquer and to convert the natives, whose inferiority in relation to himself is not even to be questioned; whereas I, without a thought of conquest, find myself among a people whose culture controls me, has even, in a sense, created me, people who have cost me more in anguish and rage than they will ever know, who yet do not even know of my existence. The astonishment with which I might have greeted them, should they have stumbled into my African village a few hundred years ago, might have rejoiced their hearts. But the astonishment with which they greet me today can only poison mine.

And this is so despite everything I may do to feel differently, despite my friendly conversations with the *bistro* owner's wife, despite their three-year-old son who has at last become my friend, despite the *saluts* and *bonsoirs* which I exchange with people as I walk, despite the fact that I know that no individual can be taken to task for what history is doing, or has done. I saw that the culture of these people controls me—but they can scarcely be held responsible for European culture. America comes out of Europe, but these people have never seen America, nor have most of them seen more of Europe than the hamlet at the foot of their mountain. Yet they move with an authority which I shall never have; and they regard me, quite rightly, not only as a stranger in their village but as a suspect latecomer, bearing no credentials, to everything they have—however unconsciously—inherited.

For this village, even were it incomparably more remote and incredibly more primitive, is the West, the West onto which I have been so strangely grafted. These people cannot be, from the point of view of power, strangers anywhere in the world; they have made the modern world, in effect, even if they do not know it. The most illiterate among them is related, in a way that I am not, to Dante, Shakespeare, Michelangelo, Aeschylus, Da Vinci, Rembrandt, and Racine; the cathedral at Chartres says something to them which it cannot say to me, as indeed would New York's Empire State Building, should anyone here ever see it. Out of their hymns and dances come Beethoven and Bach. Go back a few centuries and they are in their full glory—but I am in Africa, watching the conquerors arrive.

The rage of the disesteemed is personally fruitless, but it is also absolutely inevitable; this rage, so generally discounted, so little understood even among the people whose daily bread it is, is one of the things that makes history. Rage can only with difficulty, and never entirely, be brought under the domination of the intelligence and is therefore not susceptible to any arguments whatever. This is a fact which ordinary representatives of the *Herrenvolk*, having never felt this rage and being unable to imagine it, quite fail to understand. Also, rage cannot be hidden, it can only be dissembled. This dissembling deludes the thoughtless, and strengthens rage and adds, to rage, contempt. There are, no doubt, as many ways of coping with the resulting complex of tensions as there are black men in the world, but no black man can hope ever to be entirely liberated from this internal warfare—rage, dissembling, and contempt having inevitably accompanied his first realization of the power of white men. What is crucial here is that, since white men represent in the black man's world so heavy a weight, white men have for black men a reality which is far from being reciprocal; and hence all black men have toward all white men an attitude which is designed, really, either to rob the white man of the jewel of his naïveté, or else to make it cost him dear.

The black man insists, by whatever means he finds at his disposal, that the white man cease to regard him as an exotic rarity and recognize him as a human being. This is a very charged and difficult moment, for there is a great deal of will power involved in the white man's naïveté. Most people are not naturally reflective any more than they are naturally malicious, and the white man prefers to keep the black man at a certain human remove because it is easier for him thus to preserve his simplicity and avoid being called to account for crimes committed by his forefathers, or his neighbors. He is inescapably aware, nevertheless, that he is in a better position in the world than black men are, nor can he quite put to death the suspicion that he is hated by black men therefore. He does not wish to be hated, neither does he wish to change places, and at this point in his uneasiness he can scarcely avoid having recourse to those legends which white men have created about black men, the most usual affect of which is that the white man finds himself enmeshed, so to speak, in his own language which describes hell, as well as the attributes which lead one to hell, as being as black as night.

Every legend, moreover, contains its residuum of truth, and the root function of language is to control the universe by describing it. It is of quite considerable significance that black men remain, in the imagination, and in overwhelming numbers in fact, beyond the disciplines of salvation; and this despite the fact that the West has been "buying" African natives for centuries. There is, I should hazard, an instantaneous necessity to be divorced from this so visibly unsaved stranger, in whose heart, moreover, one cannot guess what dreams of vengeance are being nourished; and, at the same time, there are few things on earth more attractive than the idea of the unspeakable liberty which is allowed the unredeemed. When, beneath the black mask, a human being begins to make himself felt one cannot escape a certain awful wonder as to what kind of human being it is. What one's imagination makes of other people is dictated, of course, by the laws of one's own personality and it is one of the ironies of black-white relations that, by means of what the white man imagines the black man to be, the black man is enabled to know who the white man is.

I have said, for example, that I am as much a stranger in this village today as I was the first summer I arrived, but this is not quite true. The villagers wonder less about the texture of my hair than they did then, and wonder rather more about me. And the fact that their wonder now exists on another level is reflected in their attitudes and in their eyes. There are the children who make those delightful, hilarious, sometimes astonishingly grave overtures of friendship in the unpredictable fashion of children; other children, having been taught that the devil is a black man, scream in genuine anguish as I approach. Some of the older women never pass without a friendly greeting, never pass, indeed, if it seems that they will be able to engage me in conversation; other women look down or look away or rather contemptuously smirk. Some of the men drink with me and suggest that I learn how to ski—partly, I gather, because they cannot imagine what I would look like on skis—and want to know if I am married, and ask questions about my *métier*. But some of the men have accused *le sale nègre*—behind my back—of stealing wood and there is already in the eyes of some of them that peculiar, intent, paranoiac malevolence which one sometimes surprises in the eyes of American white men when, out walking with their Sunday girl, they see a Negro male approach.

There is a dreadful abyss between the streets of this village and the streets of the city in which I was born, between the children who shout *Neger!* today and those who shouted *Nigger!* yesterday—the abyss is experience, the American experience. The syllable hurled behind me today expresses, above all, wonder: I am a stranger here. But I am not a stranger in America and the same syllable riding on the American air expresses the war my presence has occasioned in the American soul.

For this village brings home to me this fact: that there was a day, and not really a very distant day, when Americans were scarcely Americans at all but discontented Europeans, facing a great unconquered continent and strolling, say, into a marketplace and seeing black men for the first time. The shock this spectacle afforded is suggested, surely, by the promptness with which they decided that these black men were not really men but cattle. It is true that the necessity on the part of the settlers of the New World of reconciling their moral assumptions with the fact—and the necessity—of slavery enhanced immensely the charm of this idea, and it is also true that this idea expresses, with a truly American bluntness, the attitude which to varying extents all masters have had toward all slaves.

But between all former slaves and slaveowners and the drama which begins for Americans over three hundred years ago at Jamestown, there are at least two differences to be observed. The American Negro slave could not suppose, for one thing, as slaves in past epochs had supposed and often done, that he would ever be able to wrest the power from his master's hands. This was a supposition which the modern era, which was to bring about such vast changes in the aims and dimensions of power, put to death; it only begins, in unprecedented fashion, and with dreadful implications, to be resurrected today. But even had this supposition persisted with undiminished force, the American Negro slave could not have used it to lend his condition dignity, for the reason that this supposition rests on another: that the slave in exile yet remains related to his past, has some means—if only in memory—of revering and sustaining the forms of his former life, is able, in short, to maintain his identity.

This was not the case with the American Negro slave. He is unique among the black men of the world in that his past was taken from him, almost literally, at one blow. One wonders what on earth the first slave found to say to the first dark child he bore. I am told that there are Haitians able to trace their ancestry back to African kings, but any American Negro wishing to go back so far will find his journey through time abruptly arrested by the signature on the bill of sale which served as the entrance paper for his ancestor. At the time— to say nothing of the circumstances—of the enslavement of the captive black man who was to become the American Negro, there was not the remotest possibility that he would ever take power from his master's hands. There was no reason to suppose that his situation would ever change, nor was there, shortly, anything to indicate that his situation had ever been different. It was his necessity, in the words of E. Franklin Frazier, to find a "motive for living under American culture or die." The identity of the American Negro comes out of this extreme situation, and the evolution of this identity was a source of the most intolerable anxiety in the minds and the lives of his masters.

For the history of the American Negro is unique also in this: that the question of his humanity, and of his rights therefore as a human being, became a burning one for several generations of Americans, so burning a question that it ultimately became one of those used to divide the nation. It is out of this argument that the venom of the epithet *Nigger!* is derived. It is an argument which Europe has never had, and hence Europe quite sincerely fails to understand how or why the argument arose in the first place, why its effects are so frequently disastrous and always so unpredictable, why it refuses until today to be entirely settled. Europe's black possessions remained—and do remain—in Europe's colonies, at which remove they represented no threat whatever to European identity. If they posed any problem at all for the European conscience, it was a problem which remained comfortingly abstract: in effect, the black man, *as a man*, did not exist for Europe. But in America, even as a slave, he was an inescapable part of the general social fabric and no American could escape having an attitude toward him. Americans attempt until today to make an abstraction of the Negro, but the very nature of these abstractions reveals the tremendous effects the presence of the Negro has had on the American character.

When one considers the history of the Negro in America it is of the greatest importance to recognize that the moral beliefs of a person, or a people, are never really as tenuous as life—which is not moral—very often causes them to appear; these create for them a frame of reference and a necessary hope, the hope being that when life has done its worst they will be enabled to rise above themselves and to triumph over life. Life would scarcely be bearable if this hope did not exist. Again, even when the worst has been said, to betray a belief is not by any means to have put oneself beyond its power; the betrayal of a belief is not the same thing as ceasing to believe. If this were not so there would be no moral standards in the world at all. Yet one must also recognize that morality is based on ideas and that all ideas are dangerous—dangerous because ideas can only lead to action and where the action leads no man can say. And dangerous in this respect: that confronted with the impossibility of remaining faithful to one's beliefs, and the equal impossibility of becoming free of them, one can be driven to the most inhuman excesses. The ideas on which American beliefs are based are not, though Americans often seem to think so, ideas which originated in America. They came out of Europe. And the establishment of democracy on the American continent was scarcely as radical a break with the past as was the necessity, which Americans faced, of broadening this concept to include black men.

This was, literally, a hard necessity. It was impossible, for one thing, for Americans to abandon their beliefs, not only because these beliefs alone seemed able to justify the sacrifices they had endured and the blood that they had spilled, but also because these beliefs afforded them their only bulwark against a moral chaos as absolute as the physical chaos of the continent it was their destiny to conquer. But in the situation in which Americans found themselves, these beliefs threatened an idea which, whether or not one likes to think so, is the very warp and woof of the heritage of the West, the idea of white supremacy.

Americans have made themselves notorious by the shrillness and the brutality with which they have insisted on this idea, but they did not invent it; and it has escaped the world's notice that those very excesses of which Americans have been guilty imply a certain, unprecedented uneasiness over the idea's life and power, if not, indeed, the idea's validity. The idea of white supremacy rests simply on the fact that white men are the creators of civilization (the present civilization, which is the only one that matters; all previous civilizations are simply "contributions" to our own) and are therefore civilization's guardians and defenders. Thus it was impossible for Americans to accept the black man as one of themselves, for to do so was to jeopardize their status as white men. But not so to accept him was to deny his human reality, his human weight and complexity, and the strain of denying the overwhelmingly undeniable forced Americans into rationalizations so fantastic that they approached the pathological.

At the root of the American Negro problem is the necessity of the American white man to find a way of living with the Negro in order to be able to live with himself. And the history of this problem can be reduced to the means used by Americans—lynch law and law, segregation and legal acceptance, terrorization and concession—either to come to terms with this necessity, or to find a way around it, or (most usually) to find a way of doing both these things at once. The resulting spectacle, at once foolish and dreadful, led someone to make the quite accurate observation that "the negro-in-America is a form of insanity which overtakes white men."

In this long battle, a battle by no means finished, the unforeseeable effects of which will be felt by many future generations, the white man's motive was the protection of this identity; the black man was motivated by the need to establish an identity. And despite the terrorization which the Negro in America endured and endures sporadically until today, despite the cruel and totally inescapable ambivalence of his status in his country, the battle for his identity has long ago been won. He is not a visitor to the West, but a citizen there, an American; as American as the Americans who despise him, the Americans who fear him, the Americans who love him—the Americans who became less than themselves, or rose to be greater than themselves by virtue of the fact that the challenge he represented was inescapable. He is perhaps the only black man in the world whose relationship to white men is more terrible, more subtle, and more meaningful than the relationship of bitter possessed to uncertain possessor. His survival depended, and his development depends, on his ability to turn his peculiar status in the Western world to his own advantage and, it may be, to the very great advantage of that world. It remains for him to fashion out of his experience that which will give him sustenance, and a voice.

The cathedral at Chartres, I have said, says something to the people of this village which it cannot say to me; but it is important to understand that this cathedral says something to me which it cannot say to them. Perhaps they are struck by the power of the spires, the glory of the windows; but they have known God, after all, longer than I have known him, and in a different way, and I am terrified by the slippery bottomless well to be found in the crypt, down which heretics were hurled to death, and by the obscene, inescapable gargoyles jutting out of the stone and seeming to say that God and the devil can never be divorced. I doubt that the villagers think of the devil when they face a cathedral because they have never been identified with the devil. But I must accept the status which myth, if nothing else, gives me in the West before I can hope to change the myth.

Yet, if the American Negro has arrived at this identity by virtue of the absoluteness of his estrangement from his past, American white men still nourish the illusion that there is some means of recovering the European innocence, of returning to a state in which black men do not exist. This is one of the greatest errors Americans can make. The identity they fought so hard to protect has, by virtue of that battle, undergone a change: Americans are as unlike any other white people in the world as it is possible to be. I do not think, for example, that it is too much to suggest that the American vision of the world—which allows so little reality, generally speaking, for any of the darker forces in human life, which tends until today to paint moral issues in glaring black and white—owes a great deal to the battle waged by Americans to maintain between themselves and black men a human separation which could not be bridged. It is only now beginning to be borne in on us—very faintly, it must be admitted, very slowly, and very much against our will—that this vision of the world is dangerously inaccurate, and perfectly useless. For it protects our moral high-mindedness at the terrible expense of weakening our grasp of reality. People who shut their eyes to reality simply invite their own destruction, and anyone who insists on remaining in a state of innocence long after that innocence is dead turns himself into a monster.

The time has come to realize that the interracial drama acted out on the American continent has not only created a new black man, it has created a new white man, too. No road whatever will lead Americans back to the simplicity of this European village where white men still have the luxury of looking on me as a stranger. I am not, really, a stranger any longer for any American alive. One of the things that distinguishes Americans from other people is that no other people have ever been so deeply involved in the lives of black men, and vice versa. This fact faced, with all its implications, it can be seen that the history of the American Negro problem is not merely shameful, it is also something of an achievement. For even when the worst has been said, it must also be added that the perpetual challenge posed by this problem was always, somehow, perpetually met. It is precisely this black-white experience which may prove of indispensable value to us in the world we face today. This world is white no longer, and it will never be white again.

Labyrinthine

Bernard Cooper

When I discovered my first maze among the pages of a coloring book, I dutifully guided the mouse in the margins toward his wedge of cheese at the center. I dragged my crayon through narrow alleys and around corners, backing out of dead ends, trying this direction instead of that. Often I had to stop and rethink my strategy, squinting until some unobstructed path became clear and I could start to move the crayon again.

I kept my sights on the small chamber in the middle of the page and knew that being lost would not be in vain; wrong turns only improved my chances, showed me that one true path toward my reward. Even when trapped in the hallways of the maze, I felt an embracing safety, as if I'd been zipped in a sleeping bag.

Reaching the cheese had about it a triumph and finality I'd never experienced after coloring a picture or connecting the dots. If only I'd known a word like "inevitable," since that's how it felt to finally slip into the innermost room. I gripped the crayon, savored the place.

The lines on the next maze in the coloring book curved and rippled like waves on water. The object of this maze was to lead a hungry dog to his bone. Mouse to cheese, dog to bone—the premise quickly ceased to matter. It was the tricky, halting travel I was after, forging a passage, finding my way.

Later that day, as I walked through our living room, a maze revealed itself to me in the mahogany coffee table. I sat on the floor, fingered the wood grain, and found a winding avenue through it. The fabric of my parents' blanket was a pattern of climbing ivy and, from one end of the bed to the other, I traced the air between the tendrils. Soon I didn't need to use a finger, mapping my path by sight. I moved through the veins of the marble heart, through the space between the paisleys on my mother's blouse. At the age of seven I changed forever, like the faithful who see Christ on the side of a barn or peering up from a corn tortilla. Everywhere I looked, a labyrinth meandered.

Soon the mazes in the coloring books, in the comic-strip section of the Sunday paper, or on the placemats of coffee shops that served "children's meals" became too easy. And so I began to make my own. I drew them on the cardboard rectangles that my father's dress shirts were folded around when they came back from the cleaner's. My frugal mother, hoarder of jelly jars and rubber bands, had saved a stack of them. She was happy to put the cardboard to use, if a bit mystified by my new obsession.

The best method was to start from the center and work outward with a sharpened pencil, creating layers of complication. I left a few gaps in every line, and after I'd gotten a feel for the architecture of the whole, I'd close off openings, reinforce walls, a slave sealing the pharaoh's tomb. My blind alleys were especially treacherous; I constructed them so that, by the time one realized he'd gotten stuck, turning back would be an exquisite ordeal.

My hobby required a twofold concentration: carefully planning a maze while allowing myself the fresh pleasure of moving through it. Alone in my bedroom, sitting at my desk, I sometimes spent the better part of an afternoon on a single maze. I worked with the patience of a redwood growing rings. Drawing myself into corners, erasing a wall if all else failed, I fooled and baffled and freed myself.

Eventually I used shelf paper, tearing off larger and larger sheets to accommodate my burgeoning ambition. Once I brought a huge maze to my mother, who was drinking a cup of coffee in the kitchen. It wafted behind me like an ostentatious cape. I draped it over the table and challenged her to try it. She hadn't looked at it for more than a second before she refused. "You've got to be kidding," she said, blotting her lips with a paper napkin. "I'm lost enough as it is." When my father returned from work that night, he hefted his briefcase into the closet, his hat wet and drooping from the rain. "Later," he said (his code word for "never") when I waved the banner of my labyrinth before him.

It was inconceivable to me that someone wouldn't want to enter a maze, wouldn't lapse into the trance it required, wouldn't sacrifice the time to find a solution. But mazes had a strange effect on my parents: they took one look at those tangled paths and seemed to wilt.

I was a late child, a "big surprise" as my mother liked to say; by the time I'd turned seven, my parents were trying to cut a swath through the forest of middle age. Their mortgage ballooned. The plumbing rusted. Old friends grew sick or moved away. The creases in their skin deepened, so complex a network of lines, my mazes paled by comparison. Father's hair receded, Mother's grayed. "When you've lived as along as we have . . . ," they'd say, which meant no surprises loomed in their future; it was repetition from here on out. The endless succession of burdens and concerns was enough to make anyone forgetful. Eggs were boiled until they turned brown, sprinklers left on till the lawn grew soggy, keys and glasses and watches misplaced. When I asked my parents about their past, they cocked their heads, stared into the distance, and often couldn't recall the details.

Thirty years later, I understand my parents' refusal. Why would anyone choose to get mired in a maze when the days encase us, loopy and confusing? Remembered events merge together or fade away. Places and dates grow dubious, a jumble of guesswork and speculation. *What's-his-name* and *thingamajig* replace the bright particular. Recollecting the past becomes as unreliable as forecasting the future; you consult yourself with a certain trepidation and take your answer with a grain of salt. The friends you turn to for confirmation are just as muddled; they furrow their brows and look at you blankly. Of course, once in a while you find the tiny, pungent details poised on your tongue like caviar. But more often than not, you settle for sloppy approximations—"I was visiting Texas or Colorado, in 1971 or '72"—and the anecdote rambles on regardless. When the face of a friend from childhood suddenly comes back to me, it's sad to think that if a certain synapse hadn't fired just then, I may never have recalled that friend again. Sometimes I'm not sure if I've overheard a story in conversation, read it in a book, or if I'm the person to whom it happened; whose adventures, besides my own, are wedged in my memory? Then there are the things I've dreamed and mistaken as fact. When you've lived as long as I have, uncertainty is virtually indistinguishable from the truth, which as far as I know is never naked, but always wearing some disguise.

Mother, Father: I'm growing middle-aged, lost in the folds and bones of my body. It gets harder to remember the days when you were here. I suppose it was inevitable that, gazing down at this piece of paper, I'd feel your weary expressions on my face. What have things been like since you've been gone? Labyrinthine. The very sound of that word sums it up—as slippery as thought, as perplexing as the truth, as long and convoluted as a life.

Transfiguration

Annie Dillard

I live on northern Puget Sound, in Washington State, alone. I have a gold cat, who sleeps on my legs, named Small. In the morning I joke to her blank face, Do you remember last night? Do you remember? I throw her out before breakfast, so I can eat.

There is a spider, too, in the bathroom, with whom I keep a sort of company. Her little outfit always reminds me of a certain moth I helped to kill. The spider herself is of uncertain lineage, bulbous at the abdomen and drab. Her six-inch mess of a web works, works somehow, works miraculously, to keep her alive and me amazed. The web itself is in a corner behind the toilet, connecting tile wall to tile wall and floor, in a place where there is, I would have thought, scant traffic. Yet under the web are sixteen or so corpses she has tossed to the floor.

The corpses appear to be mostly sow bugs, those little armadillo creatures who live to travel flat out in houses, and die round. There is also a new shred of earwig, three old spider skins crinkled and clenched, and two moth bodies, wingless and huge and empty, moth bodies I drop to my knees to see.

Today the earwig shines darkly and gleams, what there is of him: a dorsal curve of thorax and abdomen, and a smooth pair of cerci by which I knew his name. Next week, if the other bodies are any indication, he will be shrunken and gray, webbed to the floor with dust. The sow bugs beside him are hollow and empty of color, fragile, a breath away from brittle fluff. The spider skins lie on their sides, translucent and ragged, their legs drying in knots. And the moths, the empty moths, stagger against each other, headless, in a confusion of arching strips of chitin like peeling varnish, like a jumble of buttresses for cathedral domes, like nothing resembling moths, so that I should hesitate to call them moths, except that I have had some experience with the figure Moth reduced to a nub.

Two summers ago I was camping alone in the Blue Ridge Mountains in Virginia. I had hauled myself and gear up there to read, among other things, James Ramsey Ullman's *The Day on Fire*, a novel about Rimbaud that had made me want to be a writer when I was sixteen; I was hoping it would do it again. So I read, lost, every day sitting under a tree by my tent, while warblers swung in the leaves overhead and bristle worms trailed their inches over the twiggy dirt at my feet; and I read every night by candlelight, while barred owls called in the forest and pale moths massed round my head in the clearing, where my light made a ring.

Moths kept flying into the candle. They would hiss and recoil, lost upside down in the shadows among my cooking pans. Or they would singe their wings and fall, and their hot wings, as if melted, would stick to the first thing they touched—a pan, a lid, a spoon—so that the snagged moths could flutter only in tiny arcs, unable to struggle free. These I could release by a quick flip with a stick; in the morning I would find my cooking stuff gilded with torn flecks of moth wings, triangles of shiny dust here and there on the aluminum. So I read, and boiled water, and replenished candles, and read on.

One night a moth flew into the candle, was caught, burnt dry, and held. I must have been staring at the candle, or maybe I looked up when a shadow crossed my page; at any rate, I saw it all. A golden female moth, a biggish one with a two-inch wing-span, flapped into the fire, dropped her abdomen into the wet wax, stuck, flamed, frazzled and fried in a second. Her moving wings ignited like tissue paper, enlarging the circle of light in the clearing and creating out of the darkness the sudden blue sleeves of my sweater, the green leaves of jewel-weed by my side, the ragged red trunk of a pine. At once the light contracted again and the moth's wings vanished in a fine, foul smoke. At the same time her six legs clawed, curled, blackened, and ceased, disappearing utterly. And her head jerked in spasms, making a spattering noise; her antennae crisped and burned away and her heaving mouth parts crackled like pistol fire. When it was all over, her head was, so far as I could determine, gone, gone the long way of her wings and legs. Had she been new, or old? Had she mated and laid her eggs, had she done her work? All that was left was the glowing horn shell of her abdomen and thorax—a fraying, partially collapsed gold tube jammed upright in the candle's round pool.

And then this moth-essence, this spectacular skeleton, began to act as a wick. She kept burning. The wax rose in the moth's body from her soaking abdomen to her thorax to the jagged hole where her head should be, and widened into flame, a saffron-yellow flame that robed her to the ground like any immolating monk. That candle had two wicks, two flames of identical height, side by side. The moth's head was fire. She burned for two hours, until I blew her out.

She burned for two hours without changing, without bending or leaning—only glowing within, like a building fire glimpsed through silhouetted walls, like a hollow saint, like a flame-faced virgin gone to God, while I read by her light, kindled, while Rimbaud in Paris burnt out his brains in a thousand poems, while night pooled wetly at my feet.

And that is why I believe those hollow crisps on the bathroom floor are moths. I think I know moths, and fragments of moths, and chips and tatters of utterly empty moths, in any state. How many of you, I asked the people in my class, which of you want to give your lives and be writers? I was trembling from coffee, or cigarettes, or the closeness of faces all around me. (Is this what we live for? I thought; is this the only final beauty: the color of any skin in any light, and living, human eyes?) All hands rose to the question. (You, Nick? Will you? Margaret? Randy? Why do I want them to mean it?) And then I tried to tell them what the choice must mean: you can't be anything else. You must go at your life with a broadax. . . . They had no idea what I was saying. (I have two hands, don't I? And all this energy, for as long as I can remember. I'll do it in the evenings, after skiing, or on the way home from the bank; or after the children are asleep. . . .) They thought I was raving again. It's just as well.

I have three candles here on the table which I disentangle from the plants and light when visitors come. Small usually avoids them, although once she came too close and her tail caught fire; I rubbed it out before she noticed. The flames move light over everyone's skin, draw light to the surface of the faces of my friends. When the people leave I never blow the candles out, and after I'm asleep they flame and burn.

The Illusion of the Two Cultures

Loren Eiseley

Not long ago an English scientist, Sir Eric Ashby, remarked that "to train young people in the dialect between orthodoxy and dissent is the unique contribution which universities make to society." I am sure that Sir Eric meant by this remark that nowhere but in universities are the young given the opportunity to absorb past tradition and at the same time to experience the impact of new ideas—in the sense of a constant dialogue between past and present—lived in every hour of the student's existence. This dialogue, ideally, should lead to a great winnowing and sifting of experience and to a heightened consciousness of self which, in turn, should lead on to greater sensitivity and perception on the part of the individual.

Our lives are the creation of memory and the accompanying power to extend ourselves outward into ideas and relive them. The finest intellect is that which employs an invisible web of gossamer running into the past as well as across the minds of living men and which constantly responds to the vibrations transmitted through these tenuous lines of sympathy. It would be contrary to fact, however, to assume that our universities always perform this unique function of which Sir Eric speaks, with either grace or perfection; in fact our investment in man, it has been justly remarked, is deteriorating even as the financial investment in science grows.

More than thirty years ago, George Santayana had already sensed this trend. He commented, in a now-forgotten essay, that one of the strangest consequences of modern science was that as the visible wealth of nature was more and more transferred and abstracted, the mind seemed to lose courage and to become ashamed of its own fertility. "The hard-pressed natural man will not indulge his imagination," continued Santayana, "unless it poses for truth; and being half-aware of this imposition, he is more troubled at the thought of being deceived than at the fact of being mechanized or being bored; and he would wish to escape imagination altogether."

"Man would wish to escape imagination altogether." I repeat that last phrase, for it defines a peculiar aberration of the human mind found on both sides of that bipolar division between the humanities and the sciences, which C. P. Snow has popularized under the title of *The Two Cultures*. The idea is not solely a product of this age. It was already emerging with the science of the seventeenth century; one finds it in Bacon. One finds the fear of it faintly foreshadowed in Thoreau. Thomas Huxley lent it weight when he referred contemptuously to the "caterwauling of poets."

Ironically, professional scientists berated the early evolutionists such as Lamarck and Chambers for overindulgence in the imagination. Almost eighty years ago John Burroughs observed that some of the animus once directed by science toward dogmatic theology seemed in his day increasingly to be vented upon the literary naturalist. In the early 1900s a quarrel over "nature faking" raised a confused din in America and aroused W. H. Hudson to some dry and pungent comment upon the failure to distinguish the purposes of science from those of literature. I know of at least one scholar who, venturing to develop some personal ideas in an essay for the layman, was characterized by a reviewer in a leading professional journal as a worthless writer; although, as it chanced, the work under discussion had received several awards in literature, one of them international in scope. More recently, some scholars not indifferent to humanistic values have exhorted poets to leave their personal songs in order to portray the beauty and symmetry of molecular structures.

Now some very fine verse has been written on scientific subjects, but, I fear, very little under the dictate of scientists as such. Rather there is evident here precisely that restriction of imagination against which Santayana inveighed; namely, an attempt to constrain literature itself to the delineation of objective or empiric truth, and to dismiss the whole domain of value, which after all constitutes the very nature of man, as without significance and beneath contempt.

Unconsciously, the human realm is denied in favor of the world of pure techniques. Man, the tool user, grows convinced that he is himself only useful as a tool, that fertility except in the use of the scientific imagination is wasteful and without purpose, even, in some indefinable way, sinful. I was reading J. R. R. Tolkien's great symbolic trilogy, *The Fellowship of the Ring*, a few months ago, when a young scientist of my acquaintance paused and looked over my shoulder. After a little casual interchange the man departed leaving an accusing remark hovering in the air between us. "I wouldn't waste my time with a man who writes fairy stories." He might as well have added, "or with a man who reads them."

As I went back to my book I wondered vaguely in what leafless landscape one grew up without Hans Christian Andersen, or Dunsany, or even Jules Verne. There lingered about the young man's words a puritanism which seemed the more remarkable because, as nearly as I could discover, it was unmotivated by any sectarian religiosity unless a total dedication to science brings to some minds a similar authoritarian desire to shackle the human imagination. After all, it is this impossible, fertile world of our imagination which gave birth to liberty in the midst of oppression, and which persists in seeking until what is sought is seen. Against such invisible and fearful powers, there can be found in all ages and in all institutions—even the institutions of professional learning—the humorless man with the sneer, or if the sneer does not suffice, then the torch for the bright unperishing letters of the human dream.

One can contrast this recalcitrant attitude with an 1890 reminiscence from that great Egyptologist Sir Flinders Petrie, which steals over into the realm of pure literature. It was written, in unconscious symbolism, from a tomb:

"I here live, and do not scramble to fit myself to the requirements of others. In a narrow tomb, with the figure of Néfermaat standing on each side of me—as he has stood through all that we know as human history—I have just room for my bed, and a row of good reading in which I can take pleasure after dinner. Behind me is that Great Peace, the Desert. It is an entity—a power—just as much as the sea is. No wonder men fled to it from the turmoil of the ancient world."

It may now reasonably be asked why one who has similarly, if less dramatically, spent his life among the stones and broken shards of the remote past should be writing here about matters involving literature and science. While I was considering this with humility and trepidation, my eye fell upon a stone in my office. I am sure that professional journalists must recall times when an approaching deadline has keyed all their senses and led them to glance wildly around in the hope that something might leap out at them from the most prosaic surroundings. At all events my eyes fell upon this stone.

Now the stone antedated anything that the historians would call art; it had been shaped many hundreds of thousands of years ago by men whose faces would frighten us if they sat among us today. Out of old habit, since I like the feel of worked flint, I picked it up and hefted it as I groped for words over this difficult matter of the growing rift between science and art. Certainly the stone was of no help to me; it was a utilitarian thing which had cracked marrow bones, if not heads, in the remote dim morning of the human species. It was nothing if not practical. It was, in fact, an extremely early example of the empirical tradition which has led on to modern science.

The mind which had shaped this artifact knew its precise purpose. It had found out by experimental observation that the stone was tougher, sharper, more enduring than the hand which wielded it. The creature's mind had solved the question of the best form of the implement and how it could be manipulated most effectively. In its day and time this hand ax was as grand an intellectual achievement as a rocket.

As a scientist my admiration went out to that unidentified workman. How he must have labored to understand the forces involved in the fracturing of flint, and all that involved practical survival in his world. My uncalloused twentieth-century hand caressed the yellow stone lovingly. It was then that I made a remarkable discovery.

117

In the mind of this gross-featured early exponent of the practical approach to nature—the technician, the no-nonsense practitioner of survival—two forces had met and merged. There had not been room in his short and desperate life for the delicate and supercilious separation of the arts from the sciences. There did not exist then the refined distinctions set up between the scholarly percipience of reality and what has sometimes been called the vaporings of the artistic imagination.

As I clasped and unclasped the stone, running my fingers down its edges, I began to perceive the ghostly emanations from a long-vanished mind, the kind of mind which, once having shaped an object of any sort, leaves an individual trace behind it which speaks to others across the barriers of time and language. It was not the practical experimental aspect of this mind that startled me, but rather that the fellow had wasted time.

In an incalculably brutish and dangerous world he had both shaped an instrument of practical application and then, with a virtuoso's elegance, proceeded to embellish his product. He had not been content to produce a plain, utilitarian implement. In some wistful, inarticulate way, in the grip of the dim aesthetic feelings which are one of the marks of man—or perhaps I should say, some men—this archaic creature had lingered over his handiwork.

One could still feel him crouching among the stones on a long-vanished river bar, turning the thing over in his hands, feeling its polished surface, striking, here and there, just one more blow that no longer had usefulness as its criterion. He had, like myself, enjoyed the texture of the stone. With skills lost to me, he had gone on flaking the implement with an eye to beauty until it had become a kind of rough jewel, equivalent in its day to the carved and gold-inlaid pommel of the iron dagger placed in Tutankhamen's tomb.

All the later history of man contains these impractical exertions expended upon a great diversity of objects, and, with literacy, breaking even into printed dreams. Today's secular disruption between the creative aspect of art and that of science is a barbarism that would have brought lifted eyebrows in a Cro-Magnon cave. It is a product of high technical specialization, the deliberate blunting of wonder, and the equally deliberate suppression of a phase of our humanity in the name of an authoritarian institution, science, which has taken on, in our time, curious puritanical overtones. Many scientists seem unaware of the historical reasons for this development or the fact that the creative aspect of art is not so remote from that of science as may seem, at first glance, to be the case.

I am not so foolish as to categorize individual scholars or scientists. I am, however, about to remark on the nature of science as an institution. Like all such structures it is apt to reveal certain behavioral rigidities and conformities which increase with age. It is no longer the domain of the amateur, though some of its greatest discoverers could be so defined. It is now a professional body, and with professionalism there tends to emerge a greater emphasis upon a coherent system of regulations. The deviant is more sharply treated, and the young tend to imitate their successful elders. In short, an "Establishment"—a trade union—has appeared.

Similar tendencies can be observed among those of the humanities concerned with the professional analysis and interpretation of the works of the creative artist. Here too, a similar rigidity and exclusiveness make their appearance. It is not that in the case of both the sciences and the humanities standards are out of place. What I am briefly cautioning against is that too frequently they afford an excuse for stifling original thought or constricting much latent creativity within traditional molds.

Such molds are always useful to the mediocre conformist who instinctively castigates and rejects what he cannot imitate. Traditions, the continuity of learning, are, it is true, enormously important to the learned disciplines. What we must realize as scientists is that the particular institution we inhabit has its own irrational accretions and authoritarian dogmas which can be as unpleasant as some of those encountered in sectarian circles—particularly so since they are frequently unconsciously held and surrounded by an impenetrable wall of self-righteousness brought about because science is regarded as totally empiric and open-minded by tradition.

This type of professionalism, as I shall label it in order to distinguish it from what is best in both the sciences and humanities, is characterized by two assumptions: that the accretions of fact are cumulative and lead to progress, whereas the insights of art are, at best, singular, and lead nowhere, or, when introduced into the realm of science, produce obscurity and confusion. The convenient label "mystic" is, in our day, readily applied to men who pause for simple wonder, or who encounter along the borders of the known that "awful power" which Wordsworth characterized as the human imagination. It can, he says, rise suddenly from the mind's abyss and enwrap the solitary traveler like a mist.

We do not like mists in this era, and the word imagination is less and less used. We like, instead, a clear road, and we abhor solitary traveling. Indeed one of our great scientific historians remarked not long ago that the literary naturalist was obsolescent if not completely outmoded. I suppose he meant that with our penetration into the biophysical realm, life, like matter, would become increasingly represented by abstract symbols. To many it must appear that the more we can dissect life into its elements, the closer we are getting to its ultimate resolution. While I have some reservations on this score, they are not important. Rather, I should like to look at the symbols which in the one case denote science and in the other constitute those vaporings and cloud wraiths that are the abomination, so it is said, of the true scientist but are the delight of the poet and literary artist.

119

Creation in science demands a high level of imaginative insight and intuitive perception. I believe no one would deny this, even though it exists in varying degrees, just as it does, similarly, among writers, musicians, or artists. The scientist's achievement, however, is quantitatively transmissible. From a single point his discovery is verifiable by other men who may then, on the basis of corresponding data, accept the innovation and elaborate upon it in the cumulative fashion which is one of the great triumphs of science.

Artistic creation, on the other hand, is unique. It cannot be twice discovered, as, say, natural selection was discovered. It may be imitated stylistically, in a genre, a school, but, save for a few items of technique, it is not cumulative. A successful work of art may set up reverberations and is, in this, just as transmissible as science, but there is a qualitative character about it. Each reverberation in another mind is unique. As the French novelist François Mauriac has remarked, each great novel is a separate and distinct world operating under its own laws with a flora and fauna totally its own. There is communication, or the work is a failure, but the communication releases our own visions, touches some highly personal chord in our own experience.

The symbols used by the great artist are a key releasing our humanity from the solitary tower of the self. "Man," says Lewis Mumford "is first and foremost the self-fabricating animal." I shall merely add that the artist plays an enormous role in this act of self-creation. It is he who touches the hidden strings of pity, who searches our hearts, who makes us sensitive to beauty, who asks questions about fate and destiny. Such questions, though they lurk always around the corners of the external universe which is the peculiar province of science, the rigors of the scientific method do not enable us to pursue directly.

And yet I wonder.

It is surely possible to observe that it is the successful analogy or symbol which frequently allows the scientist to leap from a generalization in one field of thought to a triumphant achievement in another. For example, Progressionism in a spiritual sense later became the model contributing to the discovery of organic evolution. Such analogies genuinely resemble the figures and enchantments of great literature, whose meanings similarly can never be totally grasped because of their endless power to ramify in the individual mind.

John Donne gave powerful expression to a feeling applicable as much to science as to literature when he said devoutly of certain Biblical passages: "The literall sense is always to be preserved; but the literall sense is not always to be discerned; for the literall sense is not always that which the very letter and grammar of the place presents." A figurative sense, he argues cogently, can sometimes be the most "literall intention of the Holy Ghost."

It is here that the scientist and artist sometimes meet in uneasy opposition, or at least along lines of tension. The scientist's attitude is sometimes, I suspect, that embodied in Samuel Johnson's remark that, wherever there is mystery, roguery is not far off.

Yet surely it was not roguery when Sir Charles Lyell glimpsed in a few fossil prints of raindrops the persistence of the world's natural forces through the incredible, mysterious aeons of geologic time. The fossils were a symbol of a vast hitherto unglimpsed order. They are, in Donne's sense, both literal and symbolic. As fossils they merely denote evidence of rain in a past era. Figuratively they are more. To the perceptive intelligence they afford the hint of lengthened natural order, just as the eyes of ancient trilobites tell us similarly of the unchanging laws of light. Equally, the educated mind may discern in a scratched pebble the retreating shadow of vast ages of ice and gloom. In Donne's archaic phraseology these objects would bespeak the principal intention of the Divine Being—that is, of order beyond our power to grasp.

Such images drawn from the world of science are every bit as powerful as great literary symbolism and equally demanding upon the individual imagination of the scientist who would fully grasp the extension of meaning which is involved. It is, in fact, one and the same creative act in both domains.

Indeed evolution itself has become such a figurative symbol, as has also the hypothesis of the expanding universe. The laboratory worker may think of these concepts in a totally empirical fashion as subject to proof or disproof by the experimental method. Like Freud's doctrine of the subconscious, however, such ideas frequently escape from the professional scientist into the public domain. There they may undergo further individual transformation and embellishment. Whether the scholar approves or not, such hypotheses are now as free to evolve in the mind of the individual as are the creations of art. All the resulting enrichment and confusion will bear about it something suggestive of the world of artistic endeavor.

As figurative insights into the nature of things, such embracing conceptions may become grotesquely distorted or glow with added philosophical wisdom. As in the case of the trilobite eye or the fossil raindrop, there lurks behind the visible evidence vast shadows no longer quite of that world which we term natural. Like the words in Donne's Bible, enormous implications have transcended the literal expression of the thought. Reality itself has been superseded by a greater reality. As Donne himself asserted, "The substance of the truth is in the great images which lie behind."

It is because these two types of creation—the artistic and the scientific—have sprung from the same being and have their points of contact even in division that I have the temerity to assert that, in a sense, the "two cultures" are an illusion, that they are a product of unreasoning fear, professionalism, and misunderstanding. Because of the emphasis upon science in our society, much has been said about the necessity of educating the layman and even the professional student of the humanities upon the ways and the achievements

121

of science. I admit that a barrier exists, but I am also concerned to express the view that there persists in the domain of science itself an occasional marked intolerance of those of its own membership who venture to pursue the way of letters. As I have remarked, this intolerance can more successfully clothe itself in seeming objectivity because of the supposed open nature of the scientific society. It is not remarkable that this trait is sometimes more manifest in the younger and less secure disciplines.

There was a time, not too many centuries ago, when to be active in scientific investigation was to invite suspicion. Thus it may be that there now lingers among us, even in the triumph of the experimental method, a kind of vague fear of that other artistic world of deep emotion, of strange symbols, lest it seize upon us or distort the hard-won objectivity of our thinking— lest it corrupt, in other words, that crystalline and icy objectivity which, in our scientific guise, we erect as a model of conduct. This model, incidentally, if pursued to its absurd conclusion, would lead to a world in which the computer would determine all aspects of our existence; one in which the bomb would be as welcome as the discoveries of the physician.

Happily, the very great in science, or even those unique scientist-artists such as Leonardo, who foreran the emergence of science as an institution, have been singularly free from this folly. Darwin decried it even as he recognized that he had paid a certain price in concentrated specialization for his achievement. Einstein, it is well known, retained a simple sense of wonder; Newton felt like a child playing with pretty shells on a beach. All show a deep humility and an emotional hunger which is the prerogative of the artist. It is with the lesser men, with the institutionalization of method, with the appearance of dogma and mapped-out territories, that an unpleasant suggestion of fenced preserves begins to dominate the university atmosphere.

As a scientist, I can say that I have observed it in my own and others' specialties. I have had occasion, also, to observe its effects in the humanities. It is not science *per se*; it is, instead, in both regions of thought, the narrow professionalism which is also plainly evident in the trade union. There can be small men in science just as there are small men in government or business. In fact it is one of the disadvantages of big science, just as it is of big government, that the availability of huge sums attracts a swarm of elbowing and contentious men to whom great dreams are less than protected hunting preserves.

The sociology of science deserves at least equal consideration with the biographies of the great scientists, for powerful and changing forces are at work upon science, the institution, as contrasted with science as a dream and an ideal of the individual. Like other aspects of society, it is a construct of men and is subject, like other social structures, to human pressures and inescapable distortions.

Let me give an illustration. Even in learned journals, clashes occasionally occur between those who would regard biology as a separate and distinct domain of inquiry and the reductionists who, by contrast, perceive in the living organism only a vaster and more random chemistry. Understandably, the concern of the reductionists is with the immediate. Thomas Hobbes was expressing a similar point of view when he castigated poets as "working on mean minds with words and distinctions that of themselves signifie nothing, but betray (by their obscurity) that there walketh . . . another kingdome, as it were a kingdome of fayries in the dark." I myself have been similarly criticized for speaking of a nature "beyond the nature that we know."

Yet consider for a moment this dark, impossible realm of "fayrie." Man is not totally compounded of the nature we profess to understand. He contains, instead, a lurking unknown future, just as the man-apes of the Pliocene contained in embryo the future that surrounds us now. The world of human culture itself was an unpredictable fairy world until, in some pre-ice-age meadow, the first meaningful sounds in all the world broke through the jungle babble of the past, the nature, until that moment, "known."

It is fascinating to observe that, in the very dawn of science, Francis Bacon, the spokesman for the empirical approach to nature, shared with Shakespeare, the poet, a recognition of the creativeness which adds to nature, and which emerges from nature as "an art which nature makes." Neither the great scholar nor the great poet had renounced this "kingdome of fayries." Both had realized what Henri Bergson was later to express so effectively, that life inserts a vast "indetermination into matter." It is, in a sense, an intrusion from a realm which can never be completely subject to prophetic analysis by science. The novelties of evolution emerge; they cannot be predicted. They haunt, until their arrival, a world of unimaginable possibilities behind the living screen of events, as these last exist to the observer confined to a single point on the time scale.

Oddly enough, much of the confusion that surrounded my phrase, "a nature beyond the nature that we know," resolves itself into pure semantics. I might have pointed out what must be obvious even to the most dedicated scientific mind—that the nature which we know has been many times reinterpreted in human thinking, and that the hard, substantial matter of the nineteenth century has already vanished into a dark, bodiless void, a web of "events" in space-time. This is a realm, I venture to assert, as weird as any we have tried, in the past, to exorcise by the brave use of seeming solid words. Yet some minds exhibit an almost instinctive hostility toward the mere attempt to wonder or to ask what lies below that microcosmic world out of which emerge the particles which compose our bodies and which now take on this wraithlike quality.

Is there something here we fear to face, except when clothed in safely sterilized professional speech? Have we grown reluctant in this age of power to admit mystery and beauty into our thoughts, or to learn where power ceases? I referred earlier to one of our own forebears on a gravel bar, thumbing a pebble. If, after the ages of building and destroying, if after the measuring of light-years and the powers probed at the atom's heart, if after the last iron is rust-eaten and the last glass lies shattered in the streets, a man, some savage, some remnant of what once we were, pauses on his way to the tribal drinking place and feels rising from within his soul the inexplicable mist of terror and beauty that is evoked from old ruins—even the ruins of the greatest city in the world—then, I say, all will still be well with man.

And if that savage can pluck a stone from the gravel because it shone like crystal when the water rushed over it, and hold it against the sunset, he will be as we were in the beginning, whole—as we were when we were children, before we began to split the knowledge from the dream. All talk of the two cultures is an illusion; it is the pebble which tells man's story. Upon it is written man's two faces, the artistic and the practical. They are expressed upon one stone over which a hand once closed, no less firm because the mind behind it was submerged in light and shadow and deep wonder.

Today we hold a stone, the heavy stone of power. We must perceive beyond it, however, by the aid of the artistic imagination, those humane insights and understandings which alone can lighten our burden and enable us to shape ourselves, rather than the stone, into the forms which great art has anticipated.

The Dance of the Frogs

Loren Eiseley

I

He was a member of the Explorers Club, and he had never been outside the state of Pennsylvania. Some of us who were world travelers used to smile a little about that, even though we knew his scientific reputation had been, at one time, great. It is always the way of youth to smile. I used to think of myself as something of an adventurer, but the time came when I realized that old Albert Dreyer, huddling with his drink in the shadows close to the fire, had journeyed farther into the Country of Terror than any of us would ever go, God willing, and emerge alive.

He was a morose and aging man, without family and without intimates. His membership in the club dated back into the decades when he was a zoologist famous for his remarkable experiments upon amphibians—he had recovered and actually produced the adult stage of the Mexican axolotl, as well as achieving remarkable tissue transplants in salamanders. The club had been flattered to have him then, travel or no travel, but the end was not fortunate. The brilliant scientist had become the misanthrope; the achievement lay all in the past, and Albert Dreyer kept to his solitary room, his solitary drink, and his accustomed spot by the fire.

The reason I came to hear his story was an odd one. I had been north that year, and the club had asked me to give a little talk on the religious beliefs of the Indians of the northern forest, the Naskapi of Labrador. I had long been a student of the strange mélange of superstition and woodland wisdom that makes up the religious life of the nature peoples. Moreover, I had come to know something of the strange similarities of the "shaking tent rite" to the phenomena of the modern medium's cabinet.

"The special tent with its entranced occupant is no different from the cabinet," I contended. "The only difference is the type of voices that emerge. Many of the physical phenomena are identical—the movement of powerful forces shaking the conical hut, objects thrown, all this is familiar to Western psychical science. What is different are the voices projected. Here they are the cries of animals, the voices from the swamp and the mountain—the solitary elementals before

125

whom the primitive man stands in awe, and from whom he begs sustenance. Here the game lords reign supreme; man himself is voiceless."

A low, halting query reached me from the back of the room. I was startled, even in the midst of my discussion, to note that it was Dreyer.

"And the game lords, what are they?"

"Each species of animal is supposed to have gigantic leaders of more than normal size," I explained. "These beings are the immaterial controllers of that particular type of animal. Legend about them is confused. Sometimes they partake of human qualities, will and intelligence, but they are of animal shape. They control the movements of game, and thus their favor may mean life or death to man."

"Are they visible?" Again Dreyer's low, troubled voice came from the back of the room.

"Native belief has it that they can be seen on rare occasions," I answered. "In a sense they remind one of the concept of the archetypes, the originals behind the petty show of our small, transitory existence. They are the immortal renewers of substance—the force behind and above animate nature."

"Do they dance?" persisted Dreyer.

At this I grew nettled. Old Dreyer in a heckling mood was something new. "I cannot answer that question," I said acidly. "My informants failed to elaborate upon it. But they believe implicitly in these monstrous beings, talk to and propitiate them. It is their voices that emerge from the shaking tent."

"The Indians believe it," pursued old Dreyer relentlessly, "but do *you* believe it?"

"My dear fellow—I shrugged and glanced at the smiling audience—"I have seen many strange things, many puzzling things, but I am a scientist." Dreyer made a contemptuous sound in his throat and went back to the shadow out of which he had crept in his interest. The talk was over. I headed for the bar.

II

The evening passed. Men drifted homeward or went to their rooms. I had been a year in the woods and hungered for voices and companionship. Finally, however, I sat alone with my glass, a little mellow, perhaps, enjoying the warmth of the fire and remembering the blue snowfields of the North as they should be remembered—in the comfort of warm rooms.

I think an hour must have passed. The club was silent except for the ticking of an antiquated clock on the mantel and small night noises from the street. I must have drowsed. At all events it was some time before I grew aware that a chair had been drawn up opposite me. I started.

"A damp night," I said.

"Foggy," said the man in the shadow musingly. "But not too foggy. They like it that way."

"Eh?" I said. I knew immediately it was Dreyer speaking. Maybe I had missed something; on second thought, maybe not.

"And spring," he said. "Spring. That's part of it. God knows why, of course, but we feel it, why shouldn't they? And more intensely."

"Look—" I said. "I guess—" The old man was more human than I thought. He reached out and touched my knee with the hand that he always kept a glove over—burn, we used to speculate—and smiled softly.

"You don't know what I'm talking about," he finished for me. "And, besides, I ruffled your feelings earlier in the evening. You must forgive me. You touched on an interest of mine, and I was perhaps overeager. I did not intend to give the appearance of heckling. It was only that . . ."

"Of course," I said. "Of course." Such a confession from Deyer was astounding. The man might be ill. I rang for a drink and decided to shift the conversation to a safer topic, more appropriate to a scholar.

"Frogs," I said desperately, like any young ass in a china shop. "Always admired your experiments. Frogs. Yes."

I give the old man credit. He took the drink and held it up and looked at me across the rim. There was a faint stir of sardonic humor in his eyes.

"Frogs, no," he said, "or maybe yes. I've never been quite sure. Maybe yes. But there was no time to decide properly." The humor faded out of his eyes. "Maybe I should have let go," he said. "It was what they wanted. There's no doubting that at all, but it came too quick for me. What would you have done?"

"I don't know," I said honestly enough and pinched myself.

"You had better know," said Albert Dreyer severely, "if you're planning to become an investigator of primitive religions. Or even not. I wasn't, you know, and the things came to me just when I least suspected—But I forget, you don't believe in them."

He shrugged and half rose, and for the first time, really, I saw the black-gloved hand and the haunted face of Albert Dreyer and knew in my heart the things he had stood for in science. I got up then, as a young man in the presence of his betters should get up, and I said, and I meant it, every word: "Please, Dr. Dreyer, sit down and tell me. I'm too young to be saying what I believe or don't believe in at all. I'd be obliged if you'd tell me."

Just at that moment a strange, wonderful dignity shone out of the countenance of Albert Dreyer, and I knew the man he was. He bowed and sat down, and there were no longer the barriers of age and youthful ego between us. There were just two men under a lamp, and around them a great waiting silence. Out to the ends of the universe, I thought fleetingly, that's the way with man and his lamps. One has to huddle in, there's so little light and so much space. One—

III

"It could happen to anyone," said Albert Dreyer. "And especially in the spring. Remember that. And all I did was to skip. Just a few feet, mark you, but I skipped. Remember that, too.

"You wouldn't remember the place at all. At least not as it was then." He paused and shook the ice in his glass and spoke more easily.

"It was a road that came out finally in a marsh along the Schuykill River. Probably all industrial now. But I had a little house out there with a laboratory thrown in. It was convenient to the marsh, and that helped me with my studies of amphibia. Moreover, it was a wild, lonely road, and I wanted solitude. It is always the demand of the naturalist. You understand that?"

"Of course," I said. I knew he had gone there, after the death of his young wife, in grief and loneliness and despair. He was not a man to mention such things. "It is best for the naturalist," I agreed.

"Exactly. My best work was done there." He held up his black-gloved hand and glanced at it meditatively. "The work on the axolotl, newt neoteny. I worked hard. I had—" he hesitated "things to forget. There were times when I worked all night. Or diverted myself, while waiting the result of an experiment, by midnight walks. It was a strange road. Wild all right, but paved and close enough to the city that there were occasional street lamps. All uphill and downhill, with bits of forest leaning in over it, till you walked in a tunnel of trees. Then suddenly you were in the marsh, and the road ended at an old, unused wharf.

"A place to be alone. A place to walk and think. A place for shadows to stretch ahead of you from one dim lamp to another and spring back as you reached the next. I have seen them get tall, tall, but never like that night. It was like a road into space."

"Cold?" I asked.

"No. I shouldn't have said 'space.' It gives the wrong effect. Not cold. Spring. Frog time. The first warmth, and the leaves coming. A little fog in the hollows. The way they like it then in the wet leaves and bogs. No moon, though; secretive and dark, with just those street lamps wandered out from the town. I often wondered what graft had brought them there. They shone on nothing—except my walks at midnight and the journeys of toads but still . . ."

"Yes?" I prompted, as he paused.

"I was just thinking. The web of things. A politician in town gets a rake-off for selling useless lights on a useless road. If it hadn't been for that, I might

128

not have seen them. I might not even have skipped. Or, if I had, the effect—How can you tell about such things afterwards? Was the effect heightened? Did it magnify their power? Who is to say?"

"The skip?" I said, trying to keep things casual. "I don't understand. You mean, just skipping? Jumping?"

Something like a twinkle came into his eyes for a moment "Just that," he said. "No more. You are a young man. Impulsive? You should understand."

"I'm afraid—" I began to counter.

"But of course," he cried pleasantly. "I forget. You were not there. So how could I expect you to feel or know about this skipping. Look, look at me now. A sober man, eh?"

I nodded. "Dignified," I said cautiously.

"Very well. But, young man, there is a time to skip. On country roads in the spring. It is not necessary that there be girls. You will skip without them. You will skip because something within you knows the time—frog time. Then you will skip."

"Then I will skip," I repeated, hypnotized. Mad or not, there was a force in Albert Dreyer. Even there under the club lights, the night damp of an unused road began to gather.

IV

"It was a late spring," he said. "Fog and mist in those hollows in a way I had never seen before. And frogs, of course. Thousands of them, and twenty species, trilling, gurgling, and grunting in as many keys. The beautiful keen silver piping of spring peepers arousing as the last ice leaves the ponds—if you have heard that after a long winter alone, you will never forget it." He paused and leaned forward, listening with such an intent inner ear that one could almost hear that far-off silver piping from the wet meadows of the man's forgotten years.

I rattled my glass uneasily, and his eyes came back to me.

"They come out then," he said more calmly. "All amphibia have to return to the water for mating and egg laying. Even toads will hop miles across country to streams and waterways. You don't see them unless you go out at night in the right places as I did, but that night—

"Well, it was unusual, put it that way, as an understatement. It was late, and the creatures seemed to know it. You could feel the forces of mighty and archaic life welling up from the very ground. The water was pulling them—not water as we know it, but the mother, the ancient life force, the thing that made us in the days of creation, and that lurks around us still, unnoticed in our sterile cities.

"I was no different from any other young fool coming home on a spring night, except that as a student of life, and of amphibia in particular, I was, shall we say, more aware of the creatures. I had performed experiments"— the black glove gestured before my eyes. "I was, as it proved, susceptible.

"It began on that lost stretch of roadway leading to the river, and it began simply enough. All around, under the street lamps, I saw little frogs and big frogs hopping steadily toward the river. They were going in my direction.

"At that time I had my whimsies, and I was spry enough to feel the tug of that great movement. I joined them. There was no mystery about it. I simply began to skip, to skip gaily, and enjoy the great bobbing shadow I created as I passed onward with that leaping host all headed for the river.

"Now skipping along a wet pavement in spring is infectious, particularly going downhill, as we were. The impulse to take mightier leaps, to soar farther, increases progressively. The madness worked into me. I bounded till my lungs labored, and my shadow, at first my own shadow, bounded and labored with me.

"It was only midway in my flight that I began to grow conscious that I was not alone. The feeling was not strong at first. Normally a sober pedestrian, I was ecstatically preoccupied with the discovery of latent stores of energy and agility which I had not suspected in my subdued existence.

"It was only as we passed under a street lamp that I noticed, beside my own bobbing shadow, another great, leaping grotesquerie that had an uncanny suggestion of the frog world about it. The shocking aspect of the thing lay in its size, and the fact that, judging from the shadow, it was soaring higher and more gaily than myself.

"'Very well,' you will say"—and here Dreyer paused and looked at me tolerantly—"'Why didn't you turn around? That would be the scientific thing to do.'

"It would be the scientific thing to do, young man, but let me tell you it is not done—not on an empty road at midnight—not when the shadow is already beside your shadow and is joined by another, and then another.

"No, you do not pause. You look neither to left nor right, for fear of what you might see there. Instead, you dance on madly, hopelessly. Plunging higher, higher, in the hope the shadows will be left behind, or prove to be only leaves dancing, when you reach the next street light. Or that whatever had joined you in this midnight bacchanal will take some other pathway and depart.

"You do not look—you cannot look—because to do so is to destroy the universe in which we move and exist and have our transient being. You dare not look, because, beside the shadows, there now comes to your ears the loose-limbed slap of giant batrachian feet, not loud, not loud at all, but there, definitely there, behind you at your shoulder, plunging with the utter madness of spring, their rhythm entering your bones until you too are hurtling upward in some gigantic ecstasy that it is not given to mere flesh and blood to long endure.

"I was part of it, part of some mad dance of the elementals behind the show of things. Perhaps in that night of archaic and elemental passion, that festival of the wetlands, my careless hopping passage under the street lights had called them, attracted their attention, brought them leaping down some fourth-dimensional roadway into the world of time.

"Do not suppose for a single moment I thought so coherently then. My lungs were bursting, my physical self exhausted, but I sprang, I hurtled, I flung myself onward in a company I could not see, that never outpaced me, but that swept me with the mighty ecstasies of a thousand springs, and that bore me onward exultantly past my own doorstep, toward the river, toward some pathway long forgotten, toward some unforgettable destination in the wetlands and the spring.

"Even as I leaped, I was changing. It was this, I think, that stirred the last remnants of human fear and human caution that I still possessed. My will was in abeyance; I could not stop. Furthermore, certain sensations, hypnotic or otherwise, suggested to me that my own physical shape was modifying, or about to change. I was leaping with a growing ease. I was—

"It was just then that the wharf lights began to show. We were approaching the end of the road, and the road, as I have said, ended in the river. It was this, I suppose, that startled me back into some semblance of human terror. Man is a land animal. He does not willingly plunge off wharfs at midnight in the monstrous company of amphibious shadows.

"Nevertheless their power held me. We pounded madly toward the wharf, and under the light that hung above it, and the beam that made a cross. Part of me struggled to stop, and part of me hurtled on. But in that final frenzy of terror before the water below engulfed me I shrieked, '*Help! In the name of God, help me! In the name of Jesus, stop!*'"

Dreyer paused and drew in his chair a little closer under the light. Then he went on steadily.

"I was not, I suppose, a particularly religious man, and the cries merely revealed the extremity of my terror. Nevertheless this is a strange thing, and whether it involves the crossed beam, or the appeal to a Christian deity, I will not attempt to answer.

"In one electric instant, however, I was free. It was like the release from demoniac possession. One moment I was leaping in an inhuman company of elder things, and the next moment I was a badly shaken human being on a wharf. Strangest of all, perhaps, was the sudden silence of that midnight hour. I looked down in the circle of the arc light, and there by my feet hopped

131

feebly some tiny froglets of the great migration. There was nothing impressive about them, but you will understand that I drew back in revulsion. I have never been able to handle them for research since. My work is in the past."

He paused and drank, and then, seeing perhaps some lingering doubt and confusion in my eyes, held up his black-gloved hand and deliberately pinched off the glove.

A man should not do that to another man without warning, but I suppose he felt I demanded some proof. I turned my eyes away. One does not like a webbed batrachian hand on a human being.

As I rose embarrassedly, his voice came up to me from the depths of the chair.

"It is not the hand," Deyer said. "It is the question of choice. Perhaps I was a coward, and ill prepared. Perhaps"—his voice searched uneasily among his memories—"perhaps I should have taken them and that springtime without question. Perhaps I should have trusted them and hopped onward. Who knows? They were gay enough, at least."

He sighed and set down his glass and stared so intently into empty space that, seeing I was forgotten, I tiptoed quietly away.

Lost in Translation

Eva Hoffman

It is April 1959, I'm standing at the railing of the *Batory*'s upper deck, and I feel that my life is ending. I'm looking out at the crowd that has gathered on the shore to see the ship's departure from Gdynia—a crowd that, all of a sudden, is irrevocably on the other side—and I want to break out, run back, run toward the familiar excitement, the waving hands, the exclamations. We can't be leaving all this behind—but we are. I am thirteen years old, and we are emigrating. It's a notion of such crushing, definitive finality that to me it might as well mean the end of the world.

My sister, four years younger than I, is clutching my hand wordlessly; she hardly understands where we are, or what is happening to us. My parents are highly agitated; they had just been put through a body search by the customs police, probably as the farewell gesture of anti-Jewish harassment. Still, the officials weren't clever enough, or suspicious enough, to check my sister and me—lucky for us, since we are both carrying some silverware we were not allowed to take out of Poland in large pockets sewn onto our skirts especially for this purpose, and hidden under capacious sweaters.

When the brass band on the shore strikes up the jaunty mazurka rhythms of the Polish anthem, I am pierced by a youthful sorrow so powerful that I suddenly stop crying and try to hold still against the pain. I desperately want time to stop, to hold the ship still with the force of my will. I am suffering my first, severe attack of nostalgia, or *tesknota*—a word that adds to nostalgia the tonalities of sadness and longing. It is a feeling whose shades and degrees I'm destined to know intimately, but at this hovering moment, it comes upon me like a visitation from a whole new geography of emotions, an annunciation of how much an absence can hurt. Or a premonition of absence, because at this divide, I'm filled to the brim with what I'm about to lose—images of Cracow, which I loved as one loves a person, of the sun-baked villages where we had taken summer vacations, of the hours I spent poring over passages of music with my piano teacher, of conversations and escapades with friends. Looking ahead, I come across an enormous, cold blankness—a darkening, an erasure, of the imagination, as if a camera eye has snapped shut, or as if a heavy curtain has been pulled over the future.

133

Of the place where we're going—Canada—I know nothing. There are vague outlines of half a continent, a sense of vast spaces and little habitation. When my parents were hiding in a branch-covered forest bunker during the war, my father had a book with him called *Canada Fragrant with Resin* which, in his horrible confinement, spoke to him of majestic wilderness, of animals roaming without being pursued, of freedom. That is partly why we are going there, rather than to Israel, where most of our Jewish friends have gone. But to me, the word "Canada" has ominous echoes of the "Sahara." No, my mind rejects the idea of being taken there, I don't want to be pried out of my childhood, my pleasures, my safety, my hopes for becoming a pianist. The *Batory* pulls away, the foghorn emits its lowing, shofar sounds, but my being is engaged in a stubborn refusal to move. My parents put their hands on my shoulders consolingly; for a moment, they allow themselves to acknowledge that there's pain in this departure, much as they wanted it.

Many years later, at a stylish party in New York, I met a woman who told me that she had had an enchanted childhood. Her father was a highly positioned diplomat in an Asian country, and she had lived surrounded by sumptuous elegance, the courtesy of servants, and the delicate advances of older men. No wonder, she said, that when this part of her life came to an end, at age thirteen, she felt she had been exiled from paradise, and had been searching for it ever since.

No wonder. But the wonder is what you can make a paradise out of. I told her that I grew up in a lumpen apartment in Cracow, squeezed into three rudimentary rooms with four other people, surrounded by squabbles, dark political rumblings, memories of wartime suffering, and daily struggle for existence. And yet, when it came time to leave, I, too, felt I was being pushed out of the happy, safe enclosures of Eden.

I am lying in bed, watching the slowly moving shadows on the ceiling made by the gently blowing curtains, and the lights of an occasional car moving by. I'm trying hard not to fall asleep. Being awake is so sweet that I want to delay the loss of consciousness. I'm snuggled under an enormous goose-feather quilt covered in hand-embroidered silk. Across the room from me is my sister's crib. From the next room, "the first room," I hear my parents' breathing. The maid—one of a succession of country girls who come to work for us—is sleeping in the kitchen. It is Cracow, 1949, I'm four years old, and I don't know that this happiness is taking place in a country recently destroyed by war, a place where my father has to hustle to get us a bit more than our meager ration of meat and sugar. I only know that I'm in my room, which to me is an everywhere, and that the patterns on the ceiling are enough to fill me with a feeling of sufficiency because . . . well, just because I'm conscious, because the world exists and it flows so gently into my head. Occasionally, a few blocks away, I hear the hum of the tramway, and I'm filled by a sense of utter contentment. I love riding the tramway, with its bracing but not overly fast swaying, and I love knowing, from my bed, the street over which it is moving; I repeat to myself that I'm in Cracow; Cracow, which to me is both home and the universe.

And One More Thing . . .

An Excerpt from <u>Steve Jobs</u>

Walter Isaacson

Biographers are supposed to have the last word. But this is a biography of Steve Jobs. Even though he did not impose his legendary desire for control on this project, I suspect that I would not be conveying the right feel for him—the way he asserted himself in any situation—if I just shuffled him onto history's stage without letting him have some last words.

Over the course of our conversations, there were many times when he reflected on what he hoped his legacy would be. Here are those thoughts, in his own words:

My passion has been to build an enduring company where people were motivated to make great products. Everything else was secondary. Sure, it was great to make a profit, because that was what allowed you to make great products. But the products, not the profits, were the motivation. Sculley flipped these priorities to where the goal was to make money. It's a subtle difference, but it ends up meaning everything: the people you hire, who gets promoted, what you discuss in meetings.

Some people say, "Give the customers what they want." But that's not my approach. Our job is to figure out what they're going to want before they do. I think Henry Ford once said, "If I'd asked customers what they wanted, they would have told me, 'A faster horse!'" People don't know what they want until you show it to them. That's why I never rely on market research. Our task is to read things that are not yet on the page.

Edwin Land of Polaroid talked about the intersection of the humanities and science. I like that intersection. There's something magical about that place. There are a lot of people innovating, and that's not the main distinction of my career. The reason Apple resonates with people is that there's a deep current of humanity in our innovation. I think great artists and great engineers are similar, in that they both have a desire to express themselves. In fact some of the best people working on the original Mac were poets and musicians on the side. In the seventies computers became a way for people to express their creativity. Great artists like Leonardo da Vinci and Michelangelo were also great at science. Michelangelo knew a lot about how to quarry stone, not just how to be a sculptor.

People pay us to integrate things for them, because they don't have the time to think about this stuff 24/7. If you have an extreme passion for producing great products, it pushes you to be integrated, to connect your hardware and your software and content management. You want to break new ground, so you have to do it yourself. If you want to allow your products to be open to other hardware or software, you have to give up some of your vision.

At different times in the past, there were companies that exemplified Silicon Valley. It was Hewlett-Packard for a long time. Then, in the semiconductor era, it was Fairchild and Intel. I think that it was Apple for a while, and then that faded. And then today, I think it's Apple and Google—and a little more so Apple. I think Apple has stood the test of time. It's been around for a while, but it's still at the cutting edge of what's going on.

It's easy to throw stones at Microsoft. They've clearly fallen from their dominance. They've become mostly irrelevant. And yet I appreciate what they did and how hard it was. They were very good at the business side of things. They were never as ambitious product-wise as they should have been. Bill likes to portray himself as a man of the product, but he's really not. He's a businessperson. Winning business was more important than making great products. He ended up the wealthiest guy around, and if that was his goal, then he achieved it. But it's never been my goal, and I wonder, in the end, if it was his goal. I admire him for the company he built—it's impressive—and I enjoyed working with him. He's bright and actually has a good sense of humor. But Microsoft never had the humanities and liberal arts in its DNA. Even when they saw the Mac, they couldn't copy it well. They totally didn't get it.

I have my own theory about why decline happens at companies like IBM or Microsoft. The company does a great job, innovates and becomes a monopoly or close to it in some field, and then the quality of the product becomes less important. The company starts valuing the great salesmen, because they're the ones who can move the needle on revenues, not the product engineers and designers. So the salespeople end up running the company. John Akers at IBM was a smart, eloquent, fantastic salesperson, but he didn't know anything about product. The same thing happened at Xerox. When the sales guys run the company, the product guys don't matter so much, and a lot of them just turn off. It happened at Apple when Sculley came in, which was my fault, and it happened when Ballmer took over at Microsoft. Apple was lucky and it rebounded, but I don't think anything will change at Microsoft as long as Ballmer is running it.

I hate it when people call themselves "entrepreneurs" when what they're really trying to do is launch a startup and then sell or go public, so they can cash in and move on. They're unwilling to do the work it takes to build a real company, which is the hardest work in business. That's how you really make a contribution and add to the legacy of those who went before. You build a company that will still stand for something a generation or two from now. That's what Walt Disney did, and Hewlett and Packard, and the people who built Intel. They created a company to last, not just to make money. That's what I want Apple to be.

I don't think I run roughshod over people, but if something sucks, I tell people to their face. It's my job to be honest. I know what I'm talking about, and I usually turn out to be right. That's the culture I tried to create. We are brutally honest with each other, and anyone can tell me they think I am full of shit and I can tell them the same. And we've had some rip-roaring arguments, where we are yelling at each other, and it's some of the best times I've ever had. I feel totally comfortable saying "Ron, that store looks like shit" in front of everyone else. Or I might say, "God, we really fucked up the engineering on this" in front of the person that's responsible. That's the ante for being in the room: You've got to be able to be super honest. Maybe there's a better way, a gentlemen's club where we all wear ties and speak in this Brahmin language and velvet code-words, but I don't know that way, because I am middle class from California.

I was hard on people sometimes, probably harder than I needed to be. I remember the time when Reed was six years old, coming home, and I had just fired somebody that day, and I imagined what it was like for that person to tell his family and his young son that he had lost his job. It was hard. But somebody's got to do it. I figured that it was always my job to make sure that the team was excellent, and if I didn't do it, nobody was going to do it.

You always have to keep pushing to innovate. Dylan could have sung protest songs forever and probably made a lot of money, but he didn't. He had to move on, and when he did, by going electric in 1965, he alienated a lot of people. His 1966 Europe tour was his greatest. He would come on and do a set of acoustic guitar, and the audiences loved him. Then he brought out what became The Band, and they would all do an electric set, and the audience sometimes booed. There was one point where he was about to sing "Like a Rolling Stone" and someone from the audience yells "Judas!" And Dylan then says, "Play it fucking loud!" And they did. The Beatles were the same way. They kept evolving, moving, refining their art. That's what I've always tried to do—keep moving. Otherwise, as Dylan says, if you're not busy being born, you're busy dying.

What drove me? I think most creative people want to express appreciation for being able to take advantage of the work that's been done by others before us. I didn't invent the language or mathematics I use. I make little of my own food, none of my own clothes. Everything I do depends on other members of our species and the shoulders that we stand on. And a lot of us want to contribute something back to our species and to add something to the flow. It's about trying to express something in the only way that most of us know how—because we can't write Bob Dylan songs or Tom Stoppard plays. We try to use the talents we do have to express our deep feelings, to show our appreciation of all the contributions that came before us, and to add something to that flow. That's what has driven me.

A World of Difference

Evelyn Fox Keller

> O Lady! We receive but what we give,
> And in our life alone does Nature live:
> Ours is her wedding garment, ours her shroud!
> —Samuel Taylor Coleridge, "Dejection: An Ode"

If we want to think about the ways in which science might be different, we could hardly find a more appropriate guide than Barbara McClintock. Known to her colleagues as a maverick and a visionary, McClintock occupies a place in the history of genetics at one and the same time central and peripheral—a place that, for all its eminence, is marked by difference at every turn.

Born in 1902, McClintock began in her twenties to make contributions to classical genetics and cytology that earned her a level of recognition few women of her generation could imagine. Encouraged and supported by many of the great men of classical genetics (including T. H. Morgan, R. A. Emerson, and Lewis Stadler), McClintock was given the laboratory space and fellowship stipends she needed to pursue what had quickly become the central goal of her life: understanding the secrets of plant genetics. She rejected the more conventional opportunities then available to women in science (such as a research assistantship or a teaching post at a woman's college) and devoted herself to the life of pure research. By the mid-1930s, she had already made an indelible mark on the history of genetics. But the fellowships inevitably ran out. With no job on the horizon, McClintock thought she would have to leave science. Morgan and Emerson, arguing that "it would be a scientific tragedy if her work did not go forward" (quoted in Keller 1983, p. 74), prevailed upon the Rockefeller Foundation to provide two years' interim support. Morgan described her as "the best person in the world" in her field but deplored her "personality difficulties": "She is sore at the world because of her conviction that she would have a much freer scientific opportunity if she were a man" (p. 73). Not until 1942 was McClintock's professional survival secured: at that time, a haven was provided for her at the Carnegie Institution of Washington at Cold Spring Harbor, where she has remained ever since. Two years later she was elected to the National Academy of Science; in 1945 she became president of the Genetics Society of America.

This dual theme of success and marginality that poignantly describes the first stage of McClintock's career continues as the leitmotif of her entire professional life. Despite the ungrudging respect and admiration of her colleagues, her most important work has, until recently, gone largely unappreciated, uncomprehended, and almost entirely unintegrated into the growing corpus of biological thought. This was the work, begun in her forties, that led to her discovery that genetic elements can move, in an apparently coordinated way, from one chromosomal site to another—in short, her discovery of genetic transposition. Even today, as a Nobel laureate and deluged with other awards and prizes for this same work, McClintock regards herself as, in crucial respects, an outsider to the world of modern biology—not because she is a woman but because she is a philosophical and methodological deviant.

No doubt, McClintock's marginality and deviance are more visible—and seem more dramatic—to her than to others. During the many years when McClintock's professional survival seemed so precarious, even her most devoted colleagues seemed unaware that she had no proper job. "What do you mean?" many of them asked me. "She was so good! How could she not have had a job?" Indeed, as Morgan himself suggested, her expectation that she would be rewarded on the basis of merit, on the same footing as her male colleagues, was itself read as a mark of her ingratitude—of what he called her "personality difficulties."

When discussing the second stage of her career, during which her revolutionary work on genetic transposition earned her the reputation more of eccentricity than of greatness, her colleagues are likely to focus on the enduring admiration many of them continued to feel. She, of course, is more conscious of their lack of comprehension and of the dismissal of her work by other, less admiring colleagues. She is conscious, above all, of the growing isolation that ensued.

Today, genetic transposition is no longer a dubious or isolated phenomenon. As one prominent biologist describes it, "[Transposable elements] are everywhere, in bacteria, yeast, *Drosophila*, and plants. Perhaps even in mice and men." (Marx 1981, quoted in Keller 1983, p. 193). But the significance of transposition remains in considerable dispute. McClintock saw transposable elements as a key to developmental regulation; molecular biologists today, although much more sympathetic to this possibility than they were twenty, or even ten, years ago, are still unsure. And in evolutionary terms, McClintock's view of transposition as a survival mechanism available to the organism in times of stress seems to most (although not to all) pure heresy.

My interest here, as it has been from the beginning, is less on who was "right" than on the differences in perceptions that underlay such a discordance of views. The vicissitudes of McClintock's career give those differences not only special poignancy but special importance. In *A Feeling for the Organism: The Life and Work of Barbara McClintock* (Keller 1983), I argued that it is precisely the duality of success and marginality that lends her career its significance to the history and philosophy of science. Her success indisputably affirms her legitimacy as a scientist, while her marginality provides an opportunity to examine the role and fate of dissent in the growth of scientific knowledge. This duality illustrates the diversity of values, methodological styles, and goals that, to varying degrees, always exists in science; at the same time, it illustrates the pressures that, to equally varying degrees, operate to contain that diversity.

In the preface to that book (p. xii), I wrote:

> The story of Barbara McClintock allows us to explore the condition under which dissent in science arises, the function it serves, and the plurality of values and goals it reflects. It makes us ask: What role do interests, individual and collective, play in the evolution of scientific knowledge? Do all scientists seek the same kinds of explanations? Are the kinds of questions they ask the same? Do differences in methodology between different subdisciplines even permit the same kinds of answers? And when significant differences do arise in questions asked, explanations sought, methodologies employed, how do they affect communication between scientists? In short, why could McClintock's discovery of transposition not be absorbed by her contemporaries? We can say that her vision of biological organization was too remote from the kinds of explanations her colleagues were seeking, but we need to understand what that distance is composed of, and how such divergences develop.

I chose, in effect, not to read the story of McClintock's career as a romance— neither as "a tale of dedication rewarded after years of neglect—of prejudice or indifference eventually routed by courage and truth" (p. xii), nor as a heroic story of the scientist, years "ahead of her time," stumbling on something approximating what we now know as "the truth." Instead, I read it as a story about the languages of science—about the process by which worlds of common scientific discourse become established, effectively bounded, and yet at the same time remain sufficiently permeable to allow a given piece of work to pass from incomprehensibility in one era to acceptance (if not full comprehensibility) in another.

In this essay, my focus is even more explicitly on difference itself. I want to isolate McClintock's views of nature, of science, and of the relation between mind and nature, in order to exhibit not only their departure from more conventional views but also their own internal coherence. If we can stand inside this world view, the questions she asks, the explanations she seeks, and the methods she employs in her pursuit of scientific knowledge will take on a degree of clarity and comprehensibility they lack from outside. And at the heart of this world view lies the same respect for difference that motivates us to examine it in the first place. I begin therefore with a discussion of the implications of respect for difference (and complexity) in the general philosophy expressed in McClintock's testimony, and continue by discussing its implications for cognition and perception, for her interests as a geneticist, and for the relation between her work and molecular biology. I conclude the essay with a brief analysis of the relevance of gender to any philosophy of difference, and to McClintock's in particular.

Complexity and Difference

To McClintock, nature is characterized by an a priori complexity that vastly exceeds the capacities of the human imagination. Her recurrent remark, "Anything you can think of you will find,"[1] is a statement about the capacities not of mind but of nature. It is meant not as a description of our own ingenuity as discoverers but as a comment on the resourcefulness of natural order; in the sense not so much of adaptability as of largesse and prodigality. Organisms have a life and an order of their own that scientists can only begin to fathom. "Misrepresented, not appreciated, . . . [they] are beyond our wildest expectations. . . . They do everything we [can think of], they do it better, more efficiently, more marvelously." In comparison with the ingenuity of nature, our scientific intelligence seems pallid. It follows as a matter of course that "trying to make everything fit into set dogma won't work. . . . There's no such thing as a central dogma into which everything will fit."

In the context of McClintock's views of nature, attitudes about research that would otherwise sound romantic fall into logical place. The need to "listen to the material" follows from her sense of the order of things. Precisely because the complexity of nature exceeds our own imaginative possibilities, it becomes essential to "let the experiment tell you what to do." Her major criticism of contemporary research is based on what she sees as inadequate humility. She feels that "much of the work done is done because one wants to impose an answer on it—they have the answer ready, and they [know what] they want the material to tell them, so anything it doesn't tell them, they don't really recognize as there, or they think it's a mistake and throw it out. . . . If you'd only just let the material tell you."

---

[1] All quotations from Barbara McClintock are taken from private interviews conducted between September 24, 1978, and February 25, 1979.

Respect for complexity thus demands from observers of nature the same special attention to the exceptional case that McClintock's own example as a scientist demands from observers of science: "If the material tells you, 'It may be this,' allow that. Don't turn it aside and call it an exception, an aberration, a contaminant. . . . That's what's happened all the way along the line with so many good clues." Indeed, respect for individual difference lies at the very heart of McClintock's scientific passion. "The important thing is to develop the capacity to see one kernel [of maize] that is different, and make that understandable," she says. "If [something] doesn't fit, there's a reason, and you find out what it is." The prevailing focus on classes and numbers, McClintock believes, encourages researchers to overlook difference, to "call it an exception, an aberration, a contaminant." The consequences of this seem to her very costly. "Right and left," she says, they miss "what is going on."

She is, in fact, here describing the history of her own research. Her work on transposition in fact began with the observation of an aberrant pattern of pigmentation on a few kernels of a single corn plant. And her commitment to the significance of this singular pattern sustained her through six years of solitary and arduous investigation—all aimed at making the difference she saw understandable.

Making difference understandable does not mean making it disappear. In McClintock's world view, an understanding of nature can come to rest with difference. "Exceptions" are not there to "prove the rule"; they have meaning in and of themselves. In this respect, difference constitutes a principle for ordering the world radically unlike the principle of division of dichotomization (subject–object, mind–matter, feeling–reason, disorder–law). Whereas these oppositions are directed toward a cosmic unity typically excluding or devouring one of the pair, toward a unified, all-encompassing law, respect for difference remains content with multiplicity as an end in itself.

And just as the terminus of knowledge implied by difference can be distinguished from that implied by division, so the starting point of knowledge can also be distinguished. Above all, difference, in this world view, does not posit division as an epistemological prerequisite—it does not imply the necessity of hard and fast divisions in nature, or in mind, or in the relation between mind and nature. Division severs connection and imposes distance; the recognition of difference provides a starting point for relatedness. It serves both as a clue to new modes of connectedness in nature and as an invitation to engagement with nature. For McClintock, certainly, respect for difference serves both these functions. Seeing something that does not appear to fit is, to her, a challenge to find the larger multidimensional pattern into which it does fit. Anomalous kernels of corn were evidence not of disorder or lawlessness, but of a larger system of order, one that cannot be reduced to a single law.

Difference thus invites a form of engagement and understanding that allows for the preservation of the individual. The integrity of each kernel (or chromosome or plant) survives all our own pattern-making attempts; the order of nature transcends our capacities for ordering. And this transcendence is manifested in the enduring uniqueness of each organism: "No two plants are exactly alike. They're all different, and as a consequence, you have to know that difference," she explains. "I start with the seedling and I don't want to leave it. I don't feel I really know the story if I don't watch the plant all the way along. So I know every plant in the field. I know them intimately, and I find it a great pleasure to know them." From days, weeks, and years of patient observation comes what looks like privileged insight: "When I see things, I can interpret them right away." As one colleague described it, the result is an apparent ability to write the "autobiography" of every plant she works with.

McClintock is not here speaking of relations to other humans, but the parallels are nonetheless compelling. In the relationship she describes with plants, as in human relations, respect for difference constitutes a claim not only on our interest but on our capacity for empathy—in short on the highest form of love: love that allows for intimacy without the annihilation of difference. I use the word *love* neither loosely nor sentimentally, but out of fidelity to the language McClintock herself uses to describe a form of attention, indeed a form of thought. Her vocabulary is consistently a vocabulary of affection, of kinship, of empathy. Even with puzzles, she explains, "The thing was dear to you for a period of time, you really had an affection for it. Then after a while, it disappears and it doesn't bother you. But for a short time you feel strongly attached to that little toy." The crucial point for us is that McClintock can risk the suspension of boundaries between subject and object without jeopardy to science precisely because, to her, science is not premised on that division. Indeed, the intimacy she experiences with the objects she studies—intimacy born of a lifetime of cultivated attentiveness—is a wellspring of her powers as a scientist.

The most vivid illustration of this process comes from her own account of a breakthrough in one particularly recalcitrant piece of cytological analysis. She describes the state of mind accompanying the crucial shift in orientation that enabled her to identify chromosomes she had earlier not been able to distinguish: "I found that the more I worked with them, the bigger and bigger [the chromosomes] got, and when I was really working with them I wasn't outside, I was down there. I was part of the system. I was right down there with them, and everything got big. I even was able to see the internal parts of the chromosomes—actually everything was there. It surprised me because I actually felt as if I was right down there and these were my friends. . . . As you look at these things, they become part of you. And you forget yourself."

Cognition and Perception

In this world of difference, division is relinquished without generating chaos. Self and other, mind and nature survive not in mutual alienation, or in symbiotic fusion, but in structural integrity. The "feeling for the organism" that McClintock upholds as the sine qua non of good research need not be read as "participation mystique"; it is a mode of access—honored by time and human experience if not by prevailing conventions in science—to the reliable knowledge of the world around us that all scientists seek. It is a form of attention strongly reminiscent of the concept of "focal attention" developed by Ernest Schachtel to designate "man's [sic] capacity to *center* his attention on an object fully, so that he can perceive or understand it from *many sides,* as fully as possible" (p. 251). In Schachtel's language, "focal attention" is the principal tool that, in conjunction with our natural interest in objects per se, enables us to progress from mere wishing and wanting to thinking and knowing—that equips us for the fullest possible knowledge of reality in its own terms. Such "object-centered" perception presupposes "a temporary eclipse of all the perceiver's egocentric thoughts and strivings, of all preoccupation with self and self-esteem, and a full turning towards the object, . . . [which, in turn] leads not to a *loss* of self, but to a heightened feeling of aliveness" (p. 181). Object-centered perception, Schachtel goes on to argue, is in the service of a love "which wants to affirm others in their total and unique being . . . [which affirms objects as] part of the same world of which man is a part" (p. 226). It requires

> an experiential realization of the kinship between oneself and the other . . . a realization [that] is made difficult by fear and by arrogance—by fear because then the need to protect oneself by flight, appeasement, or attack gets in the way; by arrogance because then the other is no longer experienced as akin, but as inferior to oneself. (p. 227)

The difference between Schachtel and McClintock is that what Schachtel grants to the poet's perceptual style in contrast to that of the scientist, McClintock claims equally for science. She enlists a "feeling for the organism"—not only for living organisms but for any object that fully claims our attention—in pursuit of the goal shared by all scientists: reliable (that is, shareable and reproducible) knowledge of natural order.

This difference is a direct reflection of the limitations of Schachtel's picture of science. It is drawn not from observation of scientists like McClintock but only from the more stereotypic scientist, who "looks at the object with one or more hypotheses . . . in mind and thus 'uses' the object to corroborate or disprove a hypothesis, but does not encounter the object as such, in its own fullness." For Schachtel,

modern natural science has as its main goal prediction, i.e. the power to manipulate objects in such a way that certain predicted events will happen. . . . Hence,
the scientist usually will tend to perceive the object merely from the perspective of [this] power . . . That is to say that his view of the object will be determined by the ends which he pursues in his experimentation . . . He may achieve
a great deal in this way and add important data to our knowledge, but to the
extent to which he remains within the framework of this perspective he will
not perceive the object in its own right. {1959, p. 171)

To McClintock, science has a different goal: not prediction per se, but
understanding; not the power to manipulate, but empowerment—the kind
of power that results from an understanding of the world around us, that
simultaneously reflects and affirms our connection to that world.

What Counts as Knowledge

At the root of this difference between McClintock and the stereotypic
scientist lies that unexamined starting point of science: the naming of nature.
Underlying every discussion of science, as well as every scientific discussion,
there exists a larger assumption about the nature of the universe in which that
discussion takes place. The power of this unseen ground is to be found not
in its influence on any particular argument in science but in its framing of
the very terms of argument—in its definition of the tacit aims and goals of
science. . . . Scientists may spend fruitful careers, building theories of nature
that are astonishingly successful in their predictive power, without ever feeling the need to reflect on these fundamental philosophical issues. Yet if we
want to ask questions about that success, about the value of alternative scientific descriptions of nature, even about the possibility of alternative criteria of success, we can do so only by examining those most basic assumptions
that are normally not addressed.

We have to remind ourselves that, although all scientists share a common
ambition for knowledge, it does not follow that what counts as knowledge is
commonly agreed upon. The history of science reveals a wide diversity of questions asked, explanations sought, and methodologies employed in this common quest for knowledge of the natural world; this diversity is in turn reflected
in the kinds of knowledge acquired, and indeed in what counts as knowledge. To a large degree, both the kinds of questions one asks and the explanations that one finds satisfying depend on one's a priori relation to the objects
of study. In particular, I am suggesting that questions asked about objects with
which one feels kinship are likely to differ from questions asked about
objects one sees as unalterably alien. Similarly, explanations that satisfy us

about a natural world that is seen as "blind, simple and dumb," ontologically inferior, may seem less self-evidently satisfying for a natural world seen as complex and, itself, resourceful. I suggest that individual and communal conceptions of nature need to be examined for their role in the history of science, not as causal determinants but as frameworks upon which all scientific programs are developed. More specifically, I am claiming that the difference between McClintock's conception of nature and that prevailing in the community around her is an essential key to our understanding of the history of her life and work.

It provides, for example, the context for examining the differences between McClintock's interests *as a geneticist* and what has historically been the defining focus of both classical and molecular genetics—differences crucial to the particular route her research took. To most geneticists, the problem of inheritance is solved by knowing the mechanism and structure of genes. To McClintock, however, as to many other biologists, mechanism and structure have never been adequate answers to the question "How do genes work?" Her focus was elsewhere: on function and organization. To her, an adequate understanding would, by definition, have to include an account of how they function in relation to the rest of the cell, and of course, to the organism as a whole.

In her language, the cell itself is an organism. Indeed, "Every component of the organism is as much an organism as every other part." When she says, therefore, that "one cannot consider the [gene] as such as being all important—more important is the overall organism," she means the genome as a whole, the cell, the ensemble of cells, the organism itself. Genes are neither "beads on a string" nor functionally disjoint pieces of DNA. They are organized functional units, whose very function is defined by their position in the organization as a whole. As she says, genes function "only with respect to the environment in which [they are] found."

Interests in function and in organization are historically and conceptually related to each other. By tradition, both are primary preoccupations of developmental biology, and McClintock's own interest in development followed from and supported these interests. By the same tradition, genetics and developmental biology have been two separate subjects. But for a geneticist for whom the answer to the question of how genes work must include function and organization, the problem of heredity becomes inseparable from the problem of development. The division that most geneticists felt they had to live with (happily or not) McClintock could not accept. To her, development, as the coordination of function, was an integral part of genetics.

McClintock's views today are clearly fed by her work on transposition. But her work on transposition was itself fed by these interests. Her own account (see Keller 1983, pp. 115–17) of how she came to this work and of how she followed the clues she saw vividly illustrates the ways in which her interests in function and organization—and in development—focused her attention on the patterns she saw and framed the questions she asked about the significance of these patterns. I suggest that they also defined the terms that a satisfying explanation had to meet.

Such an explanation had to account not so much for how transposition occurred as for why it occurred. The patterns she saw indicated a programmatic disruption in normal developmental function. When she succeeded in linking this disruption to the location (and change in location) of particular genetic elements, that very link was what captured her interest. (She knew she was "on to something important.") The fact that transposition occurred—the fact that genetic sequences are not fixed—was of course interesting too, but only secondary so. To her, the paramount interest lay in the meaning of its occurrence, in the clue that transposition provided for the relation between genetics and development. Necessarily, a satisfying account of this relation would have to take due note of the complexity of the regulation process.

Transposition and the Central Dogma

Just two years after McClintock's first public presentation of her work on transposition came the culminating event in the long search for the mechanism of inheritance. Watson and Crick's discovery of the structure of DNA enabled them to provide a compelling account of the essential genetic functions of replication and instruction. According to their account, the vital information of the cell is encoded in the DNA. From there it is copied onto the RNA, which, in turn, is used as a blueprint for the production of the proteins responsible for genetic traits. In the picture that emerged—DNA to RNA to protein (which Crick himself dubbed the "central dogma")—the DNA is posited as the central actor in the cell, the executive governor of cellular organization, itself remaining impervious to influence from the subordinate agents to which it dictates. Several years later, Watson and Crick's original model was emended by Jacques Monad and François Jacob to allow for environmental control of the rates of protein synthesis. But even with this modification, the essential autonomy of DNA remained unchallenged: information flowed one way, always from, and never to, the DNA.

Throughout the 1950s and 1960s, the successes of molecular genetics were dramatic. By the end of the 1960s, it was possible to say (as Jacques Monad did say), "The Secret of Life? But this is in large part known—in principle, if not in details" (quoted in Judson 1979, p. 216). A set of values and interests wholly different from McClintock's seemed to have been vindicated. The intricacies, and difficulties, of corn genetics held little fascination in comparison with the quick returns from research on the vastly simpler and seemingly more straightforward bacterium and bacteriophage. As a result, communication between McClintock and her colleagues grew steadily more difficult; fewer and fewer biologists had the expertise required even to begin to understand her results.

McClintock of course shared in the general excitement of this period, but she did not share in the general enthusiasm for the central dogma. The same model that seemed so immediately and overwhelmingly satisfying to so many of her colleagues did not satisfy her. Although duly impressed by its explanatory power, she remained at the same time acutely aware of what it did not explain. It neither addressed the questions that were of primary interest to her—bearing on the relation between genetics and development—nor began to take into account the complexity of genetic organization that she had always assumed, and that was now revealed to her by her work on transposition.

McClintock locates the critical flaw of the central dogma in its presumption: it claimed to explain too much. Baldly put, what was true of *E. coli* (the bacterium most commonly studied) was *not* true of the elephant, as Monod (and others) would have had it (Judson 1979, p. 613). Precisely because higher organisms are multicellular, she argued, they necessarily require a different kind of economy. The central dogma was without question inordinately successful as well as scientifically productive. Yet the fact that it ultimately proved inadequate even to the dynamics of *E. coli* suggests that its trouble lay deeper than just a too hasty generalization from the simple to the complex; its presumptuousness, I suggest, was built into its form of explanation.

The central dogma is a good example of what I have earlier called (following Nanney 1957) master-molecule theories (Keller 1982). In locating the seat of genetic control in a single molecule, it posits a structure of genetic organization that is essentially hierarchical, often illustrated in textbooks by organizational charts like those of corporate structures. In this model, genetic stability is ensured by the unidirectionality of information flow, much as political and social stability is assumed in many quarters to require the unidirectional exercise of authority.

To McClintock, transposition provided evidence that genetic organization is necessarily more complex, and in fact more globally interdependent, than such a model assumes. It showed that the DNA itself is subject to rearrangement and, by implication, to reprogramming. Although she did not make the suggestion explicit, the hidden heresy of her argument lay in the inference that such reorganization could be induced by signals external to the DNA—from the cell, the organism, even from the environment.

For more than fifty years, modern biologists had labored heroically to purge biological thought of the last vestiges of teleology, particularly as they surfaced in Lamarckian notions of adaptive evolution. But even though McClintock is not a Lamarckian, she sees in transposition a mechanism enabling genetic structures to respond to the needs of the organism. Since needs are relative to the environmental context and hence subject to change, transposition, by implication, indirectly allows for the possibility of environmentally induced and genetically transmitted change. To her, such a possibility is not heresy—it is not even surprising. On the contrary, it is in direct accord with her belief in the resourcefulness of natural order. Because she has no investment in the passivity of nature, the possibility of internally generated order does not, to her, threaten the foundations of science. The capacity of organisms to reprogram their own DNA implies neither vitalism, magic, nor a countermanding will. It merely confirms the existence of forms of order more complex than we have, at least thus far, been able to account for.

The renewed interest in McClintock's work today is a direct consequence of developments (beginning in the early 1970s) in the very research programs that had seemed so philosophically opposed to her position; genetic mobility was rediscovered within molecular biology itself. That this was so was crucial, perhaps even necessary, to establishing the legitimacy of McClintock's early work, precisely because the weight of scientific authority has now come to reside in molecular biology. As a by-product, this legitimization also lends McClintock's views of science and attitudes toward research somewhat more credibility among professional biologists. To observers of science, this same historical sequence serves as a sharp reminder that the languages of science, however self-contained they seem, are not closed. McClintock's

> eventual vindication demonstrates the capacity of science to overcome its own characteristic kinds of myopia, reminding us that its limitations do not reinforce themselves indefinitely. Their own methodology allows, even obliges, scientists to continually reencounter phenomena even their best theories cannot accommodate. Or—to look at it from the other side—however severely communication between science and nature may be impeded by the preconceptions of a particular time, some channels always remain open; and, through them, nature finds ways of reasserting itself. (Keller 1983, p. 197)

In this sense, the McClintock story is a happy one.

It is important, however, not to overestimate the degree of rapprochement that has taken place. McClintock has been abundantly vindicated: transposition is acknowledged, higher organisms and development have once again captured the interest of biologists, and almost everyone agrees that genetic organization is manifestly more complex than had previously been thought. But not everyone shares her conviction that we are in the midst of a revolution that "will reorganize the way we look at things, the way we do research." Many researchers remain confident that the phenomenon of transposition can somehow be incorporated, even if they do not yet see how, into an improved version of the central dogma. Their attachment to this faith is telling. Behind the continuing skepticism about McClintock's interpretation of the role of transposition in development and evolution, there remains a major gap between her underlying interests and commitments and those of most of her colleagues.

The Issue of Gender

How much of this enduring difference reflects the fact that McClintock is a woman in a field still dominated by men? To what extent are her views indicative of a vision of "what will happen to science," as Erik Erikson asked in 1964 (1965, p. 243), "if and when women are truly represented in it—not by a few glorious exceptions, but in the rank and file of the scientific elite?"

On the face of it, it would be tempting indeed to call McClintock's vision of science "a feminist science." Its emphasis on intuition, on feeling, on connection and relatedness, all seem to confirm our most familiar stereotypes of women. And to the extent that they do, we might expect that the sheer presence of more women in science would shift the balance of community sentiment and lead to the endorsement of that vision. However, there are both general and particular reasons that argue strongly against this simple view.

. . . To the extent that science is defined by its past and present practitioners, anyone who aspires to membership in that community must conform to its existing code. As a consequence, the inclusion of new members, even from a radically different culture, cannot induce immediate or direct change. To be a successful scientist, one must first be adequately socialized. For this reason, it is unreasonable to expect a sharp differentiation between women scientists and their male colleagues, and indeed, most women scientists would be appalled by such a suggestion.

McClintock is in this sense no exception. She would disclaim any analysis of her work as a woman's work, as well as any suggestion that her views represent a woman's perspective. To her, science is not a matter of gender, either male or female; it is, on the contrary, a place where (ideally at least) "the matter of gender drops away." Furthermore, her very commitment to science is of a piece with her lifelong wish to transcend gender altogether. Indeed, her adamant rejection of female stereotypes seems to have been a prerequisite for her becoming a scientist at all (See Keller 1983, chaps. 2 and 3.) In her own image of herself, she is a maverick in all respects—as a woman, as a scientist, even as a woman scientist.

Finally, I want to reemphasize that it would be not only misleading but actually contradictory to suggest that McClintock's views of science were shared by none of her colleagues. Had that been so, she could not have had even marginal status as a scientist. It is essential to understand that, in practice, the scientific tradition is far more pluralistic than any particular description of it suggests, and certainly more pluralistic than its dominant ideology. For McClintock to be recognized as a scientist, the positions that she represents, however unrepresentative, had to be, and were, identifiable as belonging somewhere within that tradition.

But although McClintock is not a total outsider to science, she is equally clearly not an insider. And however atypical she is as a woman, what she is *not* is a man. Between these two facts lies a crucial connection—a connection signaled by the recognition that, as McClintock herself admits, the matter of gender never does drop away.

I suggest that the radical core of McClintock's stance can be located right here: Because she is not a man, in a world of men, her commitment to a gender free science has been binding; because concepts of gender have so deeply influenced the basic categories of science, that commitment has been transformative. In short, the relevance of McClintock's gender in this story is to be found not in its role in her personal socialization but precisely in the role of gender in the construction of science.

Of course, not all scientists have embraced the conception of science as one of "putting nature on the rack and torturing the answers out of her." Nor have all men embraced a conception of masculinity that demands cool detachment and domination. Nor even have all scientists been men. But most have. And however variable the attitudes of individual male scientists toward science and toward masculinity, the metaphor of a marriage between mind and nature necessarily does not look the same to them as it does to women. And this is the point.

In a science constructed around the naming of object (nature) as female and the parallel naming of subject (mind) as male, any scientist who happens to be a woman is confronted with an a priori contradiction in terms. This poses a critical problem of identity: any scientist who is not a man walks a path bounded on one side by inauthenticity and on the other by subversion. Just as surely as inauthenticity is the cost a woman suffers by joining men in misogynist jokes, so it is, equally, the cost suffered by a woman who identifies with an image of the scientist modeled on the patriarchal husband. Only if she undergoes a radical disidentification from self can she share masculine pleasure in mastering a nature cast in the image of woman as passive, inert, and blind. Her alternative is to attempt a radical redefinition of terms. Nature must be renamed as not female, or, at least, as not an alienated object. By the same token, the mind, if the female scientist is to have one, must be renamed as not necessarily male, and accordingly recast with a more inclusive subjectivity. This is not to say that the male scientist cannot claim similar redefinition (certainly many have done so) but, by contrast to the woman scientist, his identity does not require it.

For McClintock, given her particular commitments to personal integrity, to be a scientist, and not a man, with a nonetheless intact identity, meant that she had to insist on a different meaning of mind, of nature, and of the relation between them. Her need to define for herself the relation between subject and object, even the very terms themselves, came not from a feminist consciousness, or even from a female consciousness. It came from her insistence on her right to be a scientist—from her determination to claim science as a human rather than a male endeavor. For such a claim, difference makes sense of the world in ways that division cannot. It allows for the kinship that she feels with other scientists, without at the same time obligating her to share all their assumptions.

Looked at in this way, McClintock's stance is, finally, a far more radical one than that implied in Erikson's question. It implies that what could happen to science "when women are truly represented in it" is not simply, or even, "the addition, to the male kind of creative vision, of women's vision" (p. 243), but, I suggest, a thoroughgoing transformation of the very possibilities of creative vision, for everyone. It implies that the kind of change we might hope for is not a direct or readily apparent one but rather an indirect and subterranean one. A first step toward such a transformation would be the undermining of the commitment of scientists to the masculinity of their profession that would be an inevitable concomitant of the participation of large numbers of women.

However, we need to remember that, as long as success in science does not require self-reflection, the undermining of masculinist or other ideological commitments is not a sufficient guarantee of change. But nature itself is an ally that can be relied upon to provide the impetus for real change: nature's responses recurrently invite reexamination of the terms in which our understanding of science is constructed. Paying attention to those responses— "listening to the material"—may help us to reconstruct our understanding of science in terms born out of the diverse spectrum of human experience rather than out of the narrow spectrum that our culture has labeled masculine.

From Working Scientist to Feminist Critic

Evelyn Fox Keller

I begin with three vignettes, all drawn from memory.

1965. In my first few years out of graduate school, I held quite conventional beliefs about science. I believed not only in the possibility of clear and certain knowledge of the world, but also in the uniquely privileged access to this knowledge provided by science in general, and by physics in particular. I believed in the accessibility of an underlying (and unifying) "truth" about the world we live in, and I believed that the laws of physics gave us the closest possible approximation of this truth. In short, I was well trained in both the traditional realist worldviews assumed by virtually all scientists and in the conventional epistemological ordering of the sciences. I had, after all, been trained, first, by theoretical physicists, and later, by molecular biologists. This is not to say that I lived my life according to the teachings of physics (or molecular biology), only that when it came to questions about what "really is," I knew where, and how, to look. Although I had serious conflicts about my own ability to be part of this venture, I fully accepted science, and scientists, as arbiters of truth. Physics (and physicists) were, of course, the highest arbiters.

Somewhere around this time, I came across the proceedings of the first major conference held in the United States on "Women and the Scientific Professions" (Mattfield and Van Aiken 1965)—a subject of inevitable interest to me. I recall reading in those proceedings an argument for more women in science, made by both Erik Erikson and Bruno Bettelheim, based on the invaluable contributions a "specifically female genius" could make to science. Although earlier in their contributions both Erikson and Bettelheim had each made a number of eminently reasonable observations and recommendations, I flew to these concluding remarks as if waiting for them, indeed forgetting everything else they had said. From the vantage point I then occupied, my reaction was predictable: To put it quite bluntly, I laughed. Laws of nature are universal—how could they possibly depend on the sex of their discoverers? Obviously, I snickered, these psychoanalysts know little enough about science (and by implication, about truth).

157

1969. I was living in a suburban California house and found myself with time to think seriously about my own mounting conflicts (as well as those of virtually all my female cohorts) about being a scientist. I had taken a leave to accompany my husband on his sabbatical, remaining at home to care for our two small children. Weekly, I would talk to the colleague I had left back in New York and hear his growing enthusiasm as he reported the spectacular successes he was having in presenting our joint work. In between, I would try to understand why my own enthusiasm was not only not growing, but actually diminishing. How I went about seeking such an understanding is worth noting: What I did was to go to the library to gather data about the fate of women scientists in general—more truthfully, to document my own growing disenchantment (even in the face of manifest success) as part of a more general phenomenon reflecting an underlying misfit between women and science. And I wrote to Erik Erikson for further comment on the alarming (yet somehow satisfying) attrition data I was collecting. In short, only a few years after ridiculing his thoughts on the subject, I was ready to at least entertain if not embrace an argument about women in, or out of, science based on "women's nature." Not once during that entire year did it occur to me that at least part of my disenchantment might be related to the fact that I was in fact not sharing in the *kudos* my colleague was reaping for our joint work.

1974. I had not dropped out of science, but I had moved into interdisciplinary, undergraduate teaching. And I had just finished teaching my first women's studies course when I received an invitation to give a series of "Distinguished Lectures" on my work in mathematical biology at the University of Maryland. It was a great honor, and I wanted to do it, but I had a problem. In my women's studies course, I had yielded to the pressure of my students and colleagues to talk openly about what it had been like, as a woman, to become a scientist. In other words, I had been persuaded to publicly air the exceedingly painful story of the struggle that had actually been—a story I had previously only talked about in private, if at all. The effect of doing this was that I actually came to see that story as public, that is, of political significance, rather than as simply private, of merely personal significance. As a result, the prospect of continuing to present myself as a disembodied scientist, of talking about my work as if it had been done in a vacuum, as if the fact of my being a woman was entirely irrelevant, had come to feel actually dishonest.

I resolved the conflict by deciding to present in my last lecture a demographic model of women in science—an excuse to devote the bulk of that lecture to a review of the many barriers that worked against the survival of women as scientists, and to a discussion of possible solutions. I concluded my review with the observation that perhaps the most important barrier to success for women in science derived from the pervasive belief in the intrinsic masculinity of scientific thought. Where, I asked, does such a belief come from? What is it doing in science, reputedly the most objective, neutral, and abstract endeavor we know? And what consequences does that belief have for the actual doing of science?

In 1974 "women in science" was not a proper subject for academic or scientific discussion; I was aware of violating professional protocol. Having given the lecture—having "carried it off"—I felt profoundly liberated. I had passed an essential milestone.

Although I did not know it then, and wouldn't recognize it for another two years, this lecture marked the beginning of my work as a feminist critic of science. In it I raised three of the central questions that were to mark my research and writing over the next decade. I can now see that, with the concluding remarks of that lecture, I had also completed the basic shift in mindset that made it possible to begin such a venture. Even though my views about gender, science, knowledge, and truth were to evolve considerably over the years to come, I had already made the two most essential steps: I had shifted attention from the question of male and female nature to that of *beliefs* about male and female nature, that is, to gender ideology. And I had admitted the possibility that such beliefs could affect science itself.

In hindsight, these two moves may seem simple enough, but when I reflect on my own history, as well as that of other women scientists, I can see that they were not. Indeed, from my earlier vantage point, they were unthinkable. In that mind-set, there was room neither for a distinction between sexual identity and beliefs about sexual identity (not even for the prior distinction between sex and gender upon which it depends), nor for the possibility that beliefs could affect science—a possibility that requires a distinction analogous to that between sex and gender, only now between nature and science. I was, of course, able to accommodate a distinction between belief and reality, but only in the sense of "false" beliefs—that is, mere illusion, or mere prejudice; "true" beliefs I took to be synonymous with the "real."

It seems to me that in that mind-set, beliefs per se were not seen as having any real force—neither the force to shape the development of men and women, nor the force to shape the development of science. Some people may "misperceive" nature, human or otherwise, but properly seen, men and women simply *are,* faithful reflections of male and female biology—just as science simply *is,* a faithful reflection of nature. Gravity has (or is) a force, DNA has force, but beliefs do not. In other words, as scientists, we are trained to see the locus of real force in the world as physical, not mental.

There is of course a sense in which they are right: Beliefs per se cannot exert force on the world. But the people who carry such beliefs can. Furthermore, the language in which their beliefs are encoded has the force to shape what others—as men, as women, and as scientists—think, believe, and in turn, actually do. It may have taken the lens of feminist theory to reveal the popular association of science, objectivity, and masculinity as a statement about the social rather than natural (or biological) world, referring not to the bodily and mental capacities of individual men and women, but to a collective consciousness; that is, as a set of beliefs given existence by language rather than by bodies, and by that language, granted the force to shape what individual men and women might (or might not) do. But to see how much culturally laden language could contribute to the shaping of science takes a different kind of lens. That requires, first and foremost, a recognition of the social character (and force) of the enterprise we call "science," a recognition quite separable from—and in fact, historically independent of—the insights of contemporary feminism.

The Taste Makers

Raffi Khatchadourian

Growing up, Michelle Hagen lived near a large factory in Cincinnati that produced what she and her sisters called The Smell. The aroma was dynamic and unpredictable, almost like a living thing. On some hot summer days, it was thick and sweet, and when it drifted over Hagen's neighborhood—a series of row houses by the interstate—it was as if molasses had been poured through the streets. At other times, the smell was protein-rich and savory. Many of the odors triggered specific associations—birthday cake, popcorn, chicken-noodle soup—and they stayed with her. In 1992, Hagen went to the University of Cincinnati to study art, but she soon turned to science, majoring in biology. She never imagined that she would end up working in the factory that made The Smell. The factory belongs to a Swiss company called Givaudan, the largest manufacturer of flavors and fragrances in the world, and upon graduating Hagen got a temporary job there that soon grew into something permanent. After three years of grueling apprenticeship, she became a flavorist, a job that admitted her into a kind of secret society. There are fewer than five hundred flavorists in the United States, and they almost never speak about their work outside their laboratories.

Hagen is thirty-five. She is brunette, with straight hair that falls just below her shoulders. She is not thin, but her face is, and it lights up easily. She prefers things that are vivid. Beneath her lab coat, Hagen is sure to be wearing some bright-hued article of clothing—a scarf, a sweater. She holds her hair back with sunglasses, in summer and in winter. After spending even a short time with her, one can't help but think of Roald Dahl's Willy Wonka, who believed that the manufacture of flavors—particularly the sweet and flashy ones that go into candy, chewing gum, and marshmallow—demands a childlike openness. At the end of "Charlie and the Chocolate Factory," Wonka tells Charlie Bucket that an adult could never run his factory. "Mind you, there are thousands of clever men who would give anything for the chance to come in and take over from me, but I don't want that sort of person," he says. "I don't want a grown-up person at all." But Wonka surely would have hired Hagen. Her office resembles a walk-in high-school locker, if such a thing existed. The walls are covered with magazine clippings, photographs, and Post-its; a clock-size Swatch with a blue kangaroo painted on it; and a dry-erase board with lists of words meant to inspire flavor creation ("baobab," "jujube," "mamoncillo"). Tacked here and there are paint chips from Benjamin Moore, which she once used as aides to memorize the aromas of approximately a thousand chemicals. California Lilac was ethyl isovalerate; Mellow Yellow was gamma octalactone.

If you like sports drinks, or something with acai or pomegranate or huckleberry on its label, you may well have tasted one of Hagen's creations. Naming the products that contain her flavors, however, would undermine the confidentiality agreements that Givaudan keeps with its clients, and elicit a severe reprimand. Several years ago, a Givaudan employee attending a convention accidentally let slip to a reporter for Beverage World that the company had made a vanilla flavor for Coca-Cola. After the comment was published, Givaudan executives acted as if a state secret had been breached: they investigated the leak, restricted all information about their business with Coke to employees working directly for the company, and flew to Atlanta to visit the Coca-Cola headquarters and apologize in person. In the world of flavor, it is not enough to keep secret a chemical formula. (Typically, these formulas are not patented; hence the obscuring use of "natural flavoring" as an ingredient—and an omnipresent riddle—on food labels.) The Givaudan employee who attended the convention had broken a more fundamental rule. Few of the companies that sell processed foods or drinks want the public to know that outside laboratories supply them with flavors. Even after Snapple's founders admitted to me that, more than twenty years ago, a Brooklyn-based company named Virginia Dare had designed the flavors for a line of sodas that Snapple has long since discontinued, people at Virginia Dare refused to discuss the matter.

Such secrecy helps shape the story of our food. It encourages consumers to think of processed foods as fully formed objects, rather than as assemblages of disparate components. It treats a brand as sacrosanct. (This is not the case in all industries: Dell openly acknowledges that the processors for its computers come from Intel.) Perhaps this kind of deception is necessary because eating and drinking are such elemental experiences. Our evolutionary forebears did not have to wonder about the supply chain of, say, an apple, and many of us today seem unwilling to register the complexity of industrial foods.

More than half of Givaudan's business—which generates nearly four billion dollars in revenue a year—is built on deceiving our senses when we eat. The consumption of food flavorings may stand as one of the modern era's most profound collective acts of submission to illusion. When you watch a movie or look at photographs or listen to an iPod, you tend not to forget that what you are taking in has been recorded and re-created for you in some fashion. Flavor additives are no less a contrivance; in fact, flavor re-creations typically have less fidelity than digital photography or MP3s. They more closely resemble paintings: subjective creations, made by people who work in competing styles. There are the hyperrealists, who strive for molecular-level precision; the neo-primitivists, who use centuries-old palettes of extracts and essential oils; the Fauvist types, who embrace a sensually heightened sensibility. Placed in the context of art history, the flavor industry today would be in its modernist phase, somewhere in the waning days of Cubism, for even the most outlandish flavor concoctions take direct inspiration from the real world. Whereas a perfumer can invent commercially successful aromas that are totally nonrepresentational—a Pollock in a crystal bottle—the flavorist must still respect the deeply held conservatism that people tend to hold when it comes to putting food in their mouths. Snapple's use of kiwi-strawberry flavoring in a juice drink may seem unusual (and the sum flavor of it may barely approximate real strawberry combined with real kiwi), but we can imagine that the flavor is authentic—that it captures some platonic gastronomic truth.

For Hagen, the boundaries of realism are something to be pushed. She spoke to me with admiration of Miro's "Prades, the Village"—"I love the electric colors, the contrast of abstract to real, and the beautiful indigo sky in that painting"—but she could just as easily have been talking about her own artistic creations. Her flavors are charged, odd, playful, personal. One day, she plans to try slipping a touch of menthol into a butterscotch flavor, or something similarly unexpected into blueberry—something "interesting, that makes you think." Not long ago, I asked her about the sorts of flavors that she mulled over at the edges of her imagination. She responded by e-mail: "Every year, my old high-school friends and their spouses and I take a long weekend in the fall to hang out in Gatlinburg, Tennessee. There are no kids and lots of beer. We stay up late playing cards or games. I usually get up really early one morning to see the sunrise over Great Smoky Mountains National Park. I like to make coffee, sit out on the deck, and listen to the silence. The forest is majestic and usually blanketed by a thin, rolling fog over its beautiful autumnal colors. On our last trip, while I was awaiting the sun, I remember thinking what a cool flavor this moment would make. I would use a zesty lemon base to represent the sun; I would add notes of cedar and pine to include the essence of the forest, and just a hint of phenolic vanilla, which would symbolize the smoky, white fog."

In January, Hagen flew to Riverside, California, and took a cab to the Mission Inn, where Givaudan had reserved rooms for thirteen members of its staff. The hotel was to serve as a staging ground for a commercial flavor-hunting expedition—what the company calls a Taste Trek—which had been organized to study exotic citrus varietals in the area. Citrus flavors, particularly those in the orange family, are among the most popular in the world, and in 2005 Givaudan conducted a yearlong, worldwide study to map consumer preferences in citrus and identify "white spaces"—combinations of different flavor attributes, such as nuttiness and floralness, that people enjoy but that are unavailable in an existing product. Fewer and fewer beverage companies develop new flavors on their own, even as they are fiercely engaged in what can only be called the Great Flavor Rush. The fight over white spaces in the supermarket aisles has grown so furious that grocery shelves are lined with bottles promising baroque exoticism: energy drinks and waters laced with kiwi-dragonfruit, or hibiscus-orange, or jackfruit-guava, or agave-melon, or clove-cardamom-cinnamon. This is fine by Hagen. "The flavors that I create are white-space flavors—out there," she said.

The citrus trek had already generated interest from key clients, among them some of the largest beverage companies in the world. What Givaudan's team was hoping to find in Riverside was a flavor that told a story. Studies have shown that when a flavor is marketed to consumers as a specific botanical type—evocative of a place or a culture, or complete with some peculiar tale of discovery—people are more likely to enjoy it. For instance, "Georgia peach" is preferable to "peach," even if there is no real difference. Givaudan was not looking to create a juice, although many juices contain natural flavoring—even ones that would not seem to, such as Ocean Spray's 100% Juice Cranberry & Blueberry. Rather, the company was looking for something more abstract: botanical inspiration. Its discoveries would lead to the creation of nutritionally vacant additives that could be deployed in all manner of processed food, from soft drinks to ice cream. With few exceptions, even the most artificial-seeming flavored products (Tang) are based on things that are natural (orange juice). Hagen told me, "I try not to have any preconceived notions of what to expect. There aren't a lot of things that haven't already been discovered, but Mother Nature is a great flavorist."

In Riverside, oranges have long been a grand romantic calling. The city took root in 1870, when a group of Midwestern abolitionists settled at the foot of a sand-colored pile of stone they later named Mt. Rubidoux. Two years later, Luther Tibbets and his wife, Eliza, arrived from Washington, D.C. They were odd: Luther wandered about in a hat trimmed with a woman's veil, to cover his face; Eliza followed a Swedish mystic and entered trances. The Tibbetses ordered a few Brazilian navel-orange trees and planted them on their land. According to legend, one was trampled by a cow; Eliza nourished the others with dishwater. They bore fruit, and that is how the California citrus industry began,

In 1907, the University of California established the Citrus Experiment Station in Riverside, on a plot of land in the foothills of Mt. Rubidoux.

Scientists working with the university collected samples of oranges, and also lemons, limes, pomelos, mandarins, and their botanical cousins, to see what would thrive in Southern California's sun-baked soil. A hundred years later, the collection's groves have more than a thousand plant varieties, including oddities from the Far East, such as the Buddha's Hand, a citron that looks like it has been crossbred with a squid. The groves—now named the Citrus Variety Collection—are one of the largest and most diverse of their kind, and serve as a national repository for citrus germplasm. Many of the fruits there are legendary, such as the Meyer lemon, which was collected in China by Frank Meyer, who travelled as far as Turkestan and Manchuria in search of plants. A compulsive wanderer, he mysteriously drowned in the Yangtze in 1918, while traveling with specimens.

Meyer would have appreciated Givaudan's Taste Treks. Since 1999, the company has conducted them in Africa, Latin America, and the Far East. The first expedition began at a large open-air market in Libreville, Gabon, and ended in a remote logging camp deep inside a rain forest known as the Forest of the Bees. The team spent weeks exploring the jungle floor, and combed the canopy in a hot-air balloon. Givaudan's researchers sampled hundreds of species with the intention of translating their taste or fragrance into flavors, and even attempted to record the ambient aroma of the rain forest itself before sunset. (Givaudan's equipment proved incapable of registering it.) The team identified a dozen plants as having commercial potential. Landolphia owariensis has been used for rubber, arrow poison, and drugs for treating epilepsy and dizziness; it bears an aromatic red-spotted fruit, and led to the invention of a Givaudan flavor called "jungle fruit." The team also created "Gabonese pineapple" from the bristly orange berries of Diospyros mannii, a species akin to ebony. The researchers discovered varieties of tree bark that, when crushed into powder, tasted either like onion or like garlic, and they took samples of wild ginger containing aframodial and labda-8(17), 12-diene-15, 16-dial—molecules that were later analyzed in Givaudan's laboratories and patented for their ability to intensify both the pungency of spicy foods and the cooling sensation that spearmint and peppermint create in your mouth. The compounds also enhance the taste of alcohol, making low-proof spirits seem stronger; recently, Givaudan put them to use in a well-known liqueur.

It was a little past eight in the morning when Hagen and the rest of the Givaudan team entered the Citrus Variety Collection. The sun had not yet become intense, and the air was crisp, laced with the aroma of desert flora. (The exhaust from I-91, which runs between the groves and Mt. Rubidoux, had not yet thickened into smog.) Hagen wore a broad-brimmed hat and held a spiral notebook. With her were members of Givaudan's marketing staff, Ph.D.s in organic chemistry, and a research scientist who had brought a device—consisting tubes, filters, and a small bell jar—designed to capture the aroma, or "headspace," of unpicked fruit. This device can make molecular-level recordings of just about any fragrance, but the results require labor-intensive analysis, so it is used sparingly. There was a Givaudan flavorist from Amsterdam, a man of precision in comportment and in language, who told me that he was a "supertaster" capable of registering bitterness with unusual acuity. And there was Jim Hassel, a chemical engineer from New York—tall with graying hair and a Brooklyn accent—who had designed a blockbuster flavor called CitraFresh Lime, and whom Hagen regarded as a kind of guru. "Jim goes very, very, very deep in citrus," she told me. Not long ago, he created a flavor for an American beer which has generated tens of millions of dollars in sales.

Everyone walked over to a tree bearing Allspice tangelos—a hybrid of a tangerine and a grapefruit—which had lumpy exteriors, like lizard skin, and spongy rinds. Hassel described what to look for when evaluating a specimen. "You've got the essential oils in the peel," he said. "I always like to scrape the peel first, just to see what the essential oil is like. That is one aspect of the fruit. The second thing, obviously, is the juice. They can be very similar and very different, and in citrus processing we always separate the oil from the peel, and then the juice from the fruit. You never want the two to meet, because the acid in the juice will chew up the peel oil." Essential oils have been distilled from spices and other botanicals since at least the Middle Ages, later gaining wide use as natural flavorings. Hassel told me that the reason for this was stability. It doesn't take long for juice to rot, but oils, especially when refined, have a longer shelf life. (It takes a ton of lemons to press about six pounds of lemon oil.) Slices of tangelo were passed around, and Hassel dug his nail into the rind, which yielded droplets of citrus oil. He then brought the rind to his nose and inhaled. The oil, he said, wasn't especially aromatic.

Hagen was holding a slice to her nose, too. "To me, it is sweet mandarin," she said. "Light lemon."

"Not too much anthranilate, right?" Hassel said, referring to a family of chemicals commonly found in grapes and strawberries.

"No," Hagen said. "Sweet orange. Light lemon."

Hassel inhaled again. "Not too tart," he said.

"Certainly no allspice in there," Hagen said. "It's a misnomer."

Hassel said that he had expected the fruit to contain compounds that have malty, yeasty flavors, some of which are found in Gouda cheese, but they weren't there. Unimpressed, he tossed the slice away.

Hagen was still sniffing. "Just clove," she said. "That's all."

Flavor is a cognitive figment. The brain fuses into a single experience the results of different stimuli registered by the tongue, nose, eyes, and ears, in addition to memories of previously consumed meals. For reasons that are not fully understood, we perceive flavor as occurring in our mouths, and that illusion is nearly unshakable, as is made clear by our difficulty identifying, with any reasonable specificity, the way each of our various senses contributes to the experience. In 2006, Jelly Belly, the candy manufacturer, produced a jellybean that mimicked the flavor of an ice-cream sandwich. When the company manufactured a prototype with a brown exterior and a white interior, people identified the flavor accurately during a trial, and said that it was a good representation of an ice-cream sandwich. Jelly Belly then made an all-white prototype; many trial respondents found it confusing, misidentifying its flavor as vanilla or marshmallow. As Hagen told me, "Color can play tricks on your mind, for sure."

Hagen hoped to sample more than fifty of the collection's citrus specimens, but she was interested primarily in the aromas. Our sense of smell plays a much larger role in defining flavor than our sense of taste does. Taste receptors on the tongue are primarily limited to the detection of saltiness, sweetness, bitterness, sourness, and umami—a Japanese term for the brothiness that one encounters when tasting MSG. These receptors may also perceive fattiness, though this sensation is so poorly understood that it is hard to say for sure. Scientists have identified the function of fewer than thirty taste receptors, and still do not know which ones are responsible for the perception of saltiness and sourness. Jay Slack, one of Givaudan's chief research scientists, told me, "We are just beginning to scratch the surface of what happens when a molecule binds with the tongue, and then all of the biochemical events that happen after that to get a perception. If you imagine a domino trail, we've knocked off maybe four or five dominoes, and have a thousand more." Taste receptors are blunt instruments. With taste alone, one cannot distinguish a grape lollipop from a watermelon one; coffee is like hot water with a bitter aftertaste, and Coke a bland sugary solution. The limitations of taste are unsurprising when one considers its evolutionary purpose. Our biological progenitors, living in the wilderness, needed to know only what was worth eating and what wasn't. If something tasted sweet, there was a good chance that it provided energy; saltiness suggested the presence of minerals; sourness indicated the level of ripeness, and bitterness the presence of poison.

Smell is a more supple and primordial sense, and its centrality is evident in the way the human brain is arranged. Our forebrains evolved from tissues that once focused on processing smells, and there are three hundred or so olfactory receptors in the nose. When we taste or see or hear something, the information must pass through the thalamus, a kind of relay station in the brain that allows us to attend to different aspects of perception. (If you suddenly notice a stop sign on the road, for instance, the thalamus has most likely directed your attention to it.) Smells, for the most part, are fed directly from the nose to a "pre-semantic" part of the brain where cognition does not occur, and where emotions are processed. The bypassing of the thalamus may be one reason why smells can be so hard to describe in detail, and also why aromas stimulate such powerful feelings. The smell of rotten meat can trigger sudden revulsion in a way that merely looking at it cannot.

Smell probably became wrapped up with eating because of its ability to predict. Each whiff is a harmless sample of a potentially risky food. To apprehend something by smell, it must be evaporating, even if only minutely. Chemical compounds that evaporate are said to be "volatile." Chocolate has many volatile compounds. So does lemon sorbet. A hot cup of coffee contains roughly five hundred volatile chemicals. When we eat, volatile chemicals in our food flow through a cavity at the back of the mouth into the nose. Some of them are extremely potent. The smell of roast lamb comes from minute quantities of sulfur compounds. Volatile chemicals can be mysterious. For many decades, we have known that a compound called vanillin plays a large role in determining our sense of vanilla, but the beany aroma that often makes high-quality vanilla seem full-flavored had long eluded science. People in the industry call the search for a complete mapping of a substance's volatile chemistry "chasing zero," and I met with a scientist working for Givaudan who had spent a great deal of time chasing this beaniness to zero. Doing so required multidimensional chromatography—a process for separating trace molecules out of a mixture—and expensive equipment. Last year, after evaluating hundreds of chemicals, he hit upon the three relevant molecules. "We found the beany contributors!" he told me. "We were very excited." The molecules were present at the level of parts per billion.

I asked Hagen how many chemicals she thought she could identify in a single bite of food, "I want to say twenty," she said. "If I am tasting a citrus fruit in the field, I could probably pick out ten chemicals for sure, and I could probably speculate about twenty-five more." Other flavorists said they could do about the same, and hearing them speak about the bouquet of Mountain Dew or Sprite—evaluating its arc, from top notes to bottom notes—you might think they were discussing a 1980 Montrachet. (Hagen told me that she thought Dr Pepper was "amazing," with a floral note that was unique and high. She spoke with awe of orange Gatorade: "I mean, that is beautiful.") During a meeting with several flavor professionals in New Jersey, I compared a flavor chemist's ability to break down the structure of a soft drink to the skills of Robert Parker, the wine critic. I was quickly corrected. "That's kind of like hocus-pocus," one of them said. "Parker may say that a wine has a nutty note or is oaky, but a lot of things can be behind that, and I don't think he's matching aspects of the flavor to a chemical compound and going, 'O.K., this note here, it comes from methyl isobutyrate.'" And yet controlled experiments show that, no matter what a person's professional vocabulary or expertise, aromas remain a blur: the average person, with minimal training, can perceive about three or four distinct components in a given aroma; professional flavorists—without leaning on their chemical knowledge of particular types of food—can do no better.

Even the most familiar products can bewilder us. Coca-Cola, for instance, is primarily a citrus beverage, its flavor derived from lemon, orange, and lime oils, combined with vanilla, cinnamon, other spices, and corn syrup. Its flavor has little in common with the astringent-tasting kola nut, from which it takes its name, and its caramel coloring is largely imposed. For many people, describing Coke's flavor as a combination of different parts is nearly impossible. (In one study, two-thirds of the subjects could not tell the difference between Classic Coke and Diet Coke.) If you close your eyes, inhale deeply, and try to pay close attention to the volatile chemistry of Coke, it is possible to pick out a few basic elements, but for the average consumer the flavor is "cognitively impenetrable." That is, if you ask someone "What does Coke taste like?" the answer will be tautological: "It tastes like Coke." This presents a conundrum that many flavorists try not to think about. If consumers are cognitively unable to regard a flavor meaningfully, is there any point to what flavorists do? Hagen once told me, "My husband loves football, and so when I am watching the players on the sidelines drink Gatorade I'm thinking that they have no idea how complex that lemon-lime is. All they know is that it is quenching their thirst and it tastes good." Still, she was hoping to discover the next big drink. Coke's success is, in part, a testament to the sophistication of its formula, its exquisite balance, even if it does confound our senses.

By late morning, Hagen, Hassel, and the rest of the Givaudan team had begun eating salted crackers, trying to calm their palates after tasting so many citrons, oranges, and pomelos. The team had worked its way through half a dozen clementines. The Marisol clementine was a touch overripe, and its oil was oddly insectile. "It smells like crushed lightning bugs," Hagen said approvingly, as she held a Marisol rind to her nose. "Kind of like formates. When you crush an ant, there is formic acid, so formates belong to a family of molecules that are, to me, all buggy." The Nour clementine, from Morocco, was sweet. "There is something here that reminds me of bubble gum," Hagen said. "Very kid-friendly. Isoamyl acetate, which is the chemical that reminds people of Circus Peanuts." Hagen loved Hubba Bubba bubble gum as a child, and she thought that the Nour might have commercial potential. "It has a little bit of an edge," she said. "A friendly edge."

Exotic flavors rarely have immediate commercial appeal. Often, they must ease their way into the market, usually in combination with an old and well-loved companion. When, in the early nineties, Snapple paired kiwi with strawberry flavoring for its juice drink, the notion was considered highly innovative.

Snapple had been working with the oldest American flavor house, Fritzsche Dodge & Olcott, which was acquired by Givaudan in 1991. Leonard Marsh, one of Snapple's founders, told me that the flavorists made a variety of fruit flavors for him, including kiwi, which he initially rejected. "It didn't taste good on its own," he told me. "I said, 'Can you mix this with something like strawberry?'" The result was wildly popular—and highly profitable for Givaudan. A former Givaudan executive told me, "We were selling Snapple fifty-five-gallon drums of kiwi-strawberry drink. At one point, we had purchased all the kiwi juice that was available globally."

Hagen told me that her favorite white-space flavor—the one she wished she had created—was Red Bull, because it succeeded in getting consumers to embrace the surreal. The co-founder of Red Bull, Dietrich Mateschitz, acknowledges that the company went out of its way to develop a flavor that was unorthodox. ("Some people say medicine never tastes good," he told me. "You can translate this into our taste philosophy.") Other flavorists were perplexed by Red Bull, which was created in 1987. "Have you ever tasted such a crazy flavor?" Hagen said. "What is it? There is nothing like it, and every once in a while you come across a flavor that is not especially balanced but for some reason it takes off." Today, it is virtually impossible to market an energy drink that does not have the same unbalanced characteristics that Red Bull has. "It scores terribly when you put it in front of consumers who don't think it is an energy drink," a salesman for one of the top flavor houses told me. "But the spiky note in there now defines 'energy.' So when I build energy flavors with our client it has got to taste bad. If you give the consumer a great-tasting orange flavor for an energy drink, their liking drops way down, because it doesn't have that 'energy note' they expect."

Midway through the trek, it became evident that the fruits of greatest interest to the flavorists had off notes that, in combination with more palatable natural chemicals, added enough aromatic discordance to make the flavors unique. The Jamaican Ugli fruit, a large tangelo with rough greenish-yellowish skin, which has slowly been gaining a commercial following, had a sulfuric undertone that Hagen suspected was caused by prenyl mercaptan—which is often found in skunky beer. "With Corona, because it is in a clear bottle, when light hits it, it oxidizes, so that's why you put a lime in Corona—to kill this mercaptan," Hagan said. "It is this yucky bad note that people like. And you're, like, O.K., whatever." When I tasted the Ugli fruit, I didn't initially catch the prenyl mercaptan, but Hagen steered me. "Once you are past the floralness, the citrusness, then there is the sulfur note," she said—and there it was.

The team found that a rare specimen—the Oxanthera neo-caledonica hybrid—had even more divergent characteristics. The fruit's peel was smooth and yellow-green, and its oil had an aroma that was sugary, floral, and reminiscent of Juicy Fruit gum. After inhaling it, Hagen wrote in her notebook, "girlie-pink bubble gum notes, powdery fruit punch, sweet, tropical punch, very candy, reminds me of a Skittles or Starburst-type flavor, possible peach citrus notes, complex and unusual." But the fruit's taste was harshly bitter, even slightly fishy, and the juice caused a tingly, numbing sensation on the tongue—"a good example of how the peel is completely different from the taste," she told me. She found the specimen exciting.

Hassel agreed. Very few edible fruits have a numbing quality, and he thought that the tingling sensation could work in an alcoholic drink. "Even if you don't like the whole package, go in there and analyze what's giving it those unique notes," he said. Later, a Givaudan scientist tried to capture the headspace of a fruit that was still on the tree: he scraped a section of the peel, covered the exposed area with the bell jar, and activated a small pump that sent a stream of air over the fruit's surface, forcing molecules into the jar, where they collected in a filter.

Before the team moved on to the next grove, the flavorist from Amsterdam wondered if, in the laboratory, the numbing element could be extracted from the fruit's awful-tasting juice and then recombined with a flavor inspired by the peel oil. "You might add the numbing, but you wouldn't add the bitterness," he said. "Maybe just a hint. You would want something pleasant in the end."

Once you begin to consider the natural world at a molecular level, the boundaries that separate one fruit from another begin to seem like artifice. Givaudan's many scientists often refer to food as "the application," as if it were composed of malleable lines of computer code; from this perspective, adding a flavor is as simple as updating software. A garden strawberry turns out to be a very complicated application, made up of hundreds of differing molecules—some of them highly volatile, some of them inert to our senses—but among the ones that seem to matter most very few are exclusive to the strawberry. If you combine gamma-decalactone from a peach, ethyl butyrate from an apple, methyl cinnamate from a guava, and Furaneol from a pineapple, you can construct a very rudimentary strawberry flavor. As John Wright, a former vice-president for International Flavors & Fragrance, a New York-based company and a Givaudan rival, told me, "Flavors are a little bit like jigsaw puzzles." The interchangeability of nature made possible Givaudan's search for inspiration in Riverside. No matter how much the team liked the Oxanthera neo-caledonica's peel aroma, everyone on the trek knew that growing enough of the fruit to extract commercially significant quantities of its essential oil would be prohibitively expensive. An approximation of the oil would have to be constructed from more readily available materials.

In this respect, the Oxanthera neo-caledonica is just like the pomegranate or the acai berry, both of which are expensive to harvest, or even the common lemon. Unusually cold weather in California and in Argentina, along with a hot Saharan wind pushing into the Mediterranean region, destroyed roughly thirty per cent of the world's lemon crop in 2008. So Givaudan, the world's largest purchaser of citrus oil, announced that it would create a "replacement" from the many lemon-oil molecules found in other botanicals and from whatever it could derive from natural sources in the lab. Citral, a dominant chemical in most lemon oils, is also found in lemon myrtle, a leafy plant native to a subtropical rain forest in Australia, and in Litsea cubeba, a small deciduous tree. In China, Litsea cubeba, known as mountain pepper, is used as a spice, but it also contains an oil that is made up largely of citral. Every year, the Chinese harvest hundreds of tons of the oil. For many years, Litsea cubeba and lemongrass have been the world's biggest natural sources of citral. If you drink or eat something with lemon flavoring today, one of its key ingredients probably does not come from a lemon.

A little before noon, the Givaudan team made an exciting discovery when David Karp—a writer and a part-time botanical explorer who is a research associate at the Citrus Variety Collection—ran over with a large pomelo and announced that he had something to share. "Most of the pomelos I really don't care for, at least as grown here in California," he said. "To me, they have a soapy flavor, in addition to the bitterness of the membrane. Even when you fillet them, I don't care for them, but Tahitian pomelos are very different. They tend to have a much thinner skin, and sort of a greenish flesh, and a very distinctive lemon-lime flavor." He cut into the fruit, carefully holding it away from his body. Juice sprayed all around him. "Never, ever open a pomelo near your computer or camera equipment," he said. "O.K., who wants to go first?"

"Me, me, me!" Hagen said.

Karp handed her a slice, which she held to her nose. He distributed more slices, "Usually, it is at its best when we are here in February," he said. On first impression, the Tahitian pomelo was unappealing: the rind oil gave off a bitterly unpleasant scent, and the fruit was densely seedy. But the taste and aroma of the juice was candylike, with hints of rice, peppercorn, and freshly cut grass, and it had a clean fruitiness: an uplifting wash of citrus. It had aspects of strawberry in it, and other aromatic layers hard to identify. If you closed your eyes and tasted it, it would be difficult to know what kind of fruit it was.

"Ah," Hagen said, throwing her head back. "That's wonderful."

Karp, passing around more slices, declared the fruit to be one of the most promising underexplored varieties of citrus on earth. He has occasionally sold exotic specimens to grocery stores, and told me that, a number of years ago, he had shipped a pallet of Tahitian pomelos to a wholesale affiliate of Gourmet

Garage, in New York: "They said, 'What the hell are you sending us this horrible, green, seedy, nasty stuff for?' And I said, 'I'm sorry.' They said, 'We're going to put it in the Dumpster right now, you idiot.' They called me back the next day and said, 'How many more pallets can you get?' The chef tasted it, and he went wild."

Standing in the grove, the Givaudan team was going wild, too. People called out their first impressions. Except for someone who picked up "a shoe-polish note at the end," everyone was smitten. One of the flavorists declared that the Tahitian pomelo was "very different from anything I have tasted before." I turned to Hagen, and she grinned before announcing her verdict: "A good soda." It recalled, for her, the freshness of Sprite, but it had a child-like quality, too. "This is awesome," she told me. "Kind of like a lime—like the lime Life Savers, a little bit of lemon, a little bit of sweet pink grapefruit. Pink lemonade. It is really nice."

For much of human history, flavor additives were simple and direct. Spices and sauces added richness to food, and often preserved it. The pharaohs had a taste for cumin, as did the ancient Greeks, who kept it on the dinner table. But the diet of ancient Western civilization lacked many flavors that we now consider fundamental. For centuries, Rome's subjects did not know the lemon, which originated in Asia, and they never tasted a tomato, or chocolate or vanilla—derived from plants native to the New World. The ancients did not have coffee or tea. According to Andrew Dalby, the author of "Food in the Ancient World from A to Z," the Homeric epics offer the earliest record in Western civilization of a beverage infused with flavor: kykeon, a mixture of wine, herbs, and barley. ("One such drink is served to a soldier as a restorative after a hard day's work at the siege of Troy," Dalby says.) The Romans used grape syrup and spices in cooking, but perhaps the most popular additive was a fermented fish sauce called liquamen, or garum, distinguished by its saltiness. Liquamen was made throughout the Roman Empire; the earliest known manufacturer was a man from Pompeii. We know this from an advertisement that he had inscribed on his jars: "Best strained liquamen. From the factory of Umbricus Agathopus." For more than a millennium, flavor technology did not advance appreciably beyond the Agathopus workshop.

Essential oils have been used in fragrances for hundreds of years, and since at least the eighteenth century people have also consumed them. The first flavorists were typically pharmacists, who added flavors to medicines. As John Wright, the former International Flavors & Fragrance executive, has noted, their flavors were "often not very close to the character of the real food." Flavor creation did not take its present form until the development of organic chemistry, in the early nineteenth century, when scientists began to identify volatile chemical compounds with distinct aromas. In many instances, the discoveries were accidental. Benzaldehyde was among the first

173

known molecules to be identified with a flavor, in 1832, and it is still widely used today. "It is my favorite chemical," Hagen told me. "Bitter almond was the source, and it is in there at a low level, but benzaldehyde really shines when it is in fruit flavors, where it can be used at a much higher level: cherry, grape, fruit punch—childhood bliss. My dad played softball, and we always would go to games and get a Cherry Icee. When I was first exposed to benzaldehyde in the industry, it reminded me of that. It's now one of my signature compounds."

At first, most flavors were natural. (Some of the earliest volatile chemicals to be identified were for strawberry, garlic, and roasted barley.) But during the ensuing decades chemists began to find ways to create these molecules entirely in the laboratory. Vanillin was synthesized in 1874 by two German scientists, Ferdinand Tiemann and Wilhelm Haarmann, from a molecule found in coniferous trees. Today, vanilla is the world's most popular flavor, and thousands of tons of vanillin are synthesized from industrial petrochemicals and waste from the production of wood pulp. (It is possible to extract it even from cow dung, as Japanese chemists demonstrated in 2006.) There is no molecular distinction between synthesized vanillin or vanillin extracted from vanilla beans, but the way the molecule is made determines whether it will be advertised as "natural" or "artificial." Flavor chemicals often make up less than one per cent of the ingredients in processed foods, and many flavorists regard the terms "natural" and "artificial" as largely meaningless—an indulgence for consumers who happen to believe that one is more likely to be toxic than another, even if the perception is not necessarily true. (After all, snake venom is natural.) The flavor industry has long resisted the public disclosure of its formulas, and so monitoring the safety of the chemicals in them is complex. After extended negotiations, the Food and Drug Administration and the industry agreed to maintain a list of compounds "generally recognized as safe," the use of which companies are not obligated to reveal.

In 1895, Xavier and Leon Givaudan, two brothers from Lyons, opened their company, in Zurich. They expanded to America in 1924. The fragranceand-flavor industry was small, secretive, and rapidly changing, Most of the companies were clustered in lower Manhattan, near the dockyards on the East River, where drums of raw materials arrived from overseas. As the industry grew, it crept uptown. The factory owners were clubby: one of them conducted so much business at the Little Venice, a restaurant on Twelfth Street, that his Rolls-Royce became a fixture out front.

In the thirties and forties, many European flavor houses opened offices in New York, though not all of them brought their formulas. Jim Broderick, a retired flavorist, told me that he once interviewed for a job at the New York office of Firmenich, a European flavor-and-fragrance house: "When I asked them 'What's my job?' It was 'You take the flavors that we make over there and re-create them over here,' and I said, 'Well, can I see the formulas?' And they said no." At the time, flavor chemists kept formulas locked in a safe, or hid them in a drawer if someone walked into their office. "A company's soul is kept in formulas," Bill Downey, a former flavorist at Fritzsche, told me. (He created the flavoring for Snapple's original lemon iced tea one afternoon with a friend.) Flavorists can spend months trying to match a competitor's creation. When the Society of Flavor Chemists was founded, at the Little Venice in 1954, some members attended in secret because their companies did not want them there. One longtime flavor scientist called the industry "paranoid."

Today, flavor and fragrance houses bring in annual revenues of twenty billion dollars. About ninety per cent of the money that Americans spend in the supermarket goes toward processed food, much of which could not be made without companies like Givaudan. "Most of the food-and-beverage companies have become marketing-and-distribution companies," a flavor-company executive told me, only somewhat in jest. I understood what he meant when, in one of his laboratories, I saw a number of his colleagues working on a tasteless "slurry," consisting largely of starch, oil, and salt, which a client was hoping to transform into a marketable product. The client had asked the flavor company's in-house chef to develop various dips, such as guacamole, using fresh ingredients; after settling on the best recipes, the company's flavorists mimicked them chemically, with an eye toward injecting the flavor compounds into the slurry in the most stable and cost-effective way.

Given that flavor additives are generally safe, and make up a tiny percentage of any given product's ingredients, companies like Givaudan are in an unusual position when one considers how their work affects our health. A couple of older flavorists told me that the essence of their work is to bring greater enjoyment to life, which is not necessarily the same as providing food that is good for you. Eric Schlosser, in "Fast Food Nation," argues that the fast-food industry could not exist without the flavor industry: he points out that even McDonald's French fries are laced with natural flavoring to make them tastier.

In the case of junk food, flavor additives mask an absence, making cheap, nutritionally negligible ingredients seem delicious (or, at least, edible). But in many other cases, flavor additives mask a reduction in sugar or salt or trans fats—things that, in excess, are harmful. It may be too much to expect an American menu stripped of all processed food items, and such a world may not even be desirable. "Think about unflavored rice cakes," Hagen told me, when I raised the issue with her. "They would sit on the shelves, because they taste like ceiling tiles. Now, add a maple-syrup flavor or a cheddar-cheese flavor to those rice cakes. People would choose them as a snack. It's not practical or economical to use 'real' foods to add flavor. There are lots of problems with this: the availability, the stability, the over-all intensity of such things."

Taking unhealthy ingredients out of a well-loved brand—for instance, removing trans fats from Oreos—while trying to retain its flavor requires complex chemistry. Since the nineteen-seventies, flavor houses have been relying on gas chromatography and mass spectrometry to decode the secrets of natural chemistry, and their expertise has deepened considerably. (In 1948, only nine components in orange-peel oil were known; since then, nearly two hundred more have been identified.) But, as the technology has changed, the notion of what a flavor company is has changed, too—from the simple mixing of ingredients that nature provides to a highly sophisticated sensory legerdemain. As a flavor-research scientist told me, "We are almost getting to pharmaceutical-grade science."

Givaudan emerged as the world's largest flavor company over the past few decades, following the acquisition of many competitors. In the past ten years, the flavor industry has undergone rapid consolidation. Nearly every flavorist I met had fallen into the profession by chance, and only after working as a journeyman apprentice in one of the smaller firms. Givaudan's head of flavor strategy, Bob Pellegrino, told me that several years ago, when he thought about his company's future, he noticed there was virtually no one new to hire: "It was like, Oh my God, we are going to have a bunch of flavorists in retirement in the next ten years, and then what?" He announced that any Givaudan technician or scientist could apply for a training program— three years of full-time study.

Hagen was among two dozen applicants. "By that point, I had fallen in love with what I was doing," she told me. She had been working as a lab technician, assembling formulas for a flavorist. "I had made a raspberry as a technician, and I was carrying it upstairs in an elevator in a little bottle, and I was just waiting in the elevator, and then I smelled it and I was like, God, how did that happen? It was this magical moment, I had brought all these chemicals together. The result smelled just like the raspberries that I used to pick with my grandmother." Hagen was one of only six applicants who made it through rigorous testing and interviews—she turned out to have an acute sense of smell. She completed the training in 2006, and joined the Society of Flavor Chemists the following year. Her first flavor to make it into a product was a blackberry.

By May, Hagen had developed several flavors based on the fruits that she had sampled in Riverside. I flew to Givaudan's headquarters in Cincinnati to follow her progress. The company's buildings occupy dual campuses on either side of Interstate 75—the factory on one side, and laboratories, kitchens, and offices on the other. When I pulled up to the building containing the laboratories, I was hit by an intoxicating odor, a blend of savory, earthy fragrances: cumin and cinnamon, perhaps, combined with a heavy sweetness. The intense aroma was somewhat chemical, but not immediately unpleasant (though locals occasionally complain). I walked past gardeners mowing the lawn. The fragrance of cut grass was absorbed by the building's ambient aroma, and as I entered I thought of something that Hagen had told me in Riverside. "The company has a murky brown smell," she had said. "It's like when you were a kid and you mixed all your paint up."

Most of the people I met at Givaudan went about their work with detached amusement. "We have a software specialist who has spent his whole career, thirty-five years, coming up with different coefficients for chemicals in chewing gum," Hagen told me. "He is able to predict when you experience certain chemicals throughout the chew." Later, during tours of the facilities—I had to promise not to reveal the names of any product—I met with researchers who had developed an experimental gum that changed flavors three times when chewed, and a "sequential release" cereal bar that went from blueberry to orange in my mouth. Much of their work was geared toward figuring out ways to maintain the tastiness of food that had been stripped of key ingredients. They experimented with molecules that make reduced-fat foods taste creamy and full-bodied, or that fool the mouth into thinking that low-sodium chicken soup tastes good.

For more than a century, Givaudan focused on tinkering with volatile chemicals that register mainly in the nose. In the past decade, it has been investing heavily in taste research—a significant shift. After substantial sections of the human genome were decoded, in 2000, Givaudan hired a team of scientists to experiment with its application to food. Jay Slack, the research scientist, was one of them. He is now working with a chemical called hydroxy-alpha sanshool. "It is a 'tingle compound,'" he said. "If you ever put your tongue on a nine-volt battery—that buzz. So there is a chemical that evokes that sensation in your tongue. It is found in the Szechuan chili, and that is a unique sensation. It's not cooling, it's not burning, it's not warming. It is truly tingling, and so we are really interested to understand what is the receptor, or receptors, that give you that sensation in the oral cavity." Slack, along with several colleagues, is free to submit scientific papers—he recently published an article on how genetic differences shape the perception of sweetness around the world. His research on taste receptors (including some recently discovered in the intestine) has focused on a question of tremendous commercial importance: how to dampen the experience of bitterness, a persistent side effect of many sugar alternatives. "Our goal is to develop flavor molecules that will tweak the sensitivity of the sweet system but not be sweeteners, because if they become sweeteners they are no longer flavors," he told me. "It's a regulatory line that's drawn in the sand."

Later, I was shown a building that was devoted to savory flavors, which tend to be complex, because of the vast number of chemicals involved and the time-sensitive nature of their aromas. (Fresh out of the kitchen, grilled fish or roasted beef may smell wonderful, but it can become unappealing an hour later.) In 2008, Givaudan conducted a yearlong study of chicken; using the device with the bell jar, researchers attempted to capture the headspace of dishes from around the world. A molecule-for-molecule re-creation of a recipe from China—roast duck with pickled radish—was stored in a little brown jar. A scientist dipped a paper blotter into it and handed it to me for a sniff. The smell was remarkably evocative.

I visited a kitchen where celebrity chefs, among them Wylie Dufresne, of New York's wd-50, had worked on dishes that Givaudan's researchers then studied. For the chef Todd English, Givaudan had created a line of "melting powders"—chemical approximations of the sum flavor of his recipes, based upon a molecular breakdown of his entrees. The powders, which are sold on the Home Shopping Network, liquefy when they are sprinkled on cooked food, creating instant versions of English's recipes.

At one point, Hagen and I were walking through a hallway. "Hey, "she called out to a flavorist hunched over a pristine lab bench, mixing chemicals in a beaker. "What are you up to?"

"Oh, making butter," the flavorist said.

Hagen's laboratory is on the second floor. Large windows overlook a metallic sculpture inspired by machinery that sprays flavor powders onto things like tortilla chips. Her shelves are lined with thousands of sepia-tinted bottles that could be artifacts from a nineteenth-century apothecary. The range of the bottles' contents is huge, and very few of the flavors are artificial. Hagen had an entire cabinet devoted to strawberry flavors, some of them combined with other fruit, some of them designed for specific applications, such as yogurt or hard candies. She directed me to some of her favorite molecules. One smelled "like fresh rain." Another smelled like carrots, and another like a mojito. She handed me a bottle and said, "Smells earthy, kind of like root, raw vegetable." Then she said, "Here is another flavor that I love. I made this and said, 'God, this smells like a Gummi worm!'" There were flavors that Hagen had created without ever sampling an original specimen. For a recent assignment, she had been given an analytical rundown of a jackfruit—a list of more than ninety of its volatile chemicals, identified by a gas chromatograph—and built a flavor solely on that information. Afterward, during a trip to San Francisco, she found a jackfruit in Chinatown, and tried it. Her version was slightly different, as she had expected it to be. "You are trying to sell a flavor," she said. "It's not like you are getting judged on how close you are to the real fruit. At the end of the day, you are getting judged on how good the flavor tastes. And you kind of have to take some artistic liberties."

In Riverside, Hagen had made initial sketches of the flavors from the citrus collection on a proprietary device that Givaudan calls the Mini Virtual Aroma Synthesizer, or the Mini-VAS. The machine—a complex network of valves and motors housed inside a shock-resistant stainless-steel suitcase—resembles the portable nuclear-missile launching systems that Dan Aykroyd and Chevy Chase lugged around in "Spies Like Us." When plugged into a laptop computer, the Mini-VAS can re-create just about any aroma. Each suitcase has room for twenty-nine removable plastic cylinders, called "keys," and each key contains a solid filter with an aroma embedded in it, such as spicy cinnamon or sweet orange or CitraFresh Lime. By forcing air through the keys at different intensities, flavorists can combine notes, like an organist playing a chord, until they get an aroma that closely matches the smell of a food that they want to simulate in the lab. The result is emitted through a small glass cone. Once the flavorist has "recorded" his subjective impressions of a fragrance, an algorithm produces an approximate molecular formula for the corresponding flavor. Increasingly, Givaudan has been inviting representatives from food and beverage manufacturers to use the machine so that they can more easily describe what they want the flavorists to do.

The company's citrus team had decided to develop a dozen flavors from the trek in Riverside, based mostly on limes and lemons (including the Meyer lemon) but also on more exotic items, such as the Tahitian pomelo and the Jamaican Ugli fruit, both of which had attracted the attention of one of America's largest beverage manufacturers. Hagen had taken several company executives to the Riverside groves, where they sampled the fruits and refined their impressions, using the Mini-VAS. The executives were enthusiastic and said that the company might rush the flavors to market in a series of drinks by the end of the year. But they wanted Hagen to make some adjustments first.

Hagen invited me to observe while she revised a flavor that she had based on the Mency tangor—a hybrid of a Mediterranean sweet orange and a Dancy mandarin. The Mency tangor was bred at the Riverside citrus collection in 1915 and exists in a limited supply. The collection's catalogue notes that it is an "early ripening fruit of sprightly, acid flavor," and during Hagen's return visit to the collection, in February, the tangor was overripe. Hagen had eliminated that aspect of it in her re-creation, but the beverage company had said that it wanted it back. Hagen found herself, as she put it, in "an interesting predicament." She had to add to the sample a note that was typically unappealing, but in a way that would improve the over-all flavor. "This is not something I initially know how to do," she said, and then began thinking aloud. "What happens when a fruit becomes overripe? It becomes sweeter and sweeter. The acid drops, so it becomes brown and sugary. I will have to add some brown notes."

She began at her desk, scrolling through a comprehensive spreadsheet that she had made during her training; it contained her descriptions of hundreds of chemicals. When fruits ripen, they not only become sweeter; they also become more sulfuric. Hagen began looking for sulfur compounds that she had previously associated with overripe aromas. There was dimethyl disulfide, which she called "garbacious." It can be found in garlic, leeks, and human feces. "That is not necessarily something I want to put into my citrus," she said. After considering a variety of chemicals, she settled on a few options: two sulfurous compounds—one found in grapefruit, another in black currant—and a molecule, common to many berries, that had "a sweet brown note and gives the impression of sugar." The latter was one of the most widely used Givaudan flavor compounds.

Because Hagen works with minute quantities of liquids—often with ingredients measured in parts per million—her instrumentation is highly precise. Using small clear plastic cups, an electronic scale, a beaker, a pipette, and a magnetic device that stirs chemicals evenly, she began trying out different recipes. With each attempt, she sampled the flavor in a solution of water, sugar, and citric acid. The first sulfuric compound made the drink taste dull; the second made the tangor flavor seem heavy and eggy; in the third, the brown note was hard to detect.

"I have one other idea—just hang with me," she said, and began to hunt through the many bottles. "There is a note that adds overripe to strawberries." She pulled down a bottle labeled "2-OCTEN-4-ONE"—a recently "discovered" compound in strawberry. Less than a decade ago the molecule was considered artificial, but it was chased down in the natural world, and its status changed. It is now natural. "It is just the ripest note in the world to me," Hagen said, with growing excitement. Using the pipette, she carefully added a few drops to the existing flavor solution and, after diluting it with water, served it up. The change was pleasant, and, if anything, made her version of the tangor more conventional. Perhaps this was what the people at the beverage company had wanted all along. Hagen told me that she would make a few minor adjustments, but she felt that the job was done.

A few weeks later, I called her to see how the tangor revision had been received. She hadn't heard yet. There was always a period of uncertainty after she sent out a flavor, she told me. "I could sell a flavor as a strawberry, and at the end of the day it could be marketed as a mixed berry," she said. Sometimes, after a flavor leaves her lab, months, even years elapse before it is used in a product. Hagen told me that fewer than five per cent of her creations actually find their way to market. She didn't sound particularly dismayed. "It's in a bottle with a label," she said of her latest creation. "It is just waiting for an opportunity. I love it."

The secret world of the flavor factory.

In History

Jamaica Kincaid

What to call the thing that happened to me and all who look like me?
Should I call it history?

If so, what should history mean to someone like me?

Should it be an idea, should it be an open wound and each breath I take
in and expel healing and opening again and again, over and over, or is it a
moment that began in 1492 and has come to no end yet? Is it a collection
of facts, all true and precise details, and, if so, when I come across these true
and precise details, what should I do, how should I feel, where should I
place myself?

Why should I be obsessed with all these questions?

My history began like this: in 1492, Christopher Columbus discovered
the New World. Since this is only a beginning and I am not yet in the picture, I have not yet made an appearance, the word "discover" does not set off
an alarm, and I am not yet confused by this interpretation. I accept it. I am
only taken by the personality of this quarrelsome, restless man. His origins
are sometimes obscure; sometimes no one knows just where he really comes
from, who he really was. His origins are sometimes quite vivid: his father was
a tailor, he came from Genoa, he as a boy wandered up and down the Genoese
wharf, fascinated by sailors and their tales of lands far away; these lands would
be filled with treasures, as all things far away are treasures. I am far away, but
I am not yet a treasure: I am not a part of this man's consciousness, he does
not know of me, I do not yet have a name. And so the word "discover," as it
is applied to this New World, remains uninteresting to me.

He, Christopher Columbus, discovers this New World. That it is new only
to him, that it had a substantial existence, physical and spiritual, before he
became aware of it, does not occur to him. To cast blame on him now for
this child-like immaturity has all the moral substance of a certificate given to
a school girl for good behavior. To be a well-behaved school girl is not hard.
When he sees this New World, it is really new to him: he has never seen anything like it before, it was not what he had expected, he had images of China
and Japan, and, though he thought he was in China and Japan, it was not
the China or Japan that he had fixed in his mind. He couldn't find enough

words to describe what he saw before him: the people were new, the flora and fauna were new, the way the water met the sky was new, this world itself was new, it was the New World.

"If one does not know the names, one's knowledge of things is useless." This is attributed to Isidorus, and I do not know if this is the Greek Isidorus or the other Isidorus, the bishop of Seville; but now put it another way: to have knowledge of things, one must first give them a name. This, in any case, seems me to have been Christopher Columbus' principle, for he named and he named: he named places, he named people, he named things. This world he saw before him had a blankness to it, the blankness of the newly made, the newly born. It had no before—I could say that it had no history, but I would have to begin again, I would have to ask those questions again: what is history? This blankness, the one Columbus met, was more like the blankness of paradise; paradise emerges from chaos, and this chaos is not history; it is not a legitimate order of things. Paradise then is the arrangement of the ordinary and the extraordinary. But in such a way as to make it, paradise, seem as if it had fallen out of the clear air. Nothing about it suggests the messy life of the builder, the carpenter, the quarrels with the contractor, the people who are late with the delivery of materials, their defense which, when it is not accepted, is met with their back chat. This is an unpleasant arrangement; this is not paradise. Paradise is the thing just met when all the troublesome details have been vanquished, overcome.

Christopher Columbus met paradise. It would not have been paradise for the people living there; they would have had the ordinary dreariness of living anywhere day after day, the ordinary dreariness of just being alive. But someone else's ordinary dreariness is another person's epiphany.

The way in which he wanted to know these things was not in the way of satisfying curiosity, or in the way of correcting an ignorance; he wanted to know them, to possess them, and he wanted to possess them in a way that must have been a surprise to him. His ideas kept not so much changing, as they kept evolving: he wanted to prove the world was round, and even that, to know with certainty that the world was round, that it did not come to an abrupt end at a sharp cliff from which one could fall into nothing, to know that is to establish a claim also. And then after the world was round, this round world should belong to his patrons, the king and queen of Spain; and then finding himself at the other side of the circumference and far away from his patrons, human and other kind, he loses himself, for it becomes clear: the person who really can name the thing gives it a life, a reality, that it did not have before. His patrons are in Spain, looking at the balance sheet: if they invest so much, will his journey yield a return to make the investment worthwhile? But he, I am still speaking of Columbus, is in the presence of something else.

His task is easier than he thought it would be; his task is harder than he could have imagined. If he had only really reached Japan or China, places like that already had an established narrative. It was not a narrative that these places had established themselves; it was a narrative that someone like him had invented, Marco Polo, for instance; but this world, China or Japan, in the same area of the world to him (even as this familiarity with each other—between China and Japan—would surprise and even offend the inhabitants of these places), had an order and the order offered a comfort (the recognizable is always so comforting). But this new place, what was it? Sometimes it was just like Seville, Spain; sometimes it was like Seville but only more so; sometimes it was more beautiful than Seville. Mostly it was "marvelous," and this word "marvelous" is the word he uses again and again, and when he uses it, what the reader (and this is what I have been, a reader of this account of the journey, and the account is by Columbus himself) can feel, can hear, can see, is a great person whose small soul has been sundered by something unexpected. And yet the unexpected turned out to be the most ordinary things: people, the sky, the sun, the land, the water surrounding the land, the things growing on the land.

What were the things growing on the land? I pause for this. What were the things growing on that land and why do I pause for this?

I come from a place called Antigua. I shall speak of it as if no one has ever heard of it before; I shall speak of it as if it is just new. In the writings, in anything representing a record of the imagination of Christopher Columbus, I cannot find any expectation for a place like this. It is a small lump of insignificance, green, green, green, and green again. Let me describe this landscape again: it is green, and unmistakably so; another person, who would have a more specific interest, a painter, might say, it is a green that often verges on blue, a green that often is modified by reds and yellows and even other more intense or other shades of green. To me, it is green and green and green again. I have no interest other than this immediate and urgent one: the landscape is green. For it is on this green landscape that, suddenly, I and the people who look like me made an appearance.

I, me. The person standing in front of you started to think of all this while really focused on something and someone else altogether. I was standing in my garden: my garden is in a place called Vermont; it is in a village situated in a place called Vermont. From the point of view of growing things, that is the gardener's, Vermont is not the same atmosphere as that other place I am from, Antigua. But while standing in that place, Vermont, I think about the place I am from, Antigua. Christopher Columbus never saw Vermont at all; it never entered his imagination. He saw Antigua, I believe on a weekday, but if not then it would have been a Sunday, for in this life there would have been only week days or Sundays, but he never set foot on it, he only came across it while passing by. My world then—the only world I might have known if circumstances had not changed, intervened, would have entered the human imagination, the human imagination that I am familiar with, the only one that dominates the world in which I live—came into being as a footnote to someone just passing by. By the time Christopher Columbus got to the place where I am from, the place which forms the foundation of the person you see before you, he was exhausted, he was sick of the whole thing, he longed for his old home, or he longed just to sit still and enjoy the first few things that he had come upon. The first few things that he came on were named after things that were prominent in his thinking, his sponsors especially; when he came to the place I am from, he (it) had been reduced to a place of worship; the place I am from is named after a church. This church might have been an important church to Christopher Columbus, but churches are not important, originally, to people who look like me. And if people who look like me have an inheritance, among this inheritance will be this confusion of intent; nowhere in his intent when he set out from his point of embarkation (for him, too, there is not origin: he originates from Italy, he sails from Spain, and this is the beginning of another new traditional american narrative, point of origin and point of embarkation):("here is something I have never seen before, I especially like it because it has no precedent, but it is frightening because it has no precedent, and so to make it less frightening I will frame it in the thing I know; I know a church, I know the name of the church, even if I do not like or know the people connected to this church, it is more familiar to me, this church, than the very ground I am standing on; the ground has changed, the church, which is in my mind, remains the same.")

I, the person standing before you, close the quotation marks. Up to this point I and they that look like me am not yet a part of this narrative. I can look at all these events: a man setting sail with three ships, and after many, many days on the ocean, finding new lands whose existence he had never even heard of before, and then finding in these new lands people and their things and these people and their things, he had never heard of them before, and he empties the land of these people, and then he empties the people, he just empties the people. It is when this land is completely empty that I and the people who look like me begin to make an appearance, the food I eat begins to make an appearance, the trees I will see each day come from far away and begin to make an appearance, the sky is as it always was, the sun is as it always was, the water surrounding the land on which I am just making an appearance is as it always was; but these are the only things left from before that man, sailing with his three ships, reached the land on which I eventually make an appearance.

When did I begin to ask all this? When did I begin to think of all this and in just this way? What is history? Is it a theory? I no longer live in the place where I and those who look like me first made an appearance. I live in another place. It has another narrative. Its narrative, too, can start with that man sailing on his ships for days and days, for that man sailing on his ships for days and days is the source of many narratives, for he was like a deity in the simplicity of his beliefs, in the simplicity of his actions; just listen to the straightforward way many volumes featuring this man sailing on his ships began, "In fourteen hundred and ninety-two . . ." "In fourteen hundred and ninety-two." But it was while standing in this other place that has a narrative mostly different from the place in which I make an appearance, that I begin to think of this.

One day, while looking at the things that lay before me at my feet, I was having an argument with myself over the names I should use when referring to the things that lay before me at my feet. These things were plants. The plants, all of them and they were hundreds, had two names: they had a common name, that is the name assigned to them by people for whom these plants have value, and then they have a proper name, or a Latin name, and that is a name assigned to them by an agreed-on group of botanists. For a long time I resisted using the proper names of the things that lay before me. I believed that it was an affectation to say "Eupatorium" when you could say "Joe Pye Weed." I then would only say "Joe Pye Weed." The botanists are from the same part of the world as the man who sailed on the three ships, that same man who started the narrative from which I trace my beginning. And the botanists are like that man who sailed on the ships in a way, too: they emptied the worlds of things animal, mineral and vegetable, of their names, and replaced these names with names pleasing to them; the recognized names are now reasonable, as reason is a pleasure to them.

Carl Linnaeus was born on the 23rd of May, in 1707 somewhere in Sweden. (I know where, but I like the high handedness of not saying so.) His father's name was Nils Ingemarsson; the Ingemarssons were farmers. Apparently, in Sweden then, surnames were uncommon among ordinary people, and so the farmer would add "son" to his name or he was called after the farm on which he lived. Nils Ingemarsson became a Lutheran minister, and on doing so he wanted to have a proper surname, not just a name with "son" attached to it. On his family's farm grew a linden tree. It had grown there for generations and had come to be regarded with reverence among neighboring farmers; people believed that misfortune would fall on you if you harmed this tree in any way. This linden tree was so well regarded that people passing by used to pick up twigs that had dropped from it and carefully place them at the base of the tree. Nils Ingemarsson took his surname from this tree: Linnaeus is the latinized form of the Swedish word *lind*. Other branches of this family who also needed a surname drew inspiration from this tree; some took the name Tiliander—the Latin word for linden is *tilia*—and then some others again who also needed a surname took the name Lindelius from the Swedish word *lind*, which means linden.

Carl Linnaeus's father had a garden. I do not know what his mother had. His father loved growing things in this garden and would point them out to the young Carl, but, when the young Carl could not remember the names of the plants, his father gave him a scolding and told him he would not tell him the names of any more plants. (Is this story true? But how could it not be?) He grew up not far from a forest filled with Beech, a forest with pine, a grove filled with oaks, meadows. His father had a collection of rare plants in his garden (but what would be rare to him and in that place, I do not know). At the time Linnaeus was born, Sweden, this small country that I now think of as filled with well-meaning and benign people interested mainly in the well-being of children, the well-being of the unfortunate no matter their age, was the ruler of an Empire; but the remains of it are only visible in the architecture of the main square of the capital of places like Estonia. And so what to make of all this, this small detail that is the linden tree, this large volume of the Swedish empire, and a small boy whose father was a Lutheran pastor? At the beginning of this narrative, the narrative that is Linnaeus, I have not made an appearance yet; the Swedes are not overly implicated in the Atlantic slave trade, not because they did not want to, only because they weren't allowed do to so; other people were better at it than they.

He was called "the little botanist" because he would neglect his studies and go out looking for flowers; if even then he had already showed an interest in, or the ability to name and classify plants, this fact is not in any account of his life that I have come across. He went to university at Uppsala; he studied there with Olaus Rudbeck. I can pause at this name, Rudbeck, and say Rudbeckia, and say, I do not like Rudbeckia, I never have it in my garden, but then I remember that a particularly stately, beautiful yellow flower in a corner of my field garden is Rudbeckia nitida growing there. He met Olaf Celsius (the Celsius scale of temperature measurement), who was so taken with Linnaeus's familiarity and knowledge of botany that he gave Linnaeus free lodging in his house. He became one of the youngest lecturers at the University. He went to Lapland and collected plants and insects native to that region of the world; he wrote and published an account of it called Flora Lapponica. In Lapland, he acquired a set of clothing that people native to that region of the world wore on festive occasions; I have seen a picture of him dressed in these clothes, and the caption under the picture says that he is wearing his Lapland costume. Suddenly, I am made a little uneasy, I haven't really entered this narrative yet, I shall soon, in any case I do not know the Laplanders, they live far away, I don't believe they look like me.

I only enter the picture when Linnaeus takes a boat to Holland. He becomes a doctor to an obviously neurotic man (obvious, only to me, I arbitrarily deem him so; no account of him I have ever come across has described him so) named George Clifford. George Clifford is often described as a rich merchant banker; just like that, a rich merchant banker, and this description often seems to say that to be a rich merchant banker is just a type of person one could be, an ordinary type of person, anyone could be that. And now how to go on, for on hearing that George Clifford was a rich merchant in the 18th century, I now am sure I have become a part of the binomial system of plant nomenclature narrative.

George Clifford had glass houses full of vegetable materials from all over the world. This is what Linnaeus writes of it: "I was greatly amazed when I entered the greenhouses, full as they were of so many plants that a son of the North must feel bewitched, and wonder to what strange quarter of the globe he had been transported. In the first house were cultivated an abundance of flowers from southern Europe, plants from Spain, the South of France, Italy, Sicily and the isles of Greece. In the second were treasures from Asia, such as Poincianas, coconut and other palms, etc.; in the third, Africa's strangely shaped, not to say misshapen plants, such as the numerous forms of Aloe and Mesembryanthemum families, carnivorous flowers, Euphorbias, Crassula and Proteas species, and so on. And finally in the fourth greenhouse were grown the charming inhabitants of America and the rest of the New World; large masses of Cactus varieties, orchids, cruciferea, yams, magnolias, tulip-trees, calabash trees, arrow, cassias, acacias, tamarinds, pepper-plants, Anona, manicinilla, cucurbitaceous trees and many others, and surrounded by these, plantains, the most stately of all the world's plants, the most beauteous Hernandia, silver-gleaming species of Protea and camphor trees. When I then entered the positively royal residence and the extremely instructive museum, whose collections no less spoke in their owner's praise, I, a stranger, felt completely enraptured, as I had never before seen its like. My heart-felt wish was that I might lend a helping hand with its management."

In almost every account of an event that has taken place sometime in the last five hundred years, there is a always a moment when I feel like placing an asterisk somewhere in its text, and at the end of this official story place my own addition. This chapter in the history of botany is such a moment. But where shall I begin? George Clifford is interesting—shall I look at him? He has long ago entered my narrative; I now feel I must enter his. What could it possibly mean to be a merchant banker in the 18th century? He is sometimes described as making his fortune in spices. Only once have I come across an account of him that says he was a director of the Dutch East India Company. The Dutch East India Company would not have been involved in the Atlantic trade in human cargo from Africa, but human cargo from Africa was part of world trade. To read a brief account of the Dutch East India trading company in my very old encyclopedia is not unlike reading the label on an old can of paint. The entry mentions dates, the names of Dutch governors or people acting in Dutch interest; it mentions trade routes, places, commodities, incidents of war between the Dutch and other European people; it never mentions the people who lived in the area of the Dutch trading factories. Places like Ceylon, Java, the Cape of Good Hope are emptied of its people as the landscape itself was emptied of the things they were familiar with, the things that Linnaeus found in George Clifford's greenhouse.

"If one does not know the names, one's knowledge of things is useless." It was in George Clifford's greenhouse that Linnaeus gave some things names. The Adam-like quality of this effort was lost on him. "We revere the Creator's omnipotence," he says, meaning, I think, that he understood he had not made the things he was describing, he was only going to give them names. And even as a relationship exists between George Clifford's activity in the world, the world as it starts out on ships leaving the sea ports of the Netherlands, traversing the earth's seas, touching on the world's peoples and the places they are in, the things that have meant something to them being renamed and a whole new set of narratives imposed on them, narratives that place them at a disadvantage in relationship to George Clifford and his fellow Dutch, even as I can say all this in one breath or in one large volume, so too then does an invisible thread, a thread that no deep breath or large volume can contain, hang between Carolus Linnaeus, his father's desire to give himself a distinguished name, the name then coming from a tree, the Linden tree, a tree whose existence was regarded as not ordinary, and his invention of a system of naming that even I am forced to use?

The invention of this system has been a good thing. Its narrative would begin this way: in the beginning, the vegetable kingdom was chaos; people everywhere called the same things by a name that made sense to them, not by a name that they arrived at by an objective standard. But who has an interest in an objective standard? Who would need one? It makes me ask again what to call the thing that happened to me and all who look like me? Should I call it history? And if so, what should history mean to someone who looks like me? Should it be an idea, should it be an open wound and each breath I take in and expel healing and opening the wound again, over and over, or is it a long moment that begins anew each day since 1492?

No Name Woman

Maxine Hong Kingston

"You must not tell anyone," my mother said, "what I am about to tell you. In China your father had a sister who killed herself. She jumped into the family well. We say that your father has all brothers because it is as if she had never been born."

"In 1924 just a few days after our village celebrated seventeen hurry-up weddings—to make sure that every young man who went 'out on the road' would responsibly come home—your father and his brothers and your grandfather and his brothers and your aunt's new husband sailed for America, the Gold Mountain. It was your grandfather's last trip. Those lucky enough to get contracts waved good-bye from the decks. They fed and guarded the stowaways and helped them off in Cuba, New York, Bali, Hawaii. "We'll meet in California next year," they said. All of them sent money home.

"I remember looking at your aunt one day when she and I were dressing; I had not noticed before that she had such a protruding melon of a stomach. But I did not think, 'She's pregnant,' until she began to look like other pregnant women, her shirt pulling and the white tops of her black pants showing. She could not have been pregnant, you see, because her husband had been gone for years. No one said anything. We did not discuss it. In early summer she was ready to have the child, long after the time when it could have been possible.

"The village had also been counting. On the night the baby was to be born the villagers raided our house. Some were crying. Like a great saw, teeth strung with lights, files of people walked zigzag across our land, tearing the rice. Their lanterns doubled in the disturbed black water, which drained away through the broken bunds. As the villagers closed in, we could see that some of them, probably men and women we knew well, wore white masks. The people with long hair hung it over their faces. Women with short hair made it stand up on end. Some had tied white bands around their foreheads, arms, and legs.

"At first they threw mud and rocks at the house. Then they threw eggs and began slaughtering our stock. We could hear the animals scream their deaths—the roosters, the pigs, a last great roar from the ox. Familiar wild heads flared in our night windows; the villagers encircled us. Some of the faces stopped to peer at us, their eyes rushing like searchlights. The hands flattened against the panes, framed heads, and left red prints.

"The villagers broke in the front and the back doors at the same time, even though we had not locked the doors against them. Their knives dripped with the blood of our animals. They smeared blood on the doors and walls. One woman swung a chicken, whose throat she had slit, splattering blood in red arcs about her. We stood together in the middle of our house, in the family hall with the pictures and tables of the ancestors around us, and looked straight ahead.

"At that time the house had only two wings. When the men came back we would build two more to enclose our courtyard and a third one to begin a second courtyard. The villagers pushed through both wings, even your grandparents' rooms, to find your aunt's, which was also mine until the men returned. From this room a new wing for one of the younger families would grow. They ripped up her clothes and shoes and broke her combs, grinding them underfoot. They tore her work from the loom. They scattered the cooking fire and rolled the new weaving in it. We could hear them in the kitchen breaking our bowls and banging the pots. They overturned the great waist-high earthenware jugs; duck eggs, pickled fruits, vegetables burst out and mixed in acrid torrents. The old woman from the next field swept a broom through the air and loosed the spirits-of-the-broom over our heads. 'Pig.' 'Ghost.' 'Pig,' they sobbed and scolded while they ruined our house.

"When they left, they took sugar and oranges to bless themselves. They cut pieces from the dead animals. Some of them took bowls that were not broken and clothes that were not torn. Afterward we swept up the rice and sewed it back up into sacks. But the smells from the spilled preserves lasted. Your aunt gave birth in the pigsty that night. The next morning when I went up for the water, I found her and the baby plugging up the family well.

"Don't let your father know that I told you. He denies her. Now that you have started to menstruate, what happened to her could happen to you. Don't humiliate us. You wouldn't like to be forgotten as if you had never been born. The villagers are watchful."

Whenever she had to warn us about life, my mother told stories that ran like this one, a story to grow up on. She tested our strength to establish realities. Those in the emigrant generations who could not reassert brute survival died young and far from home. Those of us in the first American generations have had to figure out how the invisible world the emigrants built around our childhoods fit in solid America.

The emigrants confused the gods by diverting their curses, misleading them with crooked streets and false names. They must try to confuse their offspring as well, who, I suppose, threaten them in similar ways—always trying to get things straight, always trying to name the unspeakable. The Chinese I know hide their names; sojourners take new names when their lives change and guard their real names with silence.

Chinese-Americans, when you try to understand what things in you are Chinese, how do you separate what is peculiar to childhood, to poverty, insanities, one family, your mother who marked your growing with stories, from what is Chinese? What is Chinese tradition and what is the movies?

If I want to learn what clothes my aunt wore, whether flashy or ordinary, I would have to begin, "Remember Father's drowned-in-the-well sister?" I cannot ask that. My mother has told me once and for all the useful parts. She will add nothing unless powered by Necessity, a riverbank that guides her life. She plants vegetable gardens rather than lawns; she carries the odd-shaped tomatoes home from the fields and eats food left for the gods.

Whenever we did frivolous things, we used up energy; we flew high kites. We children came up off the ground over the melting cones our parents brought home from work and the American movie on New Year's Day—*Oh, You Beautiful Doll* with Betty Grable one year, and *She Wore a Yellow Ribbon* with John Wayne another year. After the one carnival ride each, we paid in guilt; our tired father counted his change on the dark walk home.

Adultery is extravagance. Could people who hatch their own chicks and eat the embryos and the heads for delicacies and boil the feet in vinegar for party food, leaving only the gravel, eating even the gizzard lining—could such people engender a prodigal aunt? To be a woman, to have a daughter in starvation time was a waste enough. My aunt could not have been the lone romantic who gave up everything for sex. Women in the old China did not choose. Some man had commanded her to lie with him and be his secret evil. I wonder whether he masked himself when he joined the raid on her family.

Perhaps she encountered him in the fields or on the mountain where the daughters-in-law collected fuel. Or perhaps he first noticed her in the marketplace. He was not a stranger because the village housed no strangers. She had to have dealings with him other than sex. Perhaps he worked an adjoining field, or he sold her the cloth for the dress she sewed and wore. His demand must have surprised, then terrified her. She obeyed him; she always did as she was told.

When the family found a young man in the next village to be her husband, she stood tractably beside the best rooster, his proxy, and promised before they met that she would be his forever. She was lucky that he was her age and should be the first wife, an advantage secure now. The night she first saw him, he had sex with her. Then he left for America. She had almost forgotten what he looked like. When she tried to envision him, she only saw the black and white face in the group photograph the man had had taken before leaving.

191

The other man was not, after all, much different than her husband. They both gave orders: she followed. "If you tell your family, I'll beat you. I'll kill you. Be here again next week." No one talked sex, ever. And she might have separated the rapes from the rest of living if only she did not have to buy her oil from him or gather wood in the same forest. I want her fear to have lasted just as long as rape lasted so that the fear could have been contained. No drawn-out fear. But women at sex hazarded birth and hence lifetimes. The fear did not stop but permeated everywhere. She told the man, "I think I'm pregnant." He organized the raid against her.

On nights when my mother and father talked about their life back home, sometimes they mentioned an "outcast table" whose business they still seemed to be settling, their voices tight. In a commensal tradition, where food is precious, the powerful older people made wrongdoers eat alone. Instead of letting them start separate new lives like the Japanese, who could become samurais and geishas, the Chinese family, faces averted but eyes glowering sideways, hung on to the offenders and fed them leftovers. My aunt must have lived in the same house as my parents and eaten at an outcast table. My mother spoke about the raid as if she had seen it, when she and my aunt, a daughter-in-law to a different household, should not have been living together at all. Daughters-in-law lived with their husbands' parents, not their own; a synonym for marriage in Chinese is "taking a daughter-in-law." Her husband's parents could have sold her, mortgaged her, stoned her. But they had sent her back to her own mother and father, a mysterious act hinting at disgraces not told me. Perhaps they had thrown her out to deflect the avengers.

She was the only daughter; her four brothers went with her father, husband, and uncles "out on the road" and for some years became western men. When the goods were divided among the family, three of the brothers took land, and the youngest, my father, chose an education. After my grandparents gave their daughter away to her husband's family, they had dispensed all the adventure and all the property. They expected her alone to keep the traditional ways, which her brothers, now among the barbarians, could fumble without detection. The heavy, deep-rooted women were to maintain the past against the flood, safe for returning. But the rare urge west had fixed upon our family, and so my aunt crossed boundaries not delineated in space.

The work of preservation demands that the feelings playing about in one's guts not be turned into action. Just watch their passing like cherry blossoms. But perhaps my aunt, my forerunner, caught in a slow life, let dreams grow and fade and after some months or years went toward what persisted. Fear at the enormities of the forbidden kept her desires delicate, wire and bone. She looked at a man because she liked the way the hair was tucked behind his ears, or she liked the question-mark line of a long torso curving at the shoulder and straight at the hip. For warm eyes or a soft voice or a slow walk—that's all—a few hairs, a line, a brightness, a sound, a pace, she gave up family. She offered us up for a charm that vanished with tiredness, a pigtail that didn't toss when the wind died. Why, the wrong lighting could erase the dearest thing about him.

It could very well have been, however, that my aunt did not take subtle enjoyment of her friend, but, a wild woman, kept rollicking company. Imagining her free with sex doesn't fit, though. I don't know any women like that, or men either. Unless I see her life branching into mine, she gives me no ancestral help.

To sustain her being in love, she often worked at herself in the mirror, guessing at the colors and shapes that would interest him, changing them frequently in order to hit on the right combination. She wanted to look back.

On a farm near the sea, a woman who tended her appearance reaped a reputation for eccentricity. All the married women blunt cut their hair in flaps about their ears or pulled it back in tight buns. No nonsense. Neither style blew easily into heart-catching tangles. And at their weddings they displayed themselves in their long hair for the last time. "It brushed the backs of my knees," my mother tells me. "It was braided, and even so, it brushed the backs of my knees."

At the mirror my aunt combed individuality into her bob. A bun could have been contrived to escape into black streamers blowing in the wind or in quiet wisps about her face, but only the older women in our picture album wear buns. She brushed her hair back from her forehead, tucking the flaps behind her ears. She looped a piece of thread, knotted into a circle between her index fingers and thumbs, and ran the double strand across her forehead. When she closed her fingers as if she were making a pair of shadow geese bite, the string twisted together catching the little hairs. Then she pulled the thread away from her skin, ripping the hairs out neatly, her eyes watering from the needles of pain. Opening her fingers, she cleaned the thread, then rolled it along her hairline and the tops of the eyebrows. My mother did the same to me and my sisters and herself. I used to believe that the expression "caught by the short hairs" meant a captive held with a depilatory string. It especially hurt at the temples, but my mother said we were lucky we didn't have to have our feet bound when we were seven. Sisters used to sit on their beds and cry together, she said, as their mothers or their slave removed the bandages for a few minutes each night and let the blood gush back into their veins. I hope that the man my aunt loved appreciated a smooth brow, that he wasn't just a tits-and-ass man.

Once my aunt found a freckle on her chin, at a spot that the almanac said predestined her for unhappiness. She dug it out with a hot needle and washed the wound with peroxide.

More attention to her looks than these pullings of hairs and pickings at spots would have caused gossip among the villagers. They owned work clothes and good clothes, and they wore good clothes for feasting the new seasons. But since a woman combing her hair hexes beginnings, my aunt rarely found an occasion to look her best. Women looked like great sea snails—the corded wood, babies, and laundry they carried were the whorls on their backs. The Chinese did not admire a bent back; goddesses and warriors stood straight. Still there must have been a marvelous freeing of beauty when a worker laid down her burden and stretched and arched.

Such commonplace loveliness, however, was not enough for my aunt. She dreamed of a lover for the fifteen days of New Year's the time for families to exchange visits, money, and food. She plied her secret comb. And sure enough she cursed the year, the family, the village, and herself.

Even as her hair lured her imminent lover, many other men looked at her: Uncles, cousins, nephews, brothers would have looked, too, had they been home between journeys. Perhaps they had already been restraining their curiosity, and they left, fearful that their glances, like a field of nesting birds, might be startled and caught. Poverty hurt, and that was their first reason for leaving. But another, final reason for leaving the crowded house was the never-said.

She may have been unusually beloved, the precious only daughter, spoiled and mirror-gazing because of the affection the family lavished on her. When her husband left, they welcomed the chance to take her back from the in-laws; she could live like the little daughter for just a while longer. There are stories that my grandfather was different from other people, "crazy ever since the little Jap bayoneted him in the head." He used to put his naked penis on the dinner table, laughing. And one day he brought home a baby girl, wrapped up inside his brown western-style greatcoat. He had traded one of his sons, probably my father, the youngest, for her. My grandmother made him trade back. When he finally got a daughter of his own, he doted on her. They must have all loved her, except perhaps my father, the only brother who never went back to China, having once been traded for a girl.

Brothers and sisters, newly men and women, had to efface their sexual color and present plain miens. Disturbing hair and eyes, a smile like no other, threatened the ideal of five generations living under one roof. To focus blurs, people shouted face to face and yelled from room to room. The immigrants I know have loud voices, unmodulated to American tones even after years away from the village where they called their friendships out across the fields. I have not been able to stop my mother's screams in public libraries or over telephones. Walking erect (knees straight, toes pointed forward, not pigeon-toed, which is Chinese-feminine) and speaking in an inaudible voice, I have tried to turn myself American-feminine. Chinese communication was loud, public. Only sick people had to whisper. But at the dinner table, where the family members came nearest one another, no one could talk, not the outcasts nor any eaters. Every word that falls from the mouth is a coin lost. Silently they gave and accepted food with both hands. A preoccupied child who took his bowl with one hand got a sideways glare. A complete moment of total attention is due everyone alike. Children and lovers have no singularity here, but my aunt used a secret voice, a separate attentiveness.

She kept the man's name to herself throughout her labor and dying; she did not accuse him that he be punished with her. To save her inseminator's name she gave silent birth.

He may have been somebody in her own household, but intercourse with a man outside the family would have been no less abhorrent. All the village were kinsmen, and the titles shouted in loud country voices never let kinship be forgotten. Any man within visiting distance would have been neutralized as a lover—"brother," "younger brother," "older brother"—115 relationship titles. Parents researched birth charts probably not so much to assure good fortune as to circumvent incest in a population that has but one hundred surnames. Everybody has eight million relatives. How useless then sexual mannerisms, how dangerous.

As if it came from an atavism deeper than fear, I used to add "brother" silently to boys' names. It hexed the boys, who would or would not ask me to dance, and made them less scary and as familiar and deserving of benevolence as girls.

But, of course, I hexed myself also—no dates. I should have stood up, both arms waving, and shouted out across libraries, "Hey, you! Love me back." I had no idea, though, how to make attraction selective, how to control its direction and magnitude. If I made myself American-pretty so that the five or six Chinese boys in the class fell in love with me, everyone else—the Caucasian, Negro, and Japanese boys—would too. Sisterliness, dignified and honorable, made much more sense.

Attraction eludes control so stubbornly that whole societies designed to organize relationships among people cannot keep order, not even when they bind people to one another from childhood and raise them together. Among the very poor and the wealthy, brothers married their adopted sisters, like doves. Our family allowed some romance, paying adult brides' prices and providing dowries so that their sons and daughters could marry strangers. Marriage promises to turn strangers into friendly relatives—a nation of siblings.

In the village structure, spirits shimmered among the live creatures, balanced and held in equilibrium by time and land. But one human being flaring up into violence could open up a black hole, a maelstrom that pulled in the sky. The frightened villagers, who depended on one another to maintain the real, went to my aunt to show her a personal, physical representation of the break she made in the "roundness." Misallying couples snapped off the future, which was to be embodied in true offspring. The villagers punished her for acting as if she could have a private life, secret and apart from them.

If my aunt had betrayed the family at a time of large grain yields and peace, when many boys were born, and wings were being built on many houses, perhaps she might have escaped such severe punishment. But the men—hungry, greedy, tired of planting in dry soil, cuckolded—had been forced to leave the village in order to send food-money home. There were ghost plagues, bandit plagues, wars with the Japanese, floods. My Chinese brother and sister had died of an unknown sickness. Adultery, perhaps only a mistake during good times, became a crime when the village needed food.

The round moon cakes and round doorways, the round tables of graduated size that fit one roundness inside another, round windows and rice bowls—these talismans had lost their power to warn this family of the law: A family must be whole, faithfully keeping the descent line by having sons to feed the old and the dead who in turn look after the family. The villagers came to show my aunt and lover-in-hiding a broken house. The villagers were speeding up the circling of events because she was too shortsighted to see that her infidelity had already harmed the village, that waves of consequences would return unpredictably, sometimes in disguise, as now, to hurt her. This roundness had to be made coin-sized so that she would see its circumference: Punish her at the birth of her baby. Awaken her to the inexorable. People who refused fatalism because they could invent small resources insisted on culpability. Deny accidents and wrest fault from the stars.

After the villagers left, their lanterns now scattering in various directions toward home, the family broke their silence and cursed her. "Aiaa, we're going to die. Death is coming. Death is coming. Look what you've done. You've killed us. Ghost! Dead Ghost! Ghost! You've never been born." She ran out into the fields, far enough from the house so that she could no longer hear their voices, and pressed herself against the earth, her own land no more. When she felt the birth coming, she thought that she had been hurt. Her body seized together: "They've hurt me too much," she thought. "This is gall, and it will kill me." With forehead and knees against the earth, her body convulsed and then relaxed. She turned on her back, lay on the ground. The black well of sky and stars went out and out forever; her body and her complexity seemed to disappear. She was one of the stars, a bright dot in blackness, without home, without a companion, in eternal cold and silence. An agoraphobia rose in her, speeding higher and higher, bigger and bigger; she would not be able to contain it; there would be no end to fear.

Flayed, unprotected against space, she felt pain return, focusing her body. This pain chilled her—a cold, steady kind of surface pain. Inside, spasmodically, the other pain, the pain of the child, heated her. For hours she lay on the ground, alternately body and space. Sometimes a vision of normal comfort obliterated reality: She saw the family in the evening gambling at the dinner table, the young people massaging their elders' backs. She saw them congratulating one another, high joy on the mornings the rice shoots came up. When these pictures burst, the stars drew yet further apart. Black space opened.

She got to her feet to fight better and remembered that old-fashioned women gave birth in their pigsties to fool the jealous, pain-dealing gods, who do not snatch piglets. Before the next spasms could stop her, she ran to the pigsty, each step a rushing out into emptiness. She climbed over the fence and knelt in the dirt. It was good to have a fence enclosing her, a tribal person alone.

Laboring, this woman who had carried her child as a foreign growth that sickened her everyday, expelled it at last. She reached down to touch the hot, wet, moving mass, surely smaller than anything human, and could feel that it was human after all—fingers, toes, nails, nose. She pulled it up on to her belly, and it lay curled there, butt in the air, feet precisely tucked one under the other. She opened her loose shirt and buttoned the child inside. After resting, it squirmed and thrashed and she pushed it up to her breast. It turned its head this way and that until it found her nipple. There, it made little snuffling noises. She clenched her teeth at its preciousness, lovely as a young calf, a piglet, a little dog.

She may have gone to the pigsty as a last act of responsibility: She would protect this child as she had protected its father. It would look after her soul, leaving supplies on her grave. But how would this tiny child without family find her grave when there would be no marker for her anywhere, neither in the earth nor the family hall? No one would give her a family hall name. She had taken the child with her into the wastes. At its birth the two of them had felt the same raw pain of separation, a wound that only the family pressing tight could close. A child with no descent line would not soften her life but only trail after her, ghostlike, begging her to give it purpose. At dawn the villagers on their way to the fields would stand around the fence and look.

Full of milk, the little ghost slept. When it awoke, she hardened her breasts against the milk that crying loosens. Toward morning she picked up the baby and walked to the well.

Carrying the baby to the well shows loving. Otherwise abandon it. Turn its face into the mud. Mothers who love their children take them along. It was probably a girl; there is some hope of forgiveness for boys.

"Don't tell anyone you had an aunt. Your father does not want to hear her name. She has never been born." I have believed that sex was unspeakable and words so strong and fathers so frail that "aunt" would do my father mysterious harm. I have thought that my family, having settled among immigrants who had also been their neighbors in the ancestral land, needed to clean their name, and a wrong word would incite the kinspeople even here. But there is more to this silence: They want me to participate in her punishment. And I have.

In the twenty years since I heard this story I have not asked for details nor said my aunt's name; I do not know it. People who comfort the dead can also chase after them to hurt them further—a reverse ancestor worship. The real punishment was not the raid swiftly inflicted by the villagers, but the family's deliberately forgetting her. Her betrayal so maddened them, they saw to it that she would suffer forever, even after death. Always hungry, always needing, she would have to beg food from other ghosts, snatch and steal it from those whose living descendants give them gifts. She would have to fight the ghosts massed at crossroads for the buns a few thoughtful citizens leave to decoy her away from village and home so that the ancestral spirits could feast unharassed. At peace, they could act like gods, not ghosts, their descent lines providing them with paper suits and dresses, spirit money, paper houses, paper automobiles, chicken, meat, and rice into eternity—essences delivered up in smoke and flames, steam and incense rising from each rice bowl. In an attempt to make the Chinese care for people outside the family, Chairman Mao encourages us now to give our paper replicas to the spirits of outstanding soldiers and workers, no matter whose ancestors they may be. My aunt remains forever hungry. Goods are not distributed evenly among the dead.

My aunt haunts me—her ghost drawn to me because now, after fifty years of neglect, I alone devote pages of paper to her, though not origamied into houses and clothes. I do not think she always means me well. I am telling on her, and she was a spite suicide, drowning herself in the drinking water. The Chinese are always very frightened of the drowned one, whose weeping ghost, wet hair hanging and skin bloated, waits silently by the water to pull down a substitute.

Strangers

Toni Morrison

I am in this river place—newly mine—walking in the yard when I see a woman sitting on the seawall at the edge of a neighbor's garden. A home-made fishing pole arcs into the water some twenty feet from her hand. A feeling of welcome washes over me. I walk toward her, right up to the fence that separates my place from the neighbor's, and notice with pleasure the clothes she wears: men's shoes, a man's hat, a well-worn colorless sweater over a long black dress. The woman turns her head and greets me with an easy smile and a "How you doing?" She tells me her name (Mother Something) and we talk for some time—fifteen minutes or so—about fish recipes and weather and children. When I ask her if she lives there, she answers no. She lives in a nearby village, but the owner of the house lets her come to this spot any time she wants to fish, and she comes every week, sometimes several days in a row when the perch or catfish are running and even if they aren't because she likes eel, too, and they are always there. She is witty and full of the wisdom that older women always seem to have a lock on. When we part, it is with an understanding that she will be there the next day or very soon after and we will visit again. I imagine more conversations with her. I will invite her into my house for coffee, for tales, for laughter. She reminds me of someone, something. I imagine a friendship, casual, effortless, delightful.

She is not there the next day. She is not there the following days, either. And I look for her every morning. The summer passes, and I have not seen her at all. Finally, I approach the neighbor to ask about her and am bewildered to learn that the neighbor does not know who or what I am talking about. No old woman fished from her wall—ever—and none had permission to do so. I decide that the fisherwoman fibbed about the permission and took advantage of the neighbor's frequent absences to poach. The fact of the neighbor's presence is proof that the fisherwoman would not be there. During the months following, I ask lots of people if they know Mother Something. No one, not even people who have lived in nearby villages for seventy years, has ever heard of her.

I feel cheated, puzzled, but also amused, and wonder off and on if I have dreamed her. In any case, I tell myself, it was an encounter of no value other than anecdotal. Still. Little by little, annoyance then bitterness takes the place of my original bewilderment. A certain view from my windows is now devoid of her, reminding me every morning of her deceit and my disappointment. What was she doing in that neighborhood, anyway? She didn't drive, had to walk four miles if indeed she lived where she said she did. How could she be missed on the road in that hat, those awful shoes? I try to understand the intensity of my chagrin, and why I am missing a woman I spoke to for fifteen minutes. I get nowhere except for the stingy explanation that she had come into my space (next to it, anyway—at the property line, at the edge, just at the fence, where the most interesting things always happen), and had implied promises of female camaraderie, of opportunities for me to be generous, of protection and protecting. Now she is gone, taking with her my good opinion of myself, which, of course, is unforgivable.

Isn't that the kind of thing that we fear strangers will do? Disturb. Betray. Prove they are not like us. That is why it is so hard to know what to do with them. The love that prophets have urged us to offer the stranger is the same love that Jean-Paul Sartre could reveal as the very mendacity of Hell. The signal line of "No Exit," "*L'enfer, c'est les autres*," raises the possibility that "other people" are responsible for turning a personal world into a public hell. In the admonition of a prophet and the sly warning of an artist, strangers as well as the beloved are understood to tempt our gaze, to slide away or to stake claims. Religious prophets caution against the slide, the looking away; Sartre warns against love as possession.

The resources available to us for benign access to each other, for vaulting the mere blue air that separates us, are few but powerful: language, image, and experience, which may involve both, one, or neither of the first two. Language (saying, listening, reading) can encourage, even mandate, surrender, the breach of distances among us, whether they are continental or on the same pillow, whether they are distances of culture or the distinctions and indistinctions of age or gender, whether they are the consequences of social invention or biology. Image increasingly rules the realm of shaping, sometimes becoming, often contaminating, knowledge. Provoking language or eclipsing it, an image can determine not only what we know and feel but also what we believe is worth knowing about what we feel.

Those two godlings, language and image, feed and form experience. My instant embrace of an outrageously dressed fisherwoman was due in part to an image on which my representation of her was based. I immediately sentimentalized and appropriated her. I owned her or wanted to (and I suspect she glimpsed it). I had forgotten the power of embedded images and stylish language to seduce, reveal, control. Forgot, too, their capacity to help us pursue the human project—which is to remain human and to block the dehumanization of others.

But something unforeseen has entered into this admittedly oversimplified menu of our resources. Far from our original expectations of increased intimacy and broader knowledge, routine media presentations deploy images and language that narrow our view of what humans look like (or ought to look like) and what in fact we are like. Succumbing to the perversions of media can blur vision, resisting them can do the same. I was clearly and aggressively resisting such influences in my encounter with the fisherwoman. Art as well as the market can be complicit in the sequestering of form from formula, or nature from artifice, of humanity from commodity. Art gesturing toward representation has, in some exalted quarters, become literally beneath contempt. The concept of what it is to be human has altered, and the word *truth* needs quotation marks around it so that its absence (its elusiveness) is stronger than its presence.

Why would we want to know a stranger when it is easier to estrange another? Why would we want to close the distance when we can close the gate? Appeals in arts and religion for comity in the Common Wealth are faint.

It took some time for me to understand my unreasonable claims on that fisherwoman. To understand that I was longing for and missing some aspect of myself, and that there are no strangers. There are only versions of ourselves, many of which we have not embraced, most of which we wish to protect ourselves from. For the stranger is not foreign, she is random, not alien but remembered; and it is the randomness of the encounter with our already known—although unacknowledged—selves that summons a ripple of alarm. That makes us reject the figure and the motions it provokes—especially when these emotions are profound. It is also what makes us want to own, govern, administrate the Other. To romance her, if we can, back into our own mirrors. In either instance (of alarm or false reverence), we deny her personhood, the specific individuality we insist upon for ourselves.

Robert Bergman's radiant portraits of strangers provoked this meditation. Occasionally, there arises an event or a moment that one knows immediately will forever mark a place in the history of artistic endeavor. Bergman's portraits represent such a moment, such an event. In all its burnished majesty his gallery refuses us unearned solace, and one by one by one the photographs unveil *us*, asserting a beauty, a kind of rapture, that is as close as can be to a master template of the singularity, the community, the unextinguishable sacredness of the human race.

Thinking Again:
What Do We Mean by Mind?

Marilynne Robinson

It will be a great day in the history of science if we sometime discover a damp shadow elsewhere in the universe where a fungus has sprouted. The mere fossil trace of life in its simplest form would be the crowning achievement of generations of brilliant and diligent labor.

And here we are, a gaudy efflorescence of consciousness, staggeringly improbable in light of everything we know about the reality that contains us.

There are physicists and philosophers who would correct me. They would say that if there are an infinite number of universes, as in theory there could be, then creatures like us would be very likely to emerge at some time in one of them. But to say this is only to state the fact of our improbability in other terms.

Then there is the odd privilege of existence as a coherent self, the ability to speak the word "I" and mean by it a richly individual history of experience, perception, and thought. For the religious, the sense of the soul may have as a final redoubt, not as argument but as experience, that haunting I who wakes us in the night wondering where time has gone, the I we waken to, sharply aware that we have been unfaithful to ourselves, that a life lived otherwise would have acknowledged a yearning more our own than any of the daylit motives whose behests we answer to so diligently. Our religious traditions give us as the name of God two deeply mysterious words, one deeply mysterious utterance: I AM. Putting to one side the question of their meaning as the name and character by which the God of Moses would be known, these are words any human being can say about herself, and does say, though always with a modifier of some kind. I am hungry, I am comfortable, I am a singer, I am a cook. The abrupt descent into particularity in every statement of this kind, Being itself made an auxiliary to some momentary accident of being, may only startle in the dark of night, when the intuition comes that there is no proportion between the great given of existence and the narrow vessel of circumstance into which it is inevitably forced. "I am Ozymandias, king of kings. Look on my works, ye mighty, and despair."

There is much speculation about the nature of the mind, its relation to the brain, even doubt that the word "mind" is meaningful. In his book *Consilience,* the biologist E. O. Wilson claims, "The brain and its satellite glands have now been probed to the point where no particular site remains that can reasonably be supposed to harbor a nonphysical mind." But if such a site could be found in the brain, then the mind would be physical in the same sense that anything else with a locus in the brain is physical. To define the mind as nonphysical in the first place clearly prejudices his conclusion. The experimental psychologist Steven Pinker, writing about the soul in *How the Mind Works,* asks, "How does the spook interact with solid matter? How does an ethereal nothing respond to flashes, pokes and beeps and get arms and legs to move? Another problem is the overwhelming evidence that the mind is the activity of the brain. The supposedly immaterial soul, we now know, can be bisected with a knife, altered by chemicals," and so on. By identifying the soul with the mind, the mind with the brain, and noting the brain's vulnerability as a physical object, he feels he has debunked a conception of the soul that only those who find the word meaningless would ever have entertained.

This declension, from the ethereality of the mind/soul as spirit to the reality of the mind/brain as a lump of meat, is dependent, conceptually and for its effects, on precisely the antique dualism these writers who claim to speak for science believe they reject and refute. If complex life is the marvel we all say it is, quite possibly unique to this planet, then meat is, so to speak, that marvel in its incarnate form. It was dualism that pitted the spirit against the flesh, investing spirit with all that is lofty at the expense of flesh, which is by contrast understood as coarse and base. It only perpetuates dualist thinking to treat the physical as if it were in any way sufficiently described in disparaging terms. If the mind is the activity of the brain, this means only that the brain is capable of such lofty and astonishing things that their expression has been given the names mind, and soul, and spirit. Complex life may well be the wonder of the universe, and if it is, its status is not diminished by the fact that we can indeed bisect it, that we kill it routinely.

In any case, Wilson's conception of mind clearly has also taken on the properties of the soul, at least as that entity is understood by those eager to insist that there is no ghost in the machine. As Bertrand Russell pointed out decades before Gilbert Ryle coined this potent phrase, the old, confident distinction between materiality and nonmateriality is not a thing modern science can endorse. Physicists say a change in a split photon occurs simultaneously in its severed half, at any theoretical distance. As if there were no time or space, this information of change passes instantly from one to the other. Is an event that defies any understanding we have of causality a physical event? Yes. Can the seeming timelessness and spacelessness that mediate this change also be called physical? Presumably, since they have unambiguous physical consequences. Then perhaps we cannot claim to know the nature of the physical, and perhaps we ought not to be so confident in opposing it to a real or imagined nonphysical. These terms, as conventionally used, are not identical with the terms "real" and "unreal," though the belief that they are is the oldest tenet of positivism. The old notion of dualism should be put aside, now that we know a little about the uncanny properties of the finer textures of the physical. If, as some have suggested, quantum phenomena govern the brain, evidence for the fact is not likely to be found in scrutiny of lobes or glands or by means of any primitive understanding of the brain's materiality.

Let us say the mind is what the brain does. This is a definition that makes the mind, whatever else, a participant in the whole history and experience of the body. Steven Pinker offers the same definition, but modifies it differently. He says, "The mind is what the brain does; specifically, the brain processes information, and thinking is a kind of computation"—excluding the felt experience of thinking, with all its diverse burdens and colorations. Elsewhere he says, with the certitude typical of his genre, "Family feelings are designed to help our genes replicate themselves, but we cannot see or smell genes. . . . Our emotions about kin use a kind of inverse genetics to guess which of the organisms we interact with are likely to share our genes (for example, if someone appears to have the same parents as you do, treat the person as if their genetic well-being overlaps with yours)." Here we have the self we experience at a qualitative remove from what the brain really does. Presumably we are seduced into collaborating in the perpetuation of some part of our genetic inheritance by those moments of love and embrace. But why are these seductions necessary? Why are they lovely to us? Why would nature bother to distract us with them? Why do we stand apart from nature in such a way that the interests that really move us should be concealed from us? Might there not be fewer of these interfamilial crimes, honor killings, child abandonments, if nature had made us straightforwardly aware that urgencies more or less our own were being served in our propagating and nurturing? There is more than a hint of dualism in the notion that some better self—the term seems fair—has to be distracted by ingratiating pleasures to accommodate the practical business of biology.

This automaton language of Pinker's sounds a bit like Descartes. But Descartes theorized that the pineal gland, central and singular in the symmetries of the brain, moved one way or another to permit or obstruct the actions of the body, which he knew were governed by the brain. In his theory, the impressions of the senses, integrated in this gland, were appraised by the soul, which in Descartes is a term that seems pointedly synonymous with the mind. That is to say, his interest is in cognition and reason, not sin or salvation, and this in a physical and intellectual landscape inflamed by theological controversy in which those concepts figured prominently. Still, it is the soul that appraises what the mind integrates. In this way Descartes acknowledges the complexity of thinking, judging, and in his way incorporates the feeling of consciousness and the complexity of it more adequately than most theorists do now.

What Descartes actually intended by the words "soul" and "mind" seems to me an open question for Descartes himself. Clearly they are no mere ghost or illusion. What their meanings are for us as inheritors of the thought of the modern period is a more manageable question. I am excluding the kind of thinking on this point that tends toward the model of the wager. According to this model, we place our faith in an understanding of the one thing needful, and, ultimately, suffer or triumph depending on the correctness of our choice. By these lights the soul exists primarily to be saved or lost. It is hardly more our intimate companion in mortal time than is the mind or brain by the reckoning of the positivists, behaviorists, neo-Darwinists, and Freudians. The soul, in this understanding of it, is easily characterized by the nonreligious as a fearful and self-interested idea, as the product of acculturation or a fetish of the primitive brain rather than as a name for an aspect of deep experience. Therefore it is readily dismissed as a phantom of the mind, and the mind is all the more readily dismissed for its harboring of such fears and delusions.

Steven Pinker says, "The faculty with which we ponder the world has no ability to peer inside itself or our other faculties to see what makes them tick. That makes us the victims of an illusion: that our own psychology comes from some divine force or mysterious essence or almighty principle." But the mind, or the brain, a part of the body just as E. O. Wilson says it is, is deeply sensitive to itself. Guilt, nostalgia, the pleasure of anticipation, even the shock of a realization, all arise out of an event that occurs entirely in the mind or brain, and they are as potent as other sensations. Consistency would require a belief in the nonphysical character of the mind to exclude them from the general category of experience. If it is objected that all these things are ultimately dependent on images and sensations first gleaned from the world by the senses, this might be granted, on the condition that the sensory experience retained in the mind is understood to have the character the mind has given it. And it might be granted if sensory experience is understood to function as language does, both enabling thought and conforming it in large part to its own context, its own limitations. Anyone's sensory experience of the world is circumstantial and cultural, qualified by context and perspective, a fact which again suggests that the mind's awareness of itself is of a kind with its awareness of physical reality. The mind, like the body, is very much placed in the world. Those who claim to dismiss the mind/body dichotomy actually perpetuate it when they exclude the mind's self-awareness from among the data of human nature.

By "self-awareness" I do not mean merely consciousness of one's identity, or of the complex flow of thought, perception, memory, and desire, important as these are. I mean primarily the self that stands apart from itself, that questions, reconsiders, appraises. I have read that microorganisms can equip themselves with genes useful to their survival—that is, genes conferring resistance to antibiotics—by choosing them out of the ambient flux of organic material. If a supposedly simple entity can by any means negotiate its own enhancement, then an extremely complex entity largely composed of these lesser entities—that is, a human being—should be assumed to have analogous capabilities. For the purposes of the mind, these might be called conscience or aspiration. We receive their specific forms culturally and historically, as the microorganism does also when it absorbs the consequences of other germs' encounters with the human pharmacopoeia.

If the brain at the level of complex and nuanced interaction with itself does indeed become mind, then the reductionist approach insisted upon by writers on the subject is not capable of yielding evidence of mind's existence, let alone an account of its functioning. One who has inquired into the properties of hydrogen and oxygen might reasonably conclude that water is a highly combustible gas—if there were not his own experience to discourage this conclusion. As proof of the existence of mind we have only history and civilization, art, science, and philosophy. And at the same time, of course, that extraordinary individuation. If it is true that the mind can know and seek to know itself in ways analogous to its experience of the world, then there are more, richer data to be gleaned from every age and every culture, and from every moment of introspection, of deep awareness of the self.

The strangeness of reality consistently exceeds the expectations of science, and the assumptions of science, however tried and rational, are inclined to encourage false expectations. As a notable example, no one expected to find that the expansion of the universe is accelerating, and that the rate of its acceleration is accelerating. It is a tribute to the brilliance of science that we can know such things. And it is also an illustration of the fact that science does not foreclose possibility, including discoveries that overturn very fundamental assumptions, and that it is not a final statement about reality but a highly fruitful mode of inquiry into it.

The fact of the accelerating expansion of the universe is a conclusion arrived at in the first place by observation. Theory and hypothesis have followed. What was thought to be known about the effect of gravity, that it would slow cosmic expansion, could not be reconciled with new data, and a major and novel factor, in effect an antigravitational force, emerged as a hypothesis in a changed conception of the universe. The best wisdom and the most venerable of natural laws do not have standing to preclude our acknowledging solid data, though the grounds for refusing to take account of them could perfectly well be called "scientific." The exclusion of what the brain does from an account of what the brain is is "scientific" in just the same sense. By this kind of reasoning, the laws of nature supposedly tell us what we must exclude from what we might otherwise consider entirely relevant, one example being our own inwardness. This distinction between science and parascience is important in considering the mind over against the materialist position that would understand it in reductionist terms, that is, in terms that limit the kinds of interpretation that are appropriately brought to bear on it. The neo-Darwinists argue that the brain evolved to maximize the chance of genetic survival, to negotiate access to food and sex, presumably before the species evolved to the point where the prolonged helplessness of infants made genetic survival dependent in some degree on cooperation. Therefore, they tell us, we may not assume that any motive can depart from an essential qualitative likeness to these original motives. The "evolutionary epic" explains the brain exhaustively.

But "the material" itself is an artifact of the scale at which we perceive. We know that we abide with quarks and constellations, in a reality unknowable by us in a degree we will never be able to calculate, but reality all the same, the stuff and the matrix of our supposedly quotidian existence. We know that within, throughout, the solid substantiality of our experience indeterminacy reigns. Making use of the conceptual vocabulary of science to exclude a possibility which in a present state of knowledge—or a former one—that vocabulary would seem to exclude, has been the mission of positivist thinking since Auguste Comte declared scientific knowledge effectively complete. If doing so is a reflex of the polemical impulse to assert the authority of science, understandable when the project was relatively new, it is by now an atavism that persists as a consequence of the same polemical impulse.

The ancient antagonist that has shaped positivism and parascientific thought and continues to inspire its missionary zeal is religion. For cultural and historical reasons, the religions against which it has opposed itself are Christianity and Judaism, both of which must be called anthropologies, whatever else. "What is man that thou art mindful of him?" The very question is an assertion that mindfulness is an attribute of God, as well as man, a statement of the sense of deep meaning inhering in mindfulness. If I were not myself a religious person, but wished to make an account of religion, I believe I would tend toward the Feuerbachian view that religion is a human projection of humanity's conceptions of beauty, goodness, power, and other valued things, a humanizing of experience by understanding it as structured around and mirroring back these values. Then it would resemble art, with which it is strongly associated. But this would dignify religion and characterize the mind as outwardly and imaginatively engaged with the world, as, in parascientific thought after Comte, it never is.

Steven Pinker says, "Religion is a desperate measure that people resort to when the stakes are high and they have exhausted the usual techniques for the causation of success." Then a little farther on he lists the "imponderables" that lie behind the human tendency toward religion and also philosophy. These imponderables are consciousness in the sense of sentience or subjective experience, the self, free will, conceptual meaning, knowledge, and morality. He says, "Maybe philosophical problems are hard not because they are divine or irreducible or meaningless or workaday science, but because the mind of Homo sapiens lacks the cognitive equipment to solve them. We are organisms, not angels, and our brains are organs, not pipelines to the truth."

How odd that these "imponderables" should be just the kind of thing humankind has pondered endlessly. Neo-Darwinism allows for hypertrophy, the phenomenon by which evolution overshoots its mark and produces some consequence not strictly useful to the ends of genetic replication, the human brain as case in point. How strange it would be, then, that this accident, this excess, should feel a tropism toward what Pinker himself calls "the truth."

Science has arrived at a cluster of hypotheses about the first instant of creation. They attempt description, in the manner of science. In course of time, on various grounds, one description might prove to be more satisfactory than others. A consensus might be arrived at about the nature of a very fecund particle whose eruption became everything we know, and a great deal more beside. We might learn at some point whether time was created together with this universe or exists independently of it. The questions to which science in its most sophisticated forms has come would have been the imponderables of philosophy a few generations ago, of theology a few centuries ago, of religion a few millennia ago. Why this ancient instinct for the greatest questions? It is striking that Pinker identifies religion with the high-order questions humankind has posed to itself from antiquity. Then he dismisses these things as insoluble, as if that were a legitimate reason to dismiss any question. We may never know why gravity is so much weaker than, in theory, it should be, or know if we are only one among any number of actual and potential universes. But every real question is fruitful, as the history of human thought so clearly demonstrates.

And "fruitful" is by no means a synonym for "soluble." What is man? One answer on offer is: An organism whose haunting questions perhaps ought not to be meaningful to the organ that generates them, lacking as it is in any means of "solving" them. Another answer might be: It is still too soon to tell. We might be the creature who brings life on this planet to an end, and we might be the creature who awakens to the privileges that inhere in our nature—selfhood, consciousness, even our biologically anomalous craving for "the truth"—and enjoys and enhances them. Mysteriously, neither possibility precludes the other. Our nature will describe itself as we respond to new circumstances in a world that changes continuously. So long as the human mind exists to impose itself on reality, as it has already done so profoundly, what it is and what we are must remain an open question.

In order to arrive at a parascientific view of humankind we are obliged to put to one side whatever is not to be accounted for in the apparently simple terms of genetic self-interest. I say "apparently simple" because in every instance these theorists build in devices to account for the inadequacies of their theories. The Ptolemaic model of the universe worked well enough, given certain cogs and wheels, epicycles and deferents. Wilson and Pinker speak of the old error, that notion of a ghost in the machine, the image of the felt difference between mind and body. But who and what is that other self they posit, the hypertrophic self who has considered the heavens since Babylon and considers them still, by elegant and ingenious means whose refinements express a formidable pressure of desire to see and know far beyond the limits of any conception of utility, certainly any neo-Darwinist conception of it? Who is that other self needing to be persuaded that there are more than genetic reasons for rescuing a son or daughter from drowning? The archaic conundrum, how a nonphysical spirit can move a physical body, only emerges in a more pointed form in these unaccountable presences whom evolution has supposedly contrived to make us mistake for ourselves. These epigones exist because without them the theories would fail the test of comparison with human experience. Merely shift the balance toward manifest behavior, assuming that the genes do indeed look after themselves in ways and degrees we most likely cannot yet describe, but in any case that their functioning is consistent with manifest behavior. Then human nature, in its wholeness and complexity, is restored—as an unsolved problem, but as a phenomenon endlessly offering a very burdened testimony.

Each of us lives intensely within herself or himself, continuously assimilating past and present experience to a narrative and vision that are unique in every case yet profoundly communicable, whence the arts. And we all live in a great reef of collective experience, past and present, that we receive and preserve and modify. William James says data should be thought of not as givens but as gifts, this by way of maintaining an appropriate humility in the face of what we think we know. The gifts we bring to the problem of making an account of the mind are overwhelmingly rich, severally and together. This is not an excuse for excluding them from consideration. History and civilization are an authoritative record the mind has left, is leaving, and will leave, and objectivity deserving the name would take this record as a starting point.

The universe passed through its unimaginable first moment, first year, first billion years, wresting itself from whatever state of nonexistence, inflating, contorting, resolving into space and matter, bursting into light. Matter condenses, stars live out their generations. Then, very late, there is added to the universe of being a shaped stick or stone, a jug, a cuneiform tablet. They appear on a tiny, teetering, lopsided planet, and they demand wholly new vocabularies of description for reality at every scale. What but the energies of the universe could be expressed in the Great Wall of China, the *St. Matthew Passion*? For our purposes, there is nothing else. Yet language that would have been fully adequate to describe the ages before the appearance of the first artifact would have had to be enlarged by concepts like agency and intention, words like "creation," that would query the great universe itself. Might not the human brain, that most complex object known to exist in the universe, have undergone a qualitative change as well? If my metaphor only suggests the possibility that our species is more than an optimized ape, that something terrible and glorious befell us—if this is merely another fable, it might at least encourage an imagination of humankind large enough to acknowledge some small fragment of the mystery we are.

Aria: A Memoir of a Bilingual Childhood

Richard Rodriguez

I remember to start with that day in Sacramento—a California now nearly thirty years past—when I first entered a classroom, able to understand some fifty stray English words.

The third of four children, I had been preceded to a neighborhood Roman Catholic school by an older brother and sister. But neither of them had revealed very much about their classroom experiences. They left each morning and returned each afternoon, always together, speaking Spanish as they climbed the five steps to the porch. And their mysterious books, wrapped in brown shopping-bag paper, remained on the table next to the door, closed firmly behind them.

An accident of geography sent me to a school where all my classmates were white and many were the children of doctors and lawyers and business executives. On that first day of school, my classmates must certainly have been uneasy to find themselves apart from their families, in the first institution of their lives. But I was astonished. I was fated to be the "problem student" in class.

The nun said, in a friendly but oddly impersonal voice: "Boys and girls, this is Richard Rodgriquez." (I heard her sound *it* out: *Rich-heard Road-ree-guess.*) It was the first time I had heard anyone say my name in English. "Richard," the nun repeated more slowly, writing my name down in her book. Quickly I turned to see my mother's face dissolve in a watery blur behind the pebbled-glass door.

Now, many years later, I hear of something called "bilingual education"—a scheme proposed in the late 1960s by Hispanic American social activists, later endorsed by a congressional vote. It is a program that seeks to permit non-English-speaking children (many from lower class homes) to use their "family language" as the language of school. Such, at least, is the aim its supporters announce. I hear them, and am forced to say no: It is not possible for a child, any child, ever to use his family's language in school. Not to understand this is to misunderstand the public uses of schooling and to trivialize the nature of intimate life.

Memory teaches me what I know of these matters. The boys reminds the adult. I was a bilingual child, but of a certain kind: "socially disadvantaged," the son of working-class parents, both Mexican immigrants.

In the early years of my boyhood, my parents coped very well in America. My father had steady work. My mother managed at home. They were nobody's victims. When we moved to a house many blocks from the Mexican American section of town, they were not intimidated by those two or three neighbors who initially tried to make us unwelcome. ("Keep your brats away from my sidewalk!") But despite all they achieved, or perhaps because they had so much to achieve, they lacked any deep feeling of ease, of belonging in public. They regarded the people at work or in crowds as being very distant from us. Those were the others, *los gringos*. That term was interchangeable in their speech with another, even more telling, *los americanos*.

I grew up in a house where the only regular guests were my relations. On a certain day, enormous families of relatives would visit us, and there would be so many people that the noise and the bodies would spill out to the back-yard and onto the front porch. Then for weeks no one would come. (If the doorbell rang, it was usually a salesman.) Our house stood apart—gaudy yellow in a row of white bungalows. We were the people with the noisy dog, the people who raised chickens. We were the foreigners on the block. A few neighbors would smile and wave at us. We waved back. But until I was seven years old, I did not know the name of the old couple living next door or the names of the kids living across the street.

In public, my father and mother spoke a hesitant, accented, and not always grammatical English. And then they would have to strain, their bodies tense, to catch the sense of what was rapidly said by *los gringos*. At home, they returned to Spanish. The language of their Mexican past sounded in counterpoint to the English spoken in public. The words would come quickly, with ease. Conveyed through those sounds was the pleasing, soothing, consoling reminder that one was at home.

During those years when I was first learning to speak, my mother and father addressed me only in Spanish; in Spanish I learned to reply. By contrast, English *(inglés)* was the language I came to associate with *gringos*, rarely heard in the house. I learned my first words of English overhearing my parents speaking to strangers. At six years of age, I knew just enough words for my mother to trust me on errands to stores one block away—but no more.

I was then a listening child, careful to hear the very different sounds of Spanish and English. Wide-eyed with hearing, I'd listen to sounds more than to words. First, there were English *(gringo)* sounds. So many words still were unknown to me that when the butcher or the lady at the drugstore said something, exotic polysyllabic sounds would bloom in the midst of their sentences. Often the speech of people in public seemed to me very loud, booming with confidence. The man behind the counter would literally ask, "What can I do for you?" But by being so firm and clear, the sound of his voice said that he was a *gringo*; he belonged in public society. There were also the high, nasal notes of middle-class American speech—which I rarely am conscious of hearing today because I hear them so often, but could not stop hearing when I was a boy. Crowds at Safeway or at bus stops were noisy with the birdlike sounds of *los gringos*. I'd move away from them all—all of the chirping chatter above me.

My own sounds I was unable to hear, but I knew that I spoke English poorly. My words could not extend to form complete thoughts. And the words I did speak I didn't know well enough to make distinct sounds. (Listeners would usually lower their heads to hear better what I was trying to say.) But it was one thing for *me* to speak English with difficulty; it was more troubling to hear my parents speaking in public: their high-whining vowels and guttural consonants; their sentences that got stuck with "eh" and "ah" sounds; the confused syntax; the hesitant rhythm of sounds so different from the way *gringos* spoke. I'd notice, moreover, that my parents' voices were softer than those of *gringos* we would meet.

I am tempted to say now that none of this mattered. (In adulthood I am embarrassed by childhood fears.) And, in a way, it didn't matter very much that my parents could not speak English with ease. Their linguistic difficulties had no serious consequences. My mother and father made themselves understood at the county hospital clinic and at government offices. And yet, in another way, it mattered very much. It was unsettling to hear my parents struggle with English. Hearing them, I'd grow nervous, and my clutching trust in their protection and power would be weakened.

There were many times like the night at a brightly lit gasoline station (a blaring white memory) when I stood uneasily hearing my father talk to a teenage attendant. I do not recall what they were saying, but I cannot forget the sounds my father made as he spoke. At one point his words slid together to form one long word—sounds as confused as the threads of blue and green oil in the puddle next to my shoes. His voice rushed through what he had left to say. Toward the end, he reached falsetto notes, appealing to his listener's understanding. I looked away at the lights of passing automobiles. I tried not to hear anymore. But I heard only too well the attendant's reply, his calm, easy tones. Shortly afterward, headed for home, I shivered when my father put his hand on my shoulder. The very first chance that I got, I evaded his grasp and ran on ahead into the dark, skipping with feigned boyish exuberance.

But then there was Spanish: *español*, the language rarely heard away from the house; español, the language which seemed to me therefore a private language, my family's language. To hear its sounds was to feel myself specially recognized as one of the family, apart from *los otros*. A simple remark, an inconsequential comment could convey that assurance. My parents would say something to me and I would feel embraced by the sounds of their words. Those sounds said: *I am speaking with ease in Spanish. I am addressing you in words I never use with* los gringos. *I recognize you as someone special, close, like no one outside. You belong with us. In the family. Ricardo.*

At the age of six, well past the time when most middle-class children no longer notice the difference between sounds uttered at home and words spoken in public, I had a different experience. I lived in a world compounded of sounds. I was a child longer than most. I lived in a magical world, surrounded by sounds both pleasing and fearful. I shared with my family a language enchantingly private—different from that used in the city around us.

Just opening or closing the screen door behind me was an important experience. I'd rarely leave home all alone or without feeling reluctance. Walking down the sidewalk, under the canopy of tall trees, I'd warily notice the (suddenly) silent neighborhood kids who stood warily watching me. Nervously, I'd arrive at the grocery store to hear there the sounds of the *gringos*, reminding me that in this so-big world I was a foreigner. But if leaving home was never routine, neither was coming back. Walking toward our house, climbing the steps from the sidewalk, in summer when the front door was open, I'd hear voices beyond the screen door talking in Spanish. For a second or two I'd stay, linger there listening. Smiling, I'd hear my mother call out, saying in Spanish, "Is that you, Richard?" Those were her words, but all the while her sounds would assure me: *You are home now. Come close inside. With us.*

"*Sí*," I'd reply.

Once more inside the house, I would resume my place in the family. The sounds would grow harder to hear. Once more at home, I would grow less conscious of them. It required, however, no more than the blurt of the doorbell to alert me all over again to listen to sounds. The house would turn instantly quiet while my mother went to the door. I'd hear her hard English sounds. I'd wait to hear her voice turn to soft-sounding Spanish, which assured me, as surely as did the clicking tongue of the lock on the door, that the stranger was gone.

Plainly, it is not healthy to hear such sounds so often. It is not healthy to distinguish public from private sounds so easily. I remained cloistered by sounds, timid and shy in public, too dependent on the voices at home. I remember many nights when my father would come back from work, and I'd hear him call out to my mother in Spanish, sounding relieved. In Spanish, his voice would sound the light and free notes that he never could manage in English. My brother and I would come running into the room where he was with our mother. Our laughing (so deep with the pleasure!) became screaming. Like others who feel the pain of public alienation, we transformed the knowledge of our public separateness into a consoling reminder of our intimacy. Excited, our voices joined in a celebration of sounds. *We are speaking now the way we never speak out in public—we are together*, the sounds told me. Some nights no one seemed willing to loosen the hold that sounds had on us. At dinner we invented new words that sounded Spanish, but made sense only to us. We pieced together new words by taking, say, an English verb and giving it Spanish endings. My mother's instructions at bedtime would be lacquered with mock-urgent tones. Or a word like *sí*, sounded in several notes, would convey added measures of feeling. Tongues lingered around the edges of words, especially fat vowels, and we happily sounded that military drum roll, the twirling roar of the Spanish *r*. Family language, my family's sounds: the voices of my parents and sisters and brother. Their voices insisting: *You belong here. We are family members. Related. Special to one another. Listen!* Voices singing and sighing, rising and straining, then surging, teeming with pleasure which burst syllables into fragments of laughter. At times it seemed there was steady quiet only when, from another room, the rustling whispers of my parents faded and I edged closer to sleep.

Supporters of bilingual education imply today that students like me miss a great deal by not being taught in their family's language. What they seem not to recognize is that, as a socially disadvantaged child, I regarded Spanish as a private language. It was a ghetto language that deepened and strengthened my feeling of separateness. What I needed to learn in school was that I had the right, and the obligation, to speak the public language. The odd truth is that my first-grade classmates could have become bilingual, in the conventional sense of the word, more easily than I. Had they been taught early (as upper-middle-class children often are taught) a "second language" like Spanish or French, they could have regarded it simply as another public language. In my case, such bilingualism could not have been so quickly achieved. What I did not believe was that I could speak a single public language.

Without question, it would have pleased me to have heard my teachers address me in Spanish when I entered the classroom. I would have felt much less afraid. I would have imagined that my instructors were somehow "related" to me; I would indeed have heard their Spanish as my family's language. I would have trusted them and responded with ease. But I would have delayed—postponed for how long?—having to learn the language of public society. I would have evaded—and for how long?—learning the great lesson of school: that I had a public identity.

Fortunately, my teachers were unsentimental about their responsibility. What they understood was that I needed to speak public English. So their voices would search me out, asking me questions. Each time I heard them I'd look up in surprise to see a nun's face frowning at me. I'd mumble, not really meaning to answer. The nun would persist. "Richard, stand up. Don't look at the floor. Speak-up. Speak to the entire class, not just to me!" But I couldn't believe English could be my language to use. (In part, I did not want to believe it.) I continued to mumble. I resisted the teacher's demands. (Did I somehow suspect that once I learned this public language my family life would be changed?) Silent, waiting for the bell to sound, I remained dazed, diffident, afraid.

Because I wrongly imagined that English was intrinsically a public language and Spanish was intrinsically private, I easily noted the difference between classroom language and the language at home. At school, words were directed to a general audience of listeners ("Boys and girls . . .") Words were meaningfully ordered. And the point was not self-expression alone, but to make oneself understood by many others. The teacher quizzed: "Boys and girls, why do we use that word in this sentence? Could we think of a better word to use there? Would the sentence change its meaning if the words were differently arranged? Isn't there a better way of saying much the same thing?" (I couldn't say. I wouldn't try to say.)

Three months passed. Five. A half year. Unsmiling, ever watchful, my teachers noted my silence. They began to connect my behavior with the slow progress my brother and sisters were making. Until, one Saturday morning, three nuns arrived at the house to talk to our parents. Stiffly they sat on the blue living-room sofa. From the doorway of another room, spying on the visitors, I noted the incongruity, the clash of two worlds, the faces and voices of school intruding upon the familiar setting of home. I overheard one voice gently wondering, "Do your children speak only Spanish at home, Mrs. Rodriquez?" While another voice added, "That Richard especially seems so timid and shy."

That Rich-heard!

With great tact, the visitors continued, "Is it possible for you and your husband to encourage your children to practice their English when they are home?" Of course my parents complied. What would they not do for their children's well-being? And how could they question the Church's authority which those women represented? In an instant they agreed to give up the language (the sound) which had revealed and accentuated our family's closeness. The moment after the visitors left, the change was observed. "*Ahora,* speak to us only *en inglés,*" my father and mother told us.

At first, it seemed a kind of game. After dinner each night, the family gathered together to practice "our" English. It was still then *inglés,* a language foreign to us, so we felt drawn to it as strangers. Laughing, we would try to define words we could not pronounce. We played with strange English sounds, often overanglicizing our pronunciations. And we filled the smiling gaps of our sentences with familiar Spanish sounds. But that was cheating, somebody shouted, and everyone laughed.

In school, meanwhile, like my brother and sisters, I was required to attend a daily tutoring session. I needed a full year of this special work. I also needed my teachers to keep my attention from straying in class by calling out, "*Rich-heard*"—their English voices slowly loosening the ties to my other name, with its three notes, *Ri-car-do*. Most of all, I needed to hear my mother and father speak to me in a moment of seriousness in "broken"—suddenly heartbreaking—English. This scene was inevitable. On Saturday morning I entered the kitchen where my parents were talking, but I did not realize that they were talking in Spanish until, the moment they saw me, their voices changed and they began speaking English. The *gringo* sounds they uttered startled me. Pushed me away. In that moment of trivial misunderstanding and profound insight, I felt my throat twisted by unsounded grief. I simply turned and left the room. But I had no place to escape to where I could grieve in Spanish. My brother and sisters were speaking English in another part of the house.

Again and again in the days following, as I grew increasingly angry, I was obliged to hear my mother and father encouraging me: "Speak to us *en inglés*." Only then did I determine to learn classroom English. Thus, sometime afterward it happened: One day in school, I raised my hand to volunteer an answer to a question. I spoke out in a loud voice and I did not think it remarkable when the entire class understood. That day I moved very far from being the disadvantaged child I had been only days earlier. Taken hold at last was the belief, the calming assurance, that I belonged in public.

Shortly after, I stopped hearing the high, troubling sounds of *los gringos*. A more and more confident speaker of English, I didn't listen to *how* strangers sounded when they talked to me. With so many English-speaking people around me, I no longer heard American accents. Conversations quickened. Listening to persons whose voices sounded eccentrically pitched, I might note their sounds for a few seconds, but then I'd concentrate on what they were saying. Now when I heard someone's tone of voice—angry or questioning or sarcastic or happy or sad—I didn't distinguish it from the words it expressed. Sound and word were thus tightly wedded. At the end of each day I was often bemused, and always relieved, to realize how "soundless," though crowded with words, my day in public had been. An eight-year-old boy, I finally came to accept what had been technically true since my birth: I was an American citizen.

But diminished by then was the special feeling of closeness at home. Gone was the desperate, urgent, intense feeling of being at home among those with whom I felt intimate. Our family remained a loving family, but one greatly changed. We were no longer so close, no longer bound tightly together by the knowledge of our separateness from *los gringos*. Neither my older brother nor my sisters rushed home after school anymore. Nor did I. When I arrived home, often there would be neighborhood kids in the house. Or the house would be empty of sounds.

Following the dramatic Americanization of their children, even my parents grew more publicly confident—especially my mother. First she learned the names of all the people on the block. Then she decided we needed to have a telephone in our house. My father, for his part, continued to use the word gringo, but it was no longer charged with bitterness or distrust. Stripped of any emotional content, the word simply became a name for those Americans not of Hispanic descent. Hearing him, sometimes, I wasn't sure if he was pronouncing the Spanish word *gringo*, or saying gringo in English.

There was a new silence at home. As we children learned more and more English, we shared fewer and fewer words with our parents. Sentences needed to be spoken slowly when one of us addressed our mother or father. Often the parent wouldn't understand. The child would need to repeat himself. Still the parent misunderstood. The young voice, frustrated, would end up saying, "Never mind"—the subject was closed. Dinners would be noisy with the clinking of knives and forks against dishes. My mother would smile softly between her remarks; my father, at the other end of the table, would chew and chew his food while he stared over the heads of his children.

My *mother!* My *father!* After English became my primary language, I no longer knew what words to use in addressing my parents. The old Spanish words (those tender accents of sound) I had earlier used—*mamá* and *papá*—I couldn't use anymore. They would have been all-too-painful reminders of how much had changed in my life. On the other hand, the words I heard neighborhood kids call *their* parents seemed equally unsatisfactory. *Mother* and *father*, "ma," "pa," "dad," "pop" (how I hated the all-American sound of that last word)—all these I felt were unsuitable terms of address for *my* parents. As a result, I never used them at home. Whenever I'd speak to my parents, I would try to get their attention by looking at them. In public conversations, I'd refer to them as my "parents" or my "mother" and "father."

My mother and father, for their part, responded differently, as their children spoke to them less. My mother grew restless, seemed troubled and anxious at the scarceness of words exchanged in the house. She would question me about my day when I came home from school. She smiled at my small talk. She pried at the edges of my sentences to get me to say something more. "What . . . ?") She'd join conversations she overheard, but her intrusions often stopped her children's talking. By contrast, my father seemed to grow reconciled to the new quiet. Though his English somewhat improved, he tended more and more to retire into silence. At dinner he spoke very little. One night his children and even his wife helplessly giggled at his garbled English pronunciation of the Catholic "Grace Before Meals." Thereafter he made his wife recite the prayer at the start of each meal, even on formal occasions when there were guests in the house.

Hers became the public voice of the family. On official business it was she, not my father, who would usually talk to strangers on the phone or in stores. We children grew so accustomed to his silence that, years later, we would routinely refer to his "shyness." (My mother often tried to explain: Both of his parents died when he was eight. He was raised by an uncle who treated him as little more than a menial servant. He was never encouraged to speak. He grew up alone. A man of few words.) But I realized my father was not shy, I realized whenever I'd watch him speaking Spanish with relatives. Using Spanish, he was quickly effusive. Especially when talking with other men, his voice would spark, flicker, flare alive with varied sounds. In Spanish, he expressed ideas and feelings he rarely revealed when speaking English. With firm Spanish sounds, he conveyed a confidence and authority that English would never allow him.

The silence at home, however, was not simply the result of fewer words, passing between parents and children. More profound for me was the silence created by my inattention to sounds. At about the time I no longer bothered to listen with care to the sounds of English in public, I grew careless about listening to the sounds made by the family when they spoke. Most of the time I would hear someone speaking at home and didn't distinguish his sounds from the words people uttered in public. I didn't even pay much attention to my parents' accented and ungrammatical speech. At least not at home. Only when I was with them in public would I become alert to their accents. But even then their sounds caused me less and less concern. For I was growing increasingly confident of my own public identity.

I would have been happier about my public success had I not recalled sometimes, what it had been like earlier, when my family conveyed its intimacy through a set of conveniently private sounds. Sometimes in public, hearing a stranger, I'd hark back to my lost past. A Mexican farm worker approached me one day downtown. He wanted directions to some place. "*Hijito*, . . . ?" he said. And his voice stirred old longings. Another time, I was standing beside my mother in the visiting room of a Carmelite convent, before the dense screen which rendered the nuns shadowy figures. I heard several of them speaking Spanish in their busy, singsong, overlapping voices, assuring my mother that, yes, yes, we were remembered, all our family was remembered, in their prayers. Those voices echoed faraway family sounds. Another day, a dark-faced old woman touched my shoulder lightly to steady herself as she boarded a bus. She murmured something to me I couldn't quite comprehend. Her Spanish voice came near, like the face of a never-before-seen relative in the instant before I was kissed. That voice, like so many of the Spanish voices I'd hear in public, recalled the golden age of my childhood.

Bilingual educators say today that children lose a degree of "individuality" by becoming assimilated into public society. (Bilingual schooling is a program popularized in the seventies, that decade when middle-class "ethnics" began to resist the process of assimilation—the "American melting pot.") But the bilingualists oversimplify when they scorn the value and necessity of assimilation. They do not seem to realize that a person is individualized in two ways. So they do not realize that, while one suffers a diminished sense of *private* individuality by being assimilated into public society, such assimilation makes possible the achievement of *public* individuality.

Simplistically again, the bilingualists insist that a student should be reminded of his difference from others in mass society, of his "heritage." But they equate mere separateness with individuality. The fact is that only in private—with intimates—is separateness from the crowd a prerequisite for individuality; an intimate "tells" me that I am unique, unlike all others, apart from the crowd. In public, by contrast, full individuality is achieved, paradoxically, by those who are able to consider themselves members of the crowd. Thus it happened for me. Only when I was able to think of myself as an American, no longer an alien in *gringo* society, could I seek the rights and opportunities necessary for full public individuality. The social and political advantages I enjoy as a man began on the day I came to believe that my name is indeed *Rich-heard Road-ree-guess*. It is true that my public society today is often impersonal; in fact, my public society is usually mass society. But despite the anonymity of the crowd, and despite the fact that the individuality I achieve in public is often tenuous—because it depends on my being one in a crowd— I celebrate the day I acquired my new name. Those middle-class ethnics who scorn assimilation seem to me filled with decadent self-pity, obsessed by the burden of public life. Dangerously, they romanticize public separateness and trivialize the dilemma of those who are truly socially disadvantaged.

If I rehearse here the changes in my private life after my Americanization, it is finally to emphasize a public gain. The loss implies the gain. The house I returned to each afternoon was quiet. Intimate sounds no longer greeted me at the door. Inside there were other noises. The telephone rang. Neighborhood kids ran past the door of the bedroom where I was reading my schoolbooks—covered with brown shopping-bag paper. Once I learned the public language, it would never again be easy for me to hear intimate family voices. More and more of my day was spent hearing words, not sounds. But that may only be a way of saying that on the day I raised my hand in class and spoke loudly to an entire roomful of faces, my childhood started to end.

Vermeer in Bosnia

Lawrence Weschler

I happened to be in The Hague a while back, sitting in on the preliminary hearings of the Yugoslav War Crimes Tribunal—specifically, those related to the case of Dusko Tadic, the only one of more than forty accused war criminals whom the Tribunal had actually been able to get its hands on up to that point. While there, I had occasion to talk with some of the principal figures involved in this unprecedented judicial undertaking.

At one point, for instance, I was having lunch with Antonio Cassese, a distinguished Italian jurist who has been serving for the past two years as the president of the court (the head of its international panel of eleven judges). He'd been rehearsing for me some of the more gruesome stories that have crossed his desk—maybe not the most gruesome but just the sort of thing he has to contend with every day and which perhaps accounts for the sense of urgency he brings to his mission. The story, for instance, of a soccer player. As Cassese recounted, "Famous guy, a Muslim. When he was captured, they said, "Aren't you So-and-So?" He admitted he was. So they broke both his legs, handcuffed him to a radiator, and forced him to watch as they repeatedly raped his wife and two daughters and then slit their throats. After that, he begged to be killed himself, but his tormentors must have realized that the cruelest thing they could possibly do to him now would simply be to set him free, which they did. Somehow, this man was able to make his way to some U. N. investigators, and told them about his ordeal—a few days after which, he committed suicide." Or, for instance, as Cassese went on, "some of the tales about Tadic himself, how, in addition to the various rapes and murders he's accused of, he is alleged to have supervised the torture and torments of a particular group of Muslim prisoners, at one point forcing one of his charges to emasculate another—*with his teeth*. The one fellow died, and the guy who bit him went mad."

Stories like that: one judge's daily fare. And, at one point, I asked Judge Cassese how, regularly obliged to gaze into such an appalling abyss, he had kept from going mad himself. His face brightened. "Ah," he said with a smile. "You see, as often as possible I make my way over to the Mauritshuis museum, in the center of town, so as to spend a little time with the Vermeers."

Sitting there over lunch with Cassese, I'd been struck by the perfect apt-
ness of his impulse. I, too, had been spending time with the Vermeers at
the Mauritshuis, and at the Rijksmuseum, in Amsterdam, as well. For
Vermeer's paintings, almost uniquely in the history of art, radiate "a cen-
teredness, a peacefulness, a serenity" (as Cassese put it), a sufficiency, a
sense of perfectly equipoised grace. In his exquisite *Study of Vermeer*, Edward
Snow had deployed as epigraph a line from Andrew Forge's essay "Painting
and the Struggle for the Whole Self," which reads, "In ways that I do not
pretend to understand fully, painting deals with the only issues that seem
to me to count in our benighted time—freedom, autonomy, fairness, love."
And I've often found myself agreeing with Snow's implication that somehow these issues may be more richly and fully addressed in Vermeer than
anywhere else.

But that afternoon with Cassese I had a sudden further intuition as to the
true extent of Vermeer's achievement—something I hadn't fully grasped before.
For, of course, when Vermeer was painting those images, which for us have
become the very emblem of peacefulness and serenity, *all Europe was Bosnia*
(or had only just recently ceased to be): awash in incredibly vicious wars of
religious persecution and proto-nationalist formation, wars of an at-that-time
unprecedented violence and cruelty, replete with sieges and famines and mas-
sacres and mass rapes, unspeakable tortures and wholesale devastation. To be
sure, the sense of Holland during Vermeer's lifetime which we are usually
given—that of the country's so-called Golden Age—is one of becalmed,
burgherlike efficiency; but that Holland, to the extent that it ever existed,
was of relatively recent provenance, and even then under a continual threat
of being overwhelmed once again.

Jan Vermeer was born in 1632, sixteen years before the end of the Thirty
Years' War, which virtually shredded neighboring Germany and repeatedly tore
into the Netherlands as well. Between 1652 and 1674, England and the United
Provinces of the Netherlands went to war three times, and though most of
the fighting was confined to sea battles, the wars were not without their consequences for the Dutch mainland: Vermeer's Delft, in particular, suffered
terrible devastation in 1654, when some eighty thousand pounds of gunpowder
in the town's arsenal accidentally exploded, killing hundreds, including
Vermeer's great contemporary, the painter Carel Fabritius. (By the conclusion of those wars, the Dutch had ended up ceding New Amsterdam to the
British, who quickly changed its name to New York.) These were years of
terrible religious conflict throughout Europe—the climaxes of both the
Reformation and the Counter-Reformation and their various splintering progeny. And though the Dutch achieved an enviable atmosphere of tolerance during this period, Holland was regularly overrun with refugees from religious
conflicts elsewhere. (Vermeer himself, incidentally, was a convert to

Catholicism, which was a distinctly minority creed in the Dutch context.) Finally, in 1672, the Dutch fell under the murderous assault of France's Louis XIV and were subjected to a series of campaigns that lasted until 1678. In fact, the ensuing devastation of the Dutch economy and Vermeer's own resulting bankruptcy may have constituted a proximate cause of the painter's early death, by stroke, in 1675: he was only forty-two.

Another preliminary session of the Tribunal was scheduled for late in the afternoon of the day I had lunch with Judge Cassese, and, following our conversation, I decided to spend the intervening hours at the Mauritshuis. On the taxi ride out, as I looked through a Vermeer catalogue, I began to realize that, in fact, the pressure of all that violence (remembered, imagined, foreseen) is what those paintings are all about. Of course, not directly—in fact, quite the opposite: the literary critic Harry Berger, in his essays on Vermeer, frequently invokes the notion of the "conspicuous exclusion" of themes that are saturatingly present but only as *felt absence*—themes that are being held at bay, but conspicuously so. It's almost as if Vermeer can be seen, and the horrors of his age, to have been asserting or *inventing* the very idea of peace. But Hobbes's state of nature, or state of war (Hobbes: 1588–1679; Vermeer: 1632–75), is everywhere adumbrated around the edges of Vermeer's achievement. That's what the roaring lions carved into the chair posts are all about—those and also the maps on the wall. The maps generally portray the Netherlands, but the whole point is that during Vermeer's lifetime the political and geographic dispensation of the Netherlands, the distribution of its Protestants and Catholics, the grim legacy of its only just recently departed Spanish overlords, and the still current threats posed by its English and French neighbors—all these matters were still actively, and sometimes bloodily, being contested. When soldiers visit young girls in Vermeer's paintings, where does one think they have been off soldiering—and why, one wonders, does the country need all those civic guards? When pregnant young women are standing still, bathed in the window light, intently reading those letters, where is one invited to imagine the letters are coming from?

Or consider the magisterial *View of Delft*—as I now did, having arrived at the Mauritshuis and taken a seat before the magnificent canvas up on the second floor. It is an image of unalloyed civic peace and quiet. But it is also the image of a town only just emerging from a downpour, the earth in the foreground still saturated with moisture, the walls of the town bejeweled with wet, the dark clouds breaking up at last, and the sunlight breaking through, though not just anywhere: a shaft of fresh, clean light gets lavished on one spire in particular, that of the radiantly blond Nieuwe Kerk, in whose interior, as any contemporary of Vermeer's would doubtless have known, stands the mausoleum of William the Silent, one of the heroes of the wars of Dutch independence, assassinated in Delft at the end of the previous century by a French Catholic fanatic.

I found myself being reminded of a moment in my own life, over twenty-five years ago. I was in college and Nixon had just invaded Cambodia and we were, of course, all up in arms; the college had convened as a committee of the whole in the dining commons—the students, the professors, the administrators—what were we going to do? How were we going to respond? Our distinguished American history professor got up and declared this moment *the* crisis of American history. Not to be outdone, our eminent new-age classicist got up and declared it the crisis of *universal* history. And we all nodded our fervent concurrence. But then our visiting religious historian from England—a tall, lanky lay-Catholic theologian, as it happened, with something of the physical bearing of Abraham Lincoln—got up and suggested mildly, "We really ought to have a little modesty in our crises. I suspect," he went on, "that the people during the Black Plague must have thought they were in for a bit of a scrape."

Having momentarily lanced our fervor, he went on to allegorize, deploying the story of Jesus on the Waters (from Matthew 8:23–27). "Jesus," he reminded us, "needed to get across the sea of Galilee with his disciples, so they all boarded a small boat, whereupon Jesus quickly fell into a nap. Presently a storm kicked up, and the disciples, increasingly edgy, finally woke Jesus up. He told them not to worry, everything would be all right, whereupon he fell back into his nap. The storm meanwhile grew more and more intense, winds slashing the ever-higher waves. The increasingly anxious disciples woke Jesus once again, who once again told them not to worry and again fell back asleep. And still the storm worsened, now tossing the little boat violently all to and fro. The disciples, beside themselves with terror, awoke Jesus one more time, who now said, 'Oh ye of little faith'—that's where that phrase comes from—and then proceeded to pronounce, 'Peace!' Whereupon the storm instantaneously subsided and calm returned to the water." Our historian waited a few moments as we endeavored to worry out the glancing relevance of this story. "It seems to me," he finally concluded, "that what that story is trying to tell us is simply that in times of storm, we mustn't allow the storm to enter ourselves, rather we have to find peace inside ourselves and then breathe it out."

And it now seemed to me, sitting among the Vermeers that afternoon at the Mauritshuis, that that was precisely what the Master of Delft had been about in his life's work: at a tremendously turbulent juncture in the history of his continent, he had been finding—and, yes, inventing—a zone filled with peace, a small room, an intimate vision . . .and then breathing it out.

It's one of the great things about great works of art that they can bear—and, indeed, that they invite—a superplenitude of possible readings, some of them contradictory. One of the most idiosyncratic responses to Vermeer I have ever encountered was that of the Afrikaner poet and painter Breyten Breytenbach during a walk we took one morning through the galleries of New York's Metropolitan Museum. Breytenbach, who was a clandestine anti-apartheid activist, had only recently emerged from seven years of incarceration in the monochrome dungeons of the apartheid regime, and most of his comments that morning had to do with the lusciousness of all the colors in the paintings we were passing. For the most part though, we were silent, moving at a fairly even pace from room to room—that is, until we came to Vermeer's painting of the young girl in the deep-blue skirt standing by a window, her hand poised on a silver pitcher, the window light spreading evenly across a map on the wall behind her. Here Breytenbach stopped cold for many moments, utterly absorbed. "Huh," he said finally, pointing to the gallery's caption giving the date of the painting: circa 1664–65. "It's hard to believe how from all that serenity emerge the *Boere*. Look." He jabbed a finger at the little boats delicately daubed on the painted map's painted coastline. "*That's them leaving right now!*" (And, indeed, Cape Town had been founded by the Dutch East India Company only a decade earlier, and would soon start filling up with some of the Huguenots who had flooded into Holland following a fresh upsurge of repression back in France.)

Edward Snow, for his part, makes quite a convincing case that Vermeer's art is above all about sexuality and as such provides one of the most profound explorations of the wellsprings of the erotic in the entire Western tradition. It is about female reserve and autonomy and self-sufficiency in the face of the male gaze, Snow suggests, or even in the seeming absence of such a gaze.

In this context, the pièce de résistance in his argument is a brilliantly sustained twenty-page close reading of Vermeer's magnificent (though uncannily diminutive) *Head of a Young Girl*—sometimes referred to, alternatively, as *The Girl in a Turban* or *The Girl with a Pearl* (at the Mauritshuis, it happens to face *The View of Delft*, just across the room). Snow's approach to this overexposed and by now almost depleted image is to ask, Has the girl just turned toward us or is she just about to turn away? Looked at with this question in mind, it does seem that such immanence, one way or the other, is of its essence. As Snow points out, if we momentarily blot out the face itself, everything else conspires to make us expect a simple profile of a head—so that afterward, as we allow ourselves to look again on the face unobstructed, the girl does seem to have only just now turned to face us. But if we look for a moment at the pendant of cloth cascading down from the knot at the top of her turban, it seems at first as if that pendant ought to fall behind her far shoulder; in fact it falls far forward, provoking a visual torsion precisely opposite to that of the one we'd surmised earlier: no, on second thought, she seems to be pulling away. The answer is that she's actually doing both. This is a woman who has just turned toward us and is already about to look away: and the melancholy of the moment, with its impending sense of loss, is transferred from her eyes to the tearlike pearl dangling from her ear. *It's an entire movie in a single frozen image.* (One is in turn reminded of the obverse instance of Chris Marker's ravishing short film in 1962, *La Jetée*, a Vermeer-saturated romance made up entirely of still shots unfurling evenly, hypnotically, one after the next, with the sole exception of a single moving-picture sequence: the woman asleep in bed, her eyes closed, her eyes opening to gaze up at us, and then closing once again. A sequence that passes so quickly—in the blink, we say, of an eye—that it's only moments later that we even register its having been a moving-picture sequence at all.)

The girl's lips are parted in a sudden intake of breath—much, we suddenly notice, as are our own as we gaze back upon her. And in fact an astonishing transmutation has occurred. In the moment of painting, it was Vermeer who'd been looking at the girl and registering the imminent turning-away of her attention (the speculation among some critics that Vermeer's model for this image may have been his daughter renders the conceit all the more poignant); subsequently, it was, of course, the painted image that would stay frozen in time, eternally attentive, while it was he as artist who'd eventually be the one turning away; and, still later, it would be Vermeer himself who, through the girl's gaze, would remain faithful, whereas it would be we viewers, casually wandering through the museum and tarrying before the image for a few, breath-inheld moments, who would be the ones eventually turning away. *The Head of a Young Girl* thus becomes a picture about presence and eternity, or, at any rate, posterity.

But this is only because it is first and foremost a painting about intersubjectivity: about the autonomy, the independent agency, dignity, and self-sufficiency of the Other, in whose eyes we in turn are likewise autonomous, self-sufficient, suffuse with individual dignity and potential agency. And here is where we come full circle: because if Vermeer's work can be said to be one extended invention—or assertion—of a certain concept of peace-filledness, this is precisely how he's doing it, by imagining or asserting the possibility of such an autonomous, inhabited sense of selfhood.

The scale of Vermeer's achievement becomes even clearer if, like me, you have a chance to walk among some of the genre pieces by Vermeer's Dutch contemporaries, also scattered about the Mauritshuis (it was getting late now and I wanted to make it back for the final session of the preliminary Tadic hearing, but I did tarry for a few minutes longer in some of the museum's adjoining rooms).

For many years, Vermeer's works were themselves seen primarily as instances of these sorts of moralizing genre images. The Metropolitan's *Girl Asleep* was thus cast as yet another castigating allegory of feminine sloth and drunkenness, while Berlin's *Woman Putting on Pearls* was folded into the tradition of vanity motifs. The Fricks' *Officer and Laughing Girl* was assigned to the tradition of vaguely unsavory prostitution images (as, naturally, was Dresden's *Procuress*, from earlier in Vermeer's career); conversely, the Louvre's *Lacemaker* was seen in the context of more positively tinged illustrations of industriousness, and the Rijksmuseum's *Milkmaid* was cast as yet another prototypically Dutch celebration of the domestic virtues. All of which misses the essential point, because in each of these instances and in virtually every other one of his paintings, Vermeer deploys the conventional iconography precisely so as to upend it. No, his paintings all but cry out, this person is not to be seen as merely a type, a trope, an allegory. If she is standing in for anything, she is standing for the condition of being a unique individual human being, worthy of our own unique individual response. (Which is more than can be said, generally, for the men in Vermeer's paintings, who do seem, hovering there beside the women, to stand in for the condition of being somewhat oafishly de trop.)

Or so, anyway, I found myself thinking in the taxi as I returned to the Tribunal—of that and of the way in which the entire Yugoslavian debacle has been taking place in a context wherein the Other, even one's own neighbor, is suddenly being experienced no longer as a subject like oneself but as an instance, a type, a vile expletive, a Serb, a Croat, a Turk, and, as such, preordained for an ages-old, inevitable fate. (Note that such a construction has to be as assiduously "invented" as its obverse: people who've been living in relative peace for decades have to be goaded into seeing one another, once again, in this manner.) No wonder that Cassese flees to Vermeer for surcease.

A Dutch journalist named Alfred van Cleef recently published a remarkable book, *De Verloren Wereld van de Familie Berberovic (The Lost World of the Berberovic Family)*, in which he traces the downward spiral of the last five years in Yugoslavia through the shattered prism of one Bosnian family's experience. Early in his narrative, he recounts how the war came to the Berberovic family's village, how for many months its members had been picking up the increasingly strident harangues welling out from the Belgrade and Zagreb television stations but hadn't worried because theirs was a peaceful village, where Serbs and Croats and Muslims lived equably together, with a high degree of intermarriage, and so forth. Then the war was just two valleys over, but still they didn't worry, and then it was in the very next valley, but, even so, no one could imagine its actually intruding into their quiet lives. But one day a car suddenly careered into the village's central square, four young men in militia uniforms leaping out, purposefully crossing the square, seeming to single out a particular house and cornering its occupant, whereupon the leader of the militiamen calmly leveled a gun at the young man and blew him away. The militiamen hustled back to their car and sped off. As van Cleef subsequently recounted the incident for me, "They left behind them a village almost evenly divided. Those under fifty years of age had been horrified by the seeming randomness of the act, while those over fifty realized, with perhaps even greater horror, that the young man who'd just been killed was the son of a man who, back during the partisan struggles of the Second World War, happened to have killed the uncle of the kid who'd just done the killing. And the older villagers immediately realized, with absolute clarity, that if this was now possible everything was going to be possible."

David Rieff tells a story about visiting a recent battlefield at one point during the war in the company of a small band of fellow journalists: Muslim corpses strewn across the muddy meadow, a Serb soldier grimly standing guard. "'So,' we asked the soldier, this young kid," Rieff recalls, 'What happened here?' At which point the soldier took a drag on this cigarette and began, 'Well, in 1385 . . .'"

Yugoslavia today has been turned back into one of those places where people not only seem incapable of forgetting the past but barely seem capable of thinking about anything else: the Serbs and Croats and Muslims now appear to be so deeply mired in a poisonous legacy of grievances, extending back fifty years, two hundred years—indeed, all the way back to the fourteenth century—that it's almost as if the living had been transformed into pale, wraithlike shades haunting the ghosts of the long-dead rather than the other way around.

Which is to say that we're back in the moral universe of epic poetry: the Iliad, Beowulf, the Chanson de Roland, the Mahabharata, and, of course, *Finnegans Wake*—a modernist recasting of the entire epic tradition, composed during the thirties by James Joyce, who once characterized history as "two bloody Irishmen in a bloody fight over bloody nothing." Not so much over bloody nothing, perhaps, as vengeance for vengeance for vengeance for who-longer-knows-what? That's the heart of the epic tradition: those twinned themes of the relentless maw of vengeance and the ludicrous incommensurability of its first causes recur time and again, from one culture to the next. It's worth remembering how, also during the thirties, when the great Harvard classicist Milman Parry was trying to crack the Homeric code—to determine just how the ancient Greek bards were able to improvise such incredibly long poems, and what mnemonic devices they had devised to assist them—he scoured the world for places where such oral epic traditions were still alive, and the place he finally settled on as perfect for his purposes was Yugoslavia (see his disciple Albert Lord's seminal account in *The Singer of Tales*).

Vermeer was not a painter in the epic tradition: on the contrary, his life's work can be seen, within its historical moment, as a heroic, extended attempt to steer his (and his viewers') way clear of such a depersonalizing approach to experiencing one's fellow human beings. It was a project, I now realized, as I took my seat in the visitors' gallery facing the Tribunal's glassed-in hearing room, not all that dissimilar from that of the Tribunal itself.

The day before, I'd spoken with Richard Goldstone, the eminent South African jurist who has been serving as the Yugoslav Tribunal's lead prosecutor. (He is serving the same role on the Tribunal that has been established to prosecute the war criminals in Rwanda.) I'd asked him how he envisioned the mission of the Tribunal, and he'd described it as nothing less than a breaking of the historic cycle of vengeance-inspired ethnic mayhem. He does not believe in the inevitability of such violence. "For the great majority of their histories, the Croats and Serbs and Muslims, and the Tutsis and Hutus, have lived in relative peace with one another—and they were all doing that relatively nicely once again until just recently," he told me. "Such interethnic violence usually gets stoked by specific individuals intent on immediate political or material advantage, who then call forth the legacies of earlier and previously unaddressed grievances. But the guilt for the violence that results does not adhere to the entire group. Specific individuals bear the major share of the responsibility, and it is they, not the group as a whole, who need to be held to account, through a fair and meticulously detailed presentation and evaluation of evidence, precisely so that the next time around no one will be able to claim that all Serbs did this, or all Croats or all Hutus—so that people are able to see how it is specific individuals in their communities who are continually endeavoring to manipulate them in that fashion. I really believe that this is the only way the cycle can be broken."

The preliminary hearings now resumed. Tadic was seated in a sort of aquarium of bulletproof glass, a panoply of high-text gadgetry arrayed all around him and around the various lawyers and judges: instantaneous-translation devices, video cameras and monitors, computerized evidence screens, and so forth.

Inventing peace: I found myself thinking of Vermeer with his camera obscura—an empty box fronted by a lens through which the chaos of the world might be drawn in and tamed back to a kind of sublime order. And I found myself thinking of these people here with their legal chamber, the improbably calm site for a similar effort at transmutation.

I looked up at the TV monitor: the automated camera was evidently scanning the room. It caught the prosecutors in their flowing robes shuffling papers, the judges, the defense table, and now Tadic himself. The camera lingered on him—a handsome young man, improbably dapper in a navy-blue jacket and

231

a gleaming white open-collared dress shirt—and then zeroes in for a closer shot of his face.

There he was, not some symbol or trope or a stand-in for anybody other than himself: a quite specific individual, in all his sublime self-sufficiency; a man of whom, as it happened, terrible, terrible allegations had been made, and who was now going to have to face those allegations, stripped of any rationales except his own autonomous free agency.

For a startling split second, he looked up at the camera. And then he looked away.

The Great Branches
of Learning

E.O. Wilson

You will see at once why I believe that the Enlightenment thinkers of the seventeenth and eighteenth centuries got it mostly right the first time. The assumptions they made of a lawful material world, the intrinsic unity of knowledge, and the potential of indefinite human progress are the ones we still take most readily into our hearts, suffer without, and find maximally rewarding through intellectual advance. The greatest enterprise of the mind has always been and always will be the attempted linkage of the sciences and humanities. The ongoing fragmentation of knowledge and resulting chaos in philosophy are not reflections of the real world but artifacts of scholarship. The propositions of the original Enlightenment are increasingly favored by objective evidence, especially from the natural sciences.

Consilience is the key to unification. I prefer this word over "coherence" because its rarity has preserved its precision, whereas coherence has several possible meanings, only one of which is consilience. William Whewell, in his 1840 synthesis *The Philosophy of the Inductive Sciences,* was the first to speak of consilience, literally a "jumping together" of knowledge by the linking of facts and fact-based theory across disciplines to create a common groundwork of explanation. He said, "The Consilience of Inductions takes place when an Induction, obtained from one class of facts, coincides with an Induction, obtained from another different class. This Consilience is a test of the truth of the Theory in which it occurs."

The only way either to establish or to refute consilience is by methods developed in the natural sciences—not, I hasten to add, an effort led by scientists, or frozen in mathematical abstraction, but rather one allegiant to the habits of thought that have worked so well in exploring the material universe.

The belief in the possibility of consilience beyond science and across the great branches of learning is not yet science. It is a metaphysical world view, and a minority one at that, shared by only a few scientists and philosophers. It cannot be proved with logic from first principles or grounded in any definitive set of empirical tests, at least not by any yet conceived. Its best support is no more than an extrapolation of the consistent past success of the natural sciences. Its surest test will be its effectiveness in the social sciences and humanities. The strongest appeal of consilience is in the prospect of intellectual adventure and, given even modest success, the value of understanding the human condition with a higher degree of certainty.

Bear with me while I cite an example to illustrate the claim just made. Think of two intersecting lines forming a cross, and picture the four quadrants thus created. Label one quadrant environmental policy, the next ethics, the next biology, and the final one social science.

environmental policy	ethics
social science	biology

We already intuitively think of these four domains as closely connected, so that rational inquiry in one informs reasoning in the other three. Yet undeniably each stands apart in the contemporary academic mind. Each has its own practitioners, language, modes of analysis, and standards of validation. The result is confusion, and confusion was correctly identified by Francis Bacon four centuries ago as the most fatal of errors, which "occurs wherever argument or inference passes from one world of experience to another."

Next draw a series of concentric circles around the point of intersection.

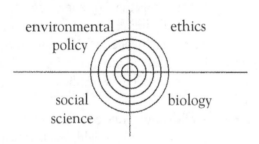

As we cross the circles inward toward the point at which the quadrants meet, we find ourselves in an increasingly unstable and disorienting region. The ring closest to the intersection, where most real-world problems exist, is the one in which fundamental analysis is most needed. Yet virtually no maps exist. Few concepts and words serve to guide us. Only in imagination can we travel clockwise from the recognition of environmental problems and the need for soundly based policy; to the selection of solutions based on moral reasoning; to the biological foundations of that reasoning; to a grasp of social institutions as the products of biology, environment, and history. And thence back to environmental policy.

Consider this example. Governments everywhere are at a loss as to the best policy for regulating the dwindling forest reserves of the world. There are few established ethical guidelines from which agreement might be reached, and those are based on an insufficient knowledge of ecology. Even if adequate scientific knowledge were available, there would still be little basis for the long-term valuation of forests. The economics of sustainable yield is still a primitive art, and the psychological benefits of natural ecosystems are almost wholly unexplored.

The time has come to achieve the tour in reality. This is not an idle exercise for the delectation of intellectuals. How wisely policy is chosen will depend on the ease with which the educated public, not just intellectuals and political leaders, can think around these and similar circuits, starting at any point and, moving in any direction.

To ask if consilience can be gained in the innermost domains of the circles, such that sound judgment will flow easily from one discipline to another, is equivalent to asking whether, in the gathering of disciplines, specialists can ever reach agreement on a common body of abstract principles and evidentiary proof. I think they can. Trust in consilience is the foundation of the natural sciences. For the material world at least, the momentum is overwhelmingly toward conceptual unity. Disciplinary boundaries within the natural sciences are disappearing, to be replaced by shifting hybrid domains in which consilience is implicit. These domains reach across many levels of complexity, from chemical physics and physical chemistry to molecular genetics, chemical ecology, and ecological genetics. None of the new specialties is considered more than a focus of research. Each is an industry of fresh ideas and advancing technology.

Given that human action comprises events of physical causation, why should the social sciences and humanities be impervious to consilience with the natural sciences? And how can they fail to benefit from that alliance? It is not enough to say that human action is historical, and that history is an unfolding of unique events. Nothing fundamental separates the course of human history from the course of physical history, whether in the stars or in organic diversity. Astronomy, geology, and evolutionary biology are examples of primarily historical disciplines linked by consilience to the rest of the natural sciences. History is today a fundamental branch of learning in its own right, down to the finest detail. But if ten thousand humanoid histories could be traced on ten thousand Earthlike planets, and from a comparative study of those histories empirical tests and principles evolved, historiography—the explanation of historical trends—would already be a natural science.

The unification agenda does not sit well with a few professional philosophers. The subject I address they consider their own, to be expressed in their language, their framework of formal thought. They will draw this indictment: *conflation, simplism, ontological reductionism, scientism,* and other sins made official by the hissing suffix. To which I plead guilty, guilty, guilty. Now let us move on, thus. Philosophy plays a vital role in intellectual synthesis, and it keeps us alive to the power and continuity of thought through the centuries. It also peers into the future to give shape to the unknown—and that has always been its vocation of choice. One of its most distinguished practitioners, Alexander Rosenberg, has recently argued that philosophy in fact addresses just two issues: the questions that the sciences—physical, biological, and social—cannot answer, and the reasons for that incapacity. "Now of course," he concludes, "there may not be any questions that the sciences cannot answer eventually, in the long run, when all the facts are in, but certainly there are questions that the sciences cannot answer *yet.*" This assessment is admirably clear and honest and convincing. It neglects, however, the obvious fact that scientists are equally qualified to judge what remains to be discovered, and why. There has never been a better time for collaboration between scientists and philosophers, especially where they meet in the borderlands between biology, the social sciences, and the humanities. We are approaching a new age of synthesis, when the testing of consilience is the greatest of all intellectual challenges. Philosophy, the contemplation of the unknown, is a shrinking dominion. We have the common goal of turning as much philosophy as possible into science.

If the world really works in a way so as to encourage the consilience of knowledge, I believe the enterprises of culture will eventually fall out into science, by which I mean the natural sciences, and the humanities, particularly the creative arts. These domains will be the two great branches of learning in the twenty-first century. The social sciences will continue to split within each of its disciplines, a process already rancorously begun, with one part folding into or becoming continuous with biology, the other fusing with the humanities. Its disciplines will continue to exist but in radically altered form. In the process the humanities, ranging from philosophy and history to moral reasoning, comparative religion, and interpretation of the arts, will draw closer to the sciences and partly fuse with them. Of these several subjects I will say more in later chapters.

I admit that the confidence of natural scientists often seems overweening. Science offers the boldest metaphysics of the age. It is a thoroughly human construct, driven by the faith that if we dream, press to discover, explain, and dream again, thereby plunging repeatedly into new terrain, the world will somehow come clearer and we will grasp the true strangeness of the universe. And the strangeness will all prove to be connected and make sense.

In his 1941 classic *Man on His Nature,* the British neurobiologist Charles Sherrington spoke of the brain as an enchanted loom, perpetually weaving a picture of the external world, tearing down and reweaving, inventing other worlds, creating a miniature universe. The communal mind of literate societies—world culture—is an immensely larger loom. Through science it has gained the power to map external reality far beyond the reach of a single mind, and through the arts the means to construct narratives, images, and rhythms immeasurably more diverse than the products of any solitary genius. The loom is the same for both enterprises, for science and for the arts, and there is a general explanation of its origin and nature and thence of the human condition, proceeding from the deep history of genetic evolution to modern culture. Consilience of causal explanation is the means by which the single mind can travel most swiftly and surely from one part of the communal mind to the other.

In education the search for consilience is the way to renew the crumbling structure of the liberal arts. During the past thirty years the ideal of the unity of learning, which the Renaissance and Enlightenment bequeathed us, has been largely abandoned. With rare exceptions American universities and colleges have dissolved their curriculum into a slurry of minor disciplines and specialized courses. While the average number of undergraduate courses per institution doubled, the percentage of mandatory courses in general education dropped by more than half. Science was sequestered in the same period; as I write, in 1997, only a third of universities and colleges require students to take at least one course in the natural sciences. The trend cannot be reversed by force-feeding students with some-of-this and some-of-that across the branches of learning. Win or lose, true reform will aim at the consilience of science with the social sciences and humanities in scholarship and teaching. Every college student should be able to answer the following question: What is the relation between science and the humanities, and how is it important for human welfare?

Every public intellectual and political leader should be able to answer that question as well. Already half the legislation coming before the United States Congress contains important scientific and technological components. Most of the issues that vex humanity daily—ethnic conflict, arms escalation, overpopulation, abortion, environment, endemic poverty, to cite several most persistently before us—cannot be solved without integrating knowledge from the natural sciences with that of the social sciences and humanities. Only fluency across the boundaries will provide a clear view of the world as it really is, not as seen through the lens of ideologies and religious dogmas or commanded by myopic response to immediate need. Yet the vast majority of our political leaders are trained exclusively in the social sciences and humanities, and have little or no knowledge of the natural sciences. The same is true of the public intellectuals, the columnists, the media interrogators, and think-tank gurus. The best of their analyses are careful and responsible, and sometimes correct, but the substantive base of their wisdom is fragmented and lopsided.

A balanced perspective cannot be acquired by studying disciplines in pieces but through pursuit of the consilience among them. Such unification will come hard. But I think it is inevitable. Intellectually it rings true, and it gratifies impulses that rise from the admirable side of human nature. To the extent that the gaps between the great branches of learning can be narrowed, diversity and depth of knowledge will increase. They will do so because of, not despite, the underlying cohesion achieved. The enterprise is important for yet another reason: It gives ultimate purpose to intellect. It promises that order, not chaos, lies beyond the horizon. I think it inevitable that we will accept the adventure, go there, and find out.

Research & Scientific Reasoning

Hiroshima

John Berger

The whole incredible problem begins with the need to reinsert those events of 6 August 1945 back into living consciousness.

I was shown a book last year at the Frankfurt Book Fair. The editor asked me some question about what I thought of its format. I glanced at it quickly and gave some reply. Three months ago I was sent a finished copy of the book. It lay on my desk unopened. Occasionally its title and cover picture caught my eye, but I did not respond. I didn't consider the book urgent, for I believed that I already knew about what I would find within it.

Did I not clearly remember the day—I was in the army in Belfast—when we first heard the news of the bomb dropped on Hiroshima? At how many meetings during the first nuclear disarmament movement had I and others not recalled the meaning of that bomb?

And then, one morning last week, I received a letter from America, accompanying an article written by a friend. This friend is a doctor of philosophy and a Marxist. Furthermore, she is a very generous and warm-hearted woman. The article was about the possibilities of a third world war. Vis-à-vis the Soviet Union she took, I was surprised to read, a position very close to Reagan's. She concluded by evoking the likely scale of destruction which would be caused by nuclear weapons, and then welcomed the positive possibilities that this would offer the socialist revolution in the United States.

It was on that morning that I opened and read the book on my desk. It is called *Unforgettable Fire*.

The book consists of drawings and paintings made by people who were in Hiroshima on the day that the bomb was dropped, thirty-six years ago today. Often the pictures are accompanied by a verbal record of what the image represents. None of them is by a professional artist. In 1974, an old man went to the television centre in Hiroshima to show to whoever was interested a picture he had painted, entitled 'At about 4pm, 6th August 1945, near Yurozuyo bridge'.

This prompted an idea of launching a television appeal to other survivors of that day to paint or draw their memories of it. Nearly a thousand

241

pictures were sent in, and these were made into an exhibition. The appeal was worded: 'Let us leave for posterity pictures about the atomic bomb, drawn by citizens.'

Clearly, my interest in these pictures cannot be an art-critical one. One does not musically analyze screams. But after repeatedly looking at them, what began as an impression became a certainty. These were images of hell.

I am not using the word as hyperbole. Between these paintings by women and men who have never painted anything else since leaving school, and who have surely, for the most part, never traveled outside Japan, between these traced memories which had to be exorcised, and the numerous representations of hell in European medieval art, there is a very close affinity.

This affinity is both stylistic and fundamental. And fundamentally it is to do with the situations depicted. The affinity lies in the degree of the multiplication of pain, in the lack of appeal or aid, in the pitilessness, in the equality of wretchedness, and in the disappearance of time.

I am 78 years old. I was living at Midorimachi on the day of the A-bomb blast. Around 9 am that morning, when I looked out of my window, I saw several women coming along the street one after another towards the Hiroshima prefectural hospital. I realized for the first time, as it is sometimes said, that when people are very much frightened hair really does stand on end. The women's hair was, in fact, standing straight up and the skin of their arms was peeled off. I suppose they were around 30 years old.

Time and again, the sober eyewitness accounts recall the surprise and horror of Dante's verses about the Inferno. The temperature at the centre of the Hiroshima fireball was 300,000 degrees centigrade. The survivors are called in Japanese *hibakuska*—'those who have seen hell'.

Suddenly, one man who was stark naked came up to me and said in a quavering voice, 'Please help me!' He was burned and swollen all over from the effects of the A-bomb. Since I did not recognize him as my neighbour, I asked who he was. He answered that he was Mr. Sasaki, the son of Mr. Ennosuke Sasaki, who had a lumber shop in Funairi town. That morning he had been doing volunteer labour service, evacuating the houses near the prefectural office in Kato town. He had been burned black all over and had started back to his home in Funairi. He looked miserable—burned and sore, and naked with only pieces of his gaiters trailing behind as he walked. Only the part of his hair covered by his soldier's hat was left, as if he was wearing a bowl. When I touched him, his burned skin slipped off. I did not know what to do, so I asked a passing driver to take him to Eba hospital.

242

Does not this evocation of hell make it easier to forget that these scenes belonged to life? Is there not something conveniently unreal about hell? The whole history of the twentieth century proves otherwise.

Very systematically in Europe the conditions of hells have been constructed. It is not even necessary to list the sites. It is not even necessary to repeat the calculations of the organizers. We know this, and we choose to forget it.

We find it ridiculous or shocking that most of the pages concerning, for example, Trotsky were torn out of official Soviet history. What has been torn out of our history are the pages concerning the experience of the two atom bombs dropped on Japan.

Of course, the facts are there in the textbooks. It may even be that school children learn the dates. But what these facts mean—and originally their meaning was so clear, so monstrously vivid, that every commentator in the world was shocked, and every politician was obliged to say (whilst planning differently), 'Never again'—what these facts mean has now been torn out. It has been a systematic, slow and thorough process of suppression and elimination. This process has been hidden within the reality of politics.

Do not misunderstand me. I am not here using the word 'reality' ironically, I am not politically naive. I have the greatest respect for political reality, and I believe that the innocence of political idealists is often very dangerous. What we are considering is how in this case in the West—not in Japan for obvious reasons and not in the Soviet Union for different reasons—political and military realities have eliminated another reality.

The eliminated reality is both physical—

Yokogawa bridge above Tenma river, 6th August 1945, 8.30 am.
People crying and moaning were running towards the city. I did not know why. Steam engines were burning at Yokogawa station.
Skin of cow tied to wire.
Skin of girl's hip was hanging down.
'My baby is dead, isn't she?'

and moral.

The political and military arguments have concerned such issues as deterrence, defense systems, relative strike parity, tactical nuclear weapons and—pathetically—so-called civil defense. Any movement for nuclear disarmament today has to contend with those considerations and dispute their false interpretation. To lose sight of them is to become as apocalyptic as the Bomb and all utopias. (The construction of hells on earth was accompanied in Europe by plans for heavens on earth.)

What has to be redeemed, reinserted, disclosed and never be allowed to be forgotten, is the other reality. Most of the mass means of communication are close to what has been suppressed.

These paintings were shown on Japanese television. Is it conceivable that the BBC would show these pictures on channel one at a peak hour? Without any reference to 'political' and 'military' realities, under the straight title, *This is How It Was, 6th August 1945*? I challenge them to do so.

What happened on that day was, of course, neither the beginning nor the end of the act. It began months, years before, with the planning of the action, and the eventual final decision to drop two bombs on Japan. However much the world was shocked and surprised by the bomb dropped on Hiroshima, it has to be emphasized that it was not a miscalculation, an error, or the result (as can happen in war) of a situation deteriorating so rapidly that it gets out of hand. What happened was consciously and precisely planned. Small scenes like this were part of the plan:

> I was walking along the Hihiyama bridge about 3 pm on 7th August. A woman, who looked like an expectant mother, was dead. At her side, a girl of about three years of age brought some water in an empty can she had found. She was trying to let her mother drink from it.
>
> As soon as I saw this miserable scene with the pitiful child, I embraced the girl close to me and cried with her, telling her that her mother was dead.

There was a preparation. And there was an aftermath. The latter included long, lingering deaths, radiation sickness, many fatal illnesses which developed later as a result of exposure to the bomb, and tragic genetical effects on generations yet to be born.

I refrain from giving the statistics: how many hundreds of thousands of dead, how many injured, how many deformed children. Just as I refrain from pointing out how comparatively 'small' were the atomic bombs dropped on Japan. Such statistics tend to distract. We consider numbers instead of pain. We calculate instead of judging. We relativize instead of refusing.

It is possible today to arouse popular indignation or anger by speaking of the threat and immorality of terrorism. Indeed, this appears to be the central plank of the rhetoric of the new American foreign policy ('Moscow is the world-base of all terrorism') and of British policy towards Ireland. What is able to shock people about terrorist acts is that often their targets are unselected and innocent—a crowd in a railway station, people waiting for a bus to go home after work. The victims are chosen indiscriminately in the hope of producing a shock effect on political decision-making by their government.

The two bombs dropped on Japan were terrorist actions. The calculation was terrorist. The indiscriminacy was terrorist. The small groups of terrorists operating today are, by comparison, humane killers.

Another comparison needs to be made. Today terrorist groups mostly represent small nations or groupings, who are disputing large powers in a position of strength. Whereas Hiroshima was perpetrated by the most powerful alliance in the world against an enemy who was already prepared to negotiate, and was admitting defeat.

To apply the epithet 'terrorist' to the acts of bombing Hiroshima and Nagasaki is logically justifiable, and I do so because it may help to re-insert that act into living consciousness today. Yet the word changes nothing in itself.

The first-hand evidence of the victims, the reading of the pages which have been torn out, provokes a sense of outrage. This outrage has two natural faces. One is a sense of horror and pity at what happened; the other face is self-defensive and declares: *this should not happen again (here)*. For some the *here* is in brackets, for others not.

The face of horror, the reaction which has now been mostly suppressed, forces us to comprehend the reality of what happened. The second reaction, unfortunately, distances us from that reality. Although it begins as a straight declaration, it quickly leads into the labyrinth of defence policies, military arguments and global strategies. Finally it leads to the sordid commercial absurdity of private fall-out shelters.

This split of the sense of outrage into, on one hand, horror and, on the other hand, expediency occurs because the concept of evil has been abandoned. Every culture, except our own in recent times, has had such a concept.

That its religious or philosophical bases vary is unimportant. The concept of evil implies a force or forces which have to be continually struggled against so that they do not triumph over life and destroy it. One of the very first written texts from Mesopotamia, 1,500 years before Homer, speaks of this struggle, which was the first condition of human life. In public thinking nowadays, the concept of evil has been reduced to a little adjective to support an opinion or hypothesis (abortions, terrorism, ayatollahs).

Nobody can confront the reality of 6th August 1945 without being forced to acknowledge that what happened was evil. It is not a question of opinion or interpretation, but of events.

The memory of these events should be continually before our eyes. This is why the thousand citizens of Hiroshima started to draw on their little scraps of paper. We need to show their drawings everywhere. These terrible images can now release an energy for opposing evil and for the life-long struggle of that opposition.

And from this a very old lesson may be drawn. My friend in the United States is, in a sense, innocent. She looks beyond a nuclear holocaust without considering its reality. This reality includes not only its victims but also its planners and those who support them. Evil from time immemorial has often worn a mask of innocence. One of evil's principal modes of being is *looking beyond* (with indifference) that which is before the eyes.

August 9th: On the west embankment of a military training field was a young boy four or five years old. He was burned black, lying on his back, with his arms pointing towards heaven.

Only by looking beyond or away can one come to believe that such evil is relative, and therefore under certain conditions justifiable. In reality—the reality to which the survivors and the dead bear witness—it can never be justified.

The Pitfalls of Not Knowing the Whole Animal

Frans B.M. de Waal

Scientists are supposed to study animals in a totally objective fashion, similar to the way in which we inspect a rock, or measure the circumference of a tree trunk. Emotions are not to interfere with the assessment.

Some scientists have proudly broken out of this mold, however. Roger Fouts, known for his work in training chimpanzees to use symbols to communicate with humans, wrote in *Next of Kin* (Morrow, 1997), "I had to break the first commandment of the behavioral sciences: Thou shalt not love thy research subject." Similarly, in *When Elephants Weep* (Delacorte, 1995), Jeffrey Masson and Susan McCarthy presented themselves as almost the first scientists interested in the emotional lives of animals.

But, really, the image of the unloving and unfeeling scientist is a caricature, a straw man erected by those wishing to pat themselves on the back for having their hearts in the right place. Unfeeling scientists do exist, but most researchers take great pleasure in the animals they study. If one reads the books of Jane Goodall, Konrad Lorenz, Cynthia Moss, E. O. Wilson, Robert Yerkes, and so on, one simply cannot maintain that researchers invariably study animals in a cold, callous way. Those authors touch large audiences precisely because they communicate, either directly or between the lines, how they feel about their animals.

I have met many other scientists who may not write in the same style—and who may not dwell on their feelings, not considering them relevant to their science—but for whom the frogs, budgerigars, cichlid fish, bats, or whatever animals they specialize in hold a deep attraction. How could it be otherwise? Can you really imagine a scientist going out every day to capture and mark wild prairie voles—getting bitten by the voles, stung by insects, drenched by rain—without some deeper motivation than the pursuit of scientific truth? Think of what it takes to study penguins on the pack ice of the Antarctic, or bonobos in hot and humid jungles overrun by armed rebels. Equally, researchers who study animals in captivity really need to like what they are doing. Care of their subjects is a round-the-clock business, and animals smell and produce waste—which chimpanzees, my favorite animals, don't mind hurling at you—something most of us hardly think about until we get visitors who hold their noses and try to escape as fast as they can.

I would turn the stereotype of the unfeeling scientist around and say that it is the rare scientist who is not at some level attached to the furry, feathered, or slippery creatures he or she works with. The maestro of observation, Konrad Lorenz, didn't believe one could effectively investigate an animal that one didn't love. Be cause our intuitive understanding of animals is based on human emotions and a sense of our connection with animals, he wrote in *The Foundations of Ethology* (Simon and Schuster, 1981), that understanding seems quite separate from the methodology of the natural sciences. To marry intuitive insight with systematic data collection is both the challenge and the joy of students of animal behavior.

Attraction to animals makes us forget the time we spend watching them, and sensitizes us to the tiniest details of behavior. The scientific mind uses the information thus gathered, formulating penetrating questions leading to more precise research. But let us not forget that things did not start with a scientific interest: The lifeblood of science is our fascination with nature. This always comes first, usually early in life.

Almost every Saturday when I was a boy, I jumped on my bike to go to the *polder*, a Dutch word for low-lying land reclaimed from the water. Bordering the Maas River, our *polder* contained freshwater ditches full of salamanders, frogs, stickleback fish, eels, water insects, and so on. Carrying a crudely constructed net, I would jump over ditches, occasionally sliding into them, to get to the best spots to catch aquatic life. I returned in a perilous zigzag, balancing a heavy bucket of water and animals in one hand while steering my bike with the other. Back home, I would release my booty in glass containers and tanks, adding plants and food. Such as water fleas caught with a net made out of one of my mother's old stockings.

Initially, the mortality in my little underwater worlds was nothing to brag about. I learned only gradually that salamanders don't eat things that don't move, that big fish shouldn't be kept with little ones, and that over feeding does more harm than good. My animals started to live longer. Then one day— I must have been around 12—I noticed a dramatic color change in one of my sticklebacks in a neglected tank with unchecked algae growth. Within days, the fish turned from silvery to sky blue with a fiery red underbelly. A plain little fish had metamorphosed into a dazzling peacock! I was astonished and spent every free minute staring into the aquarium, which I didn't clean on the assumption that perhaps the fish liked it better that way.

This is how I first saw the breeding behavior of the three-spined stickleback. The two females in the tank grew heavy bellies full of roe, while the male built a nest out of plant material in the sand. He repeatedly interrupted his hard work by performing a little dance aimed at the females, which took place closer to the nest site each time. I did not understand everything that was going on, but I did notice that the females suddenly lost their eggs, whereupon the male started moving his fins rapidly. (I later learned this was to create a current that would provide additional oxygen for the eggs.) I ended up with a tank full of fry. It was an exhilarating experience, but one that I had to enjoy all by myself. Although my family tolerated my interests, they simply could not get excited about a bunch of tiny fish in one of my aquariums.

I had a similar experience years later, when I was a biology student at the Catholic University of Nijmegen. In a welcome departure from the usual emphasis on physiology and molecular biology, one professor gave a lecture on ethology—the naturalistic study of animal behavior—showing detailed drawings of the so-called zigzag dance of the stickleback. Because of the work of Niko Tinbergen, a Dutch zoologist, the stickleback's display had become a textbook example. The drawings my professor had were wonderful, showing the male pushing out his red belly, with spines pointing outward, then leading the female to the nest while performing abrupt back-and-forth movements in front of her. When I nudged my fellow students, excitedly telling them that I knew all this, that anyone could see it in a small aquarium at home, once again I met with little interest. Why should the other students believe me, and what was the big deal about fish behavior, anyway?

A few years later, Tinbergen received a Nobel prize: The stickleback had won. By that time, however, I had moved to another university, where ethology was taken more seriously.

I now study the behavior of monkeys and apes. This may seem incongruous, given my early interests, but I have never had a fixation on a particular animal group. If there had been any chimpanzees in the *polder*, I would have brought them home as well.

Like every biologist, I have learned that one needs to build up an extensive background knowledge before one can even begin to address detailed questions. As Lorenz put it in *The Foundations of Ethology*, one needs to grasp the whole before one tries to grasp its parts: "One cannot master set research tasks if one makes a single part the focus of interest. One must, rather, continuously dart from one part to another—in a way that appears extremely flighty and unscientific to some thinkers who place value on strictly logical sequences—and one's knowledge of each of the parts must advance at the same pace."

In the study of animal behavior, this means that one follows each and every move of the species one is interested in, preferably under a wide range of circumstances. Behavior makes sense only in the larger context of the animal's natural history, social organization, general temperament, adaptations to its environment, and so on, One cannot expect predators to react the same as prey, solitary animals the same as social ones, vision-oriented animals the same as those relying on sonar, and so on.

I came across an amusing illustration in the scientific literature of the pitfalls for those who fail to pay attention to the whole animal. Bruce Moore and Susan Stuttard, psychologists at Dalhousie University, in Nova Scotia, reported in *Science* in 1979 that they had tried to replicate a 1946 study widely cited as demonstrating the ability of cats to work their way out of a puzzle box, a container whose door was operated by moving a rod. The earlier study, done by Edwin R. Guthrie and George P. Horton, documented in great detail how cats rubbed against the interior of a box with stereo-typed movements. In the process, they moved the rod and escaped. Guthrie and Horton had deemed it highly significant that all the cats in the experiment showed the same rubbing pattern, which they believed they had taught the animals through the use of food as rewards: This proved the power of conditioning.

When Moore and Stuttard repeated the experiment, their cats' behavior struck them as nothing special. The cats performed the usual head-rubbing movements that all felines—from house cats to jaguars—use in greeting and courting each other. Domestic cats often redirect these movements to inanimate objects, such as the legs of a kitchen table. Moore and Stuttard showed that food rewards were absolutely irrelevant: The only meaningful factor for the cats in the box was the visibility of people. Without training, every cat who saw people while in the box rubbed its head, flank, and tail against the rod and got out of the box. Cats who didn't see people just sat there. Instead of a learning experiment, the 1946 study had been a greeting experiment.

The lesson is painfully obvious: Before testing an animal, one needs to know a bit about its typical behavior. Yet, all too often, scientists—especially behaviorists—think of animals as interchangeable. They reason that if the laws of learning are universal, one animal is as good as another. As B. F. Skinner, the founder of behaviorism, put it in "A Case History in Scientific Method": "Pigeon, rat, monkey, which is which? It doesn't matter."

Some animals have larger brains than others, which means that they may learn a bit faster, but reward and punishment motivate all animals. Behaviorists, then, assume that all brains work the same. But is a monkey brain really no more than an expanded rat brain, and is the human brain no more than a large monkey brain? Wouldn't it be surprising if evolutionary adaptation affects every anatomical feature one can think of—from limbs and teeth to stomach, eyes, and lungs—*except* for the brain? If the architecture and function of brains were that invariable, the species with the largest brain would be superior in every respect. This is not the case, however.

Pigeons, for example, do better than humans at mentally rotating visual images, and some birds have an amazing memory for the location of hidden objects. Clark's nutcrackers store up to 33,000 seeds in caches distributed over many square kilometers, and they can find most of the caches again months later. As someone who occasionally forgets where he has parked an item as large and significant as a car, I am impressed by these peanut-brained birds.

Biologists readily accept that the ability to recall locations accurately makes perfect sense for an animal that relies on stored food—but such specializations are annoying to behaviorists. And so, when Gordon Gallup, a psychologist at the State University of New York at Albany, demonstrated in a 1970 article in *Science* a cognitive gap between apes and the rest of the animal kingdom, including monkeys, this was sufficiently upsetting that two generations of behaviorists have broken their teeth on it.

Gallup noticed that chimpanzees and monkeys respond differently to mirrors. Like most other animals, a monkey reacts to its reflection as if it were a friend or enemy, whereas an ape appears to realize that the image in the mirror is itself. Chimpanzees soon use the mirror to inspect parts of their bodies that are normally out of sight, such as the inside of their mouths or (in the case of females) their swollen pink behinds. Anyone who has ever seen an ape do this knows that the animal is not simply opening its mouth or turning around accidentally: The ape's eyes closely monitor the movements of its body in the mirror.

To corroborate the observational evidence, Gallup designed an elegant experiment in which chimpanzees needed a mirror to detect a small change in body appearance. Known as the mark test, the experiment consists of painting a dot above the eyebrow of an anesthetized animal. Once the animal wakes up, it is shown a mirror. It cannot see the dot directly, but can detect its presence only in the mirror. In these experiments, the ape would stare at the dot in the mirror, then bring a finger to the real dot on its own face and inspect the finger afterwards—a clear sign that the animals linked their reflections to themselves. Apart from humans and apes, no animals have convincingly passed this test, despite valiant efforts by many scientists.

Gallup spoke provocatively of self-awareness, and of the mental uniqueness of the hominoids, the family of animals made up of apes and humans. This triggered one of the greatest travesties in behavioral science: an attempt to demonstrate the same ability in pigeons. Surely, if pigeons have self-awareness, some scientists reasoned, the quality can't be so special. In 1981, B. F. Skinner and his colleagues reported in *Science* that, with enough trials, food rewards, and patience, they had managed to get pigeons to recognize themselves in a mirror. The birds pecked at dots projected onto their bodies, dots the birds could not see directly because they had bibs around their necks. A marvel of conditioning, no doubt, but the experiment did not con-vince many people that what these birds were doing after extensive human intervention was the same as what chimpanzees do spontaneously, without any help. Furthermore, attempts to replicate the results have remained sus-piciously unsuccessful.

Fifteen years later, another skeptical behaviorist tried a different approach. Cecilia Heyes, a reader in psychology at University College London, who was making a name for herself in Great Britain as a critic of the growing field of ape-intelligence studies, zoomed in on apes' responses to mirrors. Without the benefit of familiarity with primates, she came up with the creative sug-gestion that self-recognition might be a byproduct of the anesthesia that is part of the mark test. Perhaps a chimpanzee recovering from anesthesia has a tendency to touch its own face, in a random manner that produces occa-sional contacts with the dot. What other scientists had interpreted as self-inspection guided by a mirror might be a mere accident.

Heye's idea was quickly disproved by an experiment in which Daniel Povinelli and his colleagues at the New Iberia Research Center at the University of Southwestern Louisiana carefully recorded which area of the face chim-panzees touched in the mark test, and how soon after recovery from the anes-thesia. They found that touching is far from random: It is specifically targeted at the marked areas, and it peaks right after the animal's exposure to the mirror. That is, of course, exactly what ape experts had been claiming all along, but now it was official.

What makes critics such as Heyes unfathomable to me is their total absence of humility when faced with a group of animals they have never worked with. Behaviorists really do believe that they can generalize from rats and pigeons to all other species. But their "which is which?" approach to the diversity of life, and their talk of higher and lower forms, is essentially pre-Darwinian: It ignores the fact that every animal is a unique product of natural selection. in both body and mind. Only those scientists who try to learn everything there is to know about a particular animal have any chance of unlocking its secrets—all others will keep tripping over the cat.

And so we return to scientists who erect no artificial barriers between them-selves and other life forms, and who are not afraid to identify with them, project emotions onto them, or trust their own intuitions about them rather than relying on preconceived notions.

I often see a parallel with so-called "computer geeks." In the same way that some kids love animals, others spend all their time clicking away at com-puters, playing electronic games, browsing the World-Wide Web, testing soft-ware, and so on. A few lucky people with this inclination are now highly visible billionaires, but they didn't start out with wealth in mind. They were just obsessed with the technology. Similarly, ethologists and naturalists are driven by a power beyond their control to work with animals, watching them for inordinate amounts of time. Their science follows naturally. The only difference, sadly, is that they never get rich.

The study of animal behavior is among the oldest of human endeavors. As hunter-gatherers, our ancestors needed intimate knowledge of flora and fauna, including the habits of their prey as well as the animals that prey on humans. The human-animal relationship must have been relatively egalitarian during that period. Hunters exercise little control: They need to anticipate the moves of their prey and are impressed by the animals' cunning if they escape. A more practical kind of knowledge became necessary when our ancestors took up agriculture and began to domesticate animals for food and muscle power. Animals became dependent on us and subservient to our will. Instead of anticipating their moves, we began to dictate them.

Both perspectives are recognizable today in the study of animal behavior, and, to be successful, we need both—the observer/hunter and the experimenter/farmer. But whereas the first can easily exist without the second, the second gets into all sorts of trouble without the first.

Sex, Drugs, Disasters, and the Extinction of the Dinosaurs

Stephen J. Gould

Science, in its most fundamental definition, is a fruitful mode of inquiry, not a list of enticing conclusions. The conclusions are the consequence, not the essence.

My greatest unhappiness with most popular presentations of science concerns their failure to separate fascinating claims from the methods that scientists use to establish the facts of nature. Journalists, and the public, thrive on controversial and stunning statements. But science is, basically, a way of knowing—in P. B. Medawar's apt words, "the art of the soluble." If the growing corps of popular science writers would focus on *how* scientists develop and defend those fascinating claims, they would make their greatest possible contribution to public understanding.

Consider three ideas, proposed in perfect seriousness to explain that greatest of all titillating puzzles—the extinction of dinosaurs. Since these three notions invoke the primarily fascinating themes of our culture—sex, drugs, and violence—they surely reside in the category of fascinating claims. I want to show why two of them rank as silly speculation, while the other represents science at its grandest and most useful.

Science works with testable proposals. If, after much compilation and scrutiny of data, new information continues to affirm a hypothesis, we may accept it provisionally and gain confidence as further evidence mounts. We can never be completely sure that a hypothesis is right, though we may be able to show with confidence that it is wrong. The best scientific hypotheses are also generous and expansive: They suggest extensions and implications that enlighten related, and even far distant, subjects. Simply consider how the idea of evolution has influenced virtually every intellectual field.

Useless speculation, on the other hand, is restrictive. It generates no testable hypothesis, and offers no way to obtain potentially refuting evidence. Please note that I am not speaking of truth or falsity. The speculation may well be true; still, if it provides, in principle, no material for affirmation or rejection, we can make nothing of it. It must simply stand forever as an intriguing idea.

Useless speculation turns in on itself and leads nowhere; good science, containing both seeds for its potential refutation and implications for more and different testable knowledge, reaches out. But, enough preaching. Let's move on to dinosaurs, and the three proposals for their extinction.

1. *Sex.* Testes function only in a narrow range of temperature (those of mammals hang externally in a scrotal sac because internal body temperatures are too high for their proper function). A worldwide rise in temperature at the close of the Cretaceous period caused the testes of dinosaurs to stop functioning and led to their extinction by sterilization of males.

2. *Drugs.* Angiosperms (flowering plants) first evolved toward the end of the dinosaurs' reign. Many of these plants contain psychoactive agents, avoided by mammals today as a result of their bitter taste. Dinosaurs had neither means to taste the bitterness nor livers effective enough to detoxify the substances. They died of massive overdoses.

3. *Disasters.* A large comet or asteroid struck the earth some 65 million years ago, lofting a cloud of dust into the sky and blocking sunlight, thereby suppressing photosynthesis and so drastically lowering world temperatures that dinosaurs and hosts of other creatures became extinct.

Before analyzing these three tantalizing statements, we must establish a basic ground rule often violated in proposals for the dinosaurs' demise. *There is no separate problem of the extinction of dinosaurs.* Too often we divorce specific events from their wider contexts and systems of cause and effect. The fundamental fact of dinosaur extinction is its synchrony with the demise of so many other groups across a wide range of habitats, from terrestrial to marine.

The history of life has been punctuated by brief episodes of mass extinction. A recent analysis by University of Chicago paleontologists Jack Sepkoski and Dave Raup, based on the best and most exhaustive tabulation of data ever assembled, shows clearly that five episodes of mass dying stand well above the "background" extinctions of normal times (when we consider all mass extinctions, large and small, they seem to fall in a regular 26-million-year cycle). The Cretaceous debacle, occurring 65 million years ago and separating the Mesozoic and Cenozoic eras of our geological time scale, ranks prominently among the five. Nearly all the marine plankton (single-celled floating creatures) died with geological suddenness; among marine invertebrates, nearly 15 percent of all families perished, including many previously dominant groups, especially the ammonites (relatives of squids in coiled shells). On land, the dinosaurs disappeared after more than 100 million years of unchallenged domination.

In this context, speculations limited to dinosaurs alone ignore the larger phenomenon. We need a coordinated explanation for a system of events that includes the extinction of dinosaurs as one component. Thus it makes little sense, though it may fuel our desire to view mammals as inevitable inheritors of the earth, to guess that dinosaurs died because small mammals ate their eggs (a perennial favorite among untestable speculations). It seems most unlikely that some disaster peculiar to dinosaurs befell these massive beasts—and that the debacle happened to strike just when one of history's five great dyings had enveloped the earth for completely different reasons.

The testicular theory, an old favorite from the 1940s, had its root in an interesting and thoroughly respectable study of temperature tolerances in the American alligator, published in the staid *Bulletin of the American Museum of Natural History* in 1946 by three experts on living and fossil reptiles—E. H. Colbert, my own first teacher in paleontology; R. B. Cowles; and C. M. Bogert.

The first sentence of their summary reveals a purpose beyond alligators: "This report describes an attempt to infer the reactions of extinct reptiles, especially the dinosaurs, to high temperatures as based upon reactions observed in the modern alligator." They studied, by rectal thermometry, the body temperatures of alligators under changing conditions of heating and cooling. (Well, let's face it, you wouldn't want to try sticking a thermometer under a 'gator's tongue.) The predictions under test go way back to an old theory first stated by Galileo in the 1630s—the unequal scaling of surfaces and volumes. As an animal, or any object, grows (provided its shape doesn't change), surface areas must increase more slowly than volumes—since surfaces get larger as length squared, while volumes increase much more rapidly, as length cubed. Therefore, small animals have high ratios of surface to volume, while large animals cover themselves with relatively little surface.

Among cold-blooded animals lacking any physiological mechanism for keeping their temperatures constant, small creatures have a hell of a time keeping warm—because they lose so much heat through their relatively large surfaces. On the other hand, large animals, with their relatively small surfaces, may lose heat so slowly that, once warm, they may maintain effectively constant temperatures against ordinary fluctuations of climate. (In fact, the resolution of the "hot-blooded dinosaur" controversy that burned so brightly a few years back may simply be that, while large dinosaurs possessed no physiological mechanism for constant temperature, and were not therefore warm-blooded in the technical sense, their large size and relatively small surface area kept them warm.)

Colbert, Cowles, and Bogert compared the warming rates of small and large alligators. As predicted, the small fellows heated up (and cooled down) more quickly. When exposed to a warm sun, a tiny 50-gram (1.76-ounce) alligator heated up one degree Celsius every minute and a half, while a large alligator, 260 times bigger at 13,000 grams (28.7 pounds), took seven and a half minutes to gain a degree. Extrapolating up to an adult 10-ton dinosaur, they concluded that a one degree rise in body temperature would take eighty-six hours. If large animals absorb heat so slowly (through their relatively small surfaces), they will also be unable to shed any excess heat gained when temperatures rise above a favorable level.

The authors then guessed that large dinosaurs lived at or near their optimum temperatures; Cowles suggested that a rise in global temperatures just before the Cretaceous extinction caused the dinosaurs to heat up beyond their optimal tolerance—and, being so large, they couldn't shed the unwanted heat. (In a most unusual statement within a scientific paper, Colbert and Bogert then explicitly disavowed this speculative extension of their empirical work on alligators.) Cowles conceded that this excess heat probably wasn't enough to kill or even to enervate the great beasts, but since testes often function only within a narrow range of temperature, he proposed that this global rise might have sterilized all the males, causing extinction by natural contraception.

The overdose theory has recently been supported by UCLA psychiatrist Ronald K. Siegel. Siegel has gathered, he claims, more than 2,000 records of animals who, when given access, administer various drugs to themselves—from a mere swig of alcohol to massive doses of the big H. Elephants will swill the equivalent of twenty beers at a time, but do not like alcohol in concentrations greater than 7 percent. In a silly bit of anthropocentric speculation, Siegel states that "elephants drink, perhaps, to forget . . . the anxiety produced by shrinking rangeland and the competition for food." Since fertile imaginations can apply almost any hot idea to the extinction of dinosaurs, Siegel found a way. Flowering plants did not evolve until late in the dinosaurs' reign. These plants also produced an array of aromatic, aminoacid-based alkaloids—the major group of psychoactive agents. Most mammals are "smart" enough to avoid these potential poisons. The alkaloids simply don't taste good (they are bitter); in any case, we mammals have livers happily supplied with the capacity to detoxify them. But, Siegel speculates, perhaps dinosaurs could neither taste the bitterness nor detoxify the substances once ingested. He recently told members of the American Psychological Association: "I'm not suggesting that all dinosaurs OD'd on plant drugs, but it certainly was a factor." He also argued that death by overdose may help explain why so many dinosaur fossils are found in contorted positions. (Do not go gently into that good night.)

Extraterrestrial catastrophes have long pedigrees in the popular literature of extinction, but the subject exploded again in 1979, after a long lull, when the father-son, physicist-geologist team of Luis and Walter Alvarez proposed that an asteroid, some 10 km in diameter, struck the earth 65 million years ago. (Comets, rather than asteroids, have since gained favor. Good science is self-corrective.)

The force of such a collision would be immense, greater by far than the megatonnage of all the world's nuclear weapons. In trying to reconstruct a scenario that would explain the simultaneous dying of dinosaurs on land and so many creatures in the sea, the Alvarezes proposed that a gigantic dust cloud, generated by particles blown aloft in the impact, would so darken the earth that photosynthesis would cease and temperatures drop precipitously. (Rage, rage against the dying of the light.) The single-celled photosynthetic oceanic plankton, with life cycles measured in weeks, would perish outright, but land plants might survive through the dormancy of their seeds (land plants were not much affected by the Cretaceous extinction, and any adequate theory must account for the curious pattern of differential survival). Dinosaurs would die by starvation and freezing; small, warm-blooded mammals, with more modest requirements for food and better regulation of body temperature, would squeak through. "Let the bastards freeze in the dark," as bumper stickers of our chauvinistic neighbors in sunbelt states proclaimed several years ago, during the Northeast's winter oil crisis.

All three theories, testicular malfunction, psychoactive overdosing, and asteroidal zapping, grab our attention mightily. As pure phenomenology, they rank about equally high on any hit parade of primal fascination. Yet, one represents expansive science, the others restrictive and untestable speculation. The proper criterion lies in evidence and methodology; we must probe behind the superficial fascination of particular claims.

How could we possibly decide whether the hypothesis of testicular frying is right or wrong? We would have to know things that the fossil record cannot provide. What temperatures were optimal for dinosaurs? Could they avoid the absorption of excess heat by staying in the shade, or in caves? At what temperatures did their testicles cease to function? Were late Cretaceous climates ever warm enough to drive the internal temperatures of dinosaurs close to this ceiling? Testicles simply don't fossilize, and how could we infer their temperature tolerances even if they did? In short, Cowles's hypothesis is only an intriguing speculation leading nowhere. The most damning statement against it appeared right in the conclusion of Colbert, Cowles, and Bogert's paper, when they admitted: "It is difficult to advance any definite arguments against this hypothesis." My statement may seem paradoxical—isn't a hypothesis really good if you can't devise any arguments against it? Quite the contrary. It is simply untestable and unusable.

Siegel's overdosing has even less going for it. At least Cowles extrapolated his conclusion from some good data on alligators. And he didn't completely violate the primary guideline of siting dinosaur extinction in the context of a general mass dying—for rise in temperature could be the root cause of a general catastrophe, zapping dinosaurs by testicular malfunction and different groups for other reasons. But Siegel's speculation cannot touch the extinction of ammonites or oceanic plankton (diatoms make their own food with good sweet sunlight; they don't OD on the chemicals of terrestrial plants).

259

It is simply a gratuitous, attention-grabbing guess. It cannot be tested, for how can we know what dinosaurs tasted and what their livers could do? Livers don't fossilize any better than testicles.

The hypothesis doesn't even make any sense in its own context. Angiosperms were in full flower ten million years before dinosaurs went the way of all flesh. Why did it take so long? As for the pains of a chemical death recorded in contortions of fossils, I regret to say (or rather I'm pleased to note for the dinosaurs' sake) that Siegel's knowledge of geology must be a bit deficient: Muscles contract after death and geological strata rise and fall with motions of the earth's crust after burial—more than enough reason to distort a fossil's pristine appearance.

The impact story, on the other hand, has a sound basis in evidence. It can be tested, extended, refined, and, if wrong, disproved. The Alvarezes did not just construct an arresting guess for public consumption. They proposed their hypothesis after laborious geochemical studies with Frank Asaro and Helen Michael had revealed a massive increase of iridium in rocks deposited right at the time of extinction. Iridium, a rare metal of the platinum group, is virtually absent from indigenous rocks of the earth's crust; most of our iridium arrives on extraterrestrial objects that strike the earth.

The Alvarez hypothesis bore immediate fruit. Based originally on evidence from two European localities, it led geochemists throughout the world to examine other sediments of the same age. They found abnormally high amounts of iridium everywhere—from continental rocks of the western United States to deep sea cores from the South Atlantic.

Cowles proposed his testicular hypothesis in the mid-1940s. Where has it gone since then? Absolutely nowhere, because scientists can do nothing with it. The hypothesis must stand as a curious appendage to a solid study of alligators. Siegel's overdose scenario will also win a few press notices and fade into oblivion. The Alvarezes' asteroid falls into a different category altogether, and much of the popular commentary has missed this essential distinction by focusing on the impact and its attendant results, and forgetting what really matters to a scientist—the iridium. If you talk just about asteroids, dust, and darkness, you tell stories no better and no more entertaining than fried testicles or terminal trips. It is the iridium—the source of testable evidence—that counts and forges the crucial distinction between speculation and science.

The proof, to twist a phrase, lies in the doing. Cowles's hypothesis has generated nothing in thirty-five years. Since its proposal in 1979, the Alvarez hypothesis has spawned hundreds of studies, a major conference, and attendant publications. Geologists are fired up. They are looking for iridium at all other extinction boundaries. Every week exposes a new wrinkle in the scientific press. Further evidence that the Cretaceous iridium represents extra-terrestrial impact and not indigenous volcanism continues to accumulate. As I revise this essay in November 1984 (this paragraph will be out of date when [it] is published), new data include chemical "signatures" of other isotopes indicating unearthly provenance, glass spherules of a size and sort produced by impact and not by volcanic eruptions, and high-pressure varieties of silica formed (so far as we know) only under the tremendous shock of impact.

My point is simply this: Whatever the eventual outcome (I suspect it will be positive), the Alvarez hypothesis is exciting, fruitful science because it gen-erates tests, provides us with things to do, and expands outward. We are having fun, battling back and forth, moving toward a resolution, and extend-ing beyond its original scope.

As just one example of the unexpected, distant cross-fertilization that good science engenders, the Alvarez hypothesis made a major contribution to a theme that has riveted public attention in the past few months—so-called nuclear winter. In a speech delivered in April 1982, Luis Alvarez calculated the energy that a ten-kilometer asteroid would release on impact. He com-pared such an explosion with a full nuclear exchange and implied that all-out atomic war might unleash similar consequences.

This theme of impact leading to massive dust clouds and falling temper-atures formed an important input to the decision of Carl Sagan and a group of colleagues to model the climatic consequences of nuclear holocaust. Full nuclear exchange would probably generate the same kind of dust cloud and darkening that may have wiped out the dinosaurs. Temperatures would drop precipitously and agriculture might become impossible. Avoidance of nuclear war is fundamentally an ethical and political imperative, but we must know the factual consequences to make firm judgments. I am heartened by a final link across disciplines and deep concerns—another criterion, by the way, of science at its best: A recognition of the very phenomenon that made our evolution possible by exterminating the previously dominant dinosaurs and clearing a way for the evolution of large mammals, including us, might actu-ally help to save us from joining those magnificent beasts in contorted poses among the strata of the earth.

Women's Brains

Stephen J. Gould

In the prelude to *Middlemarch*, George Eliot lamented the unfulfilled lives of talented women:

> Some have felt that these blundering lives are due to the inconvenient indefiniteness with which the Supreme Power has fashioned the natures of women: if there were one level of feminine incompetence as strict as the ability to count three and no more, the social lot of women might be treated with scientific certitude.

Eliot goes on to discount the idea of innate limitation, but while she wrote in 1872, the leaders of European anthropometry were trying to measure "with scientific certitude" the inferiority of women. Anthropometry, or measurement of the human body, is not so fashionable a field these days, but it dominated the human sciences for much of the nineteenth century and remained popular until intelligence testing replaced skull measurement as a favored device for making invidious comparisons among races, classes, and sexes. Craniometry, or measurement of the skull, commanded the most attention and respect. Its unquestioned leader, Paul Broca (1824–80), professor of clinical surgery at the Faculty of Medicine in Paris, gathered a school of disciples and imitators around himself. Their work, so meticulous and apparently irrefutable, exerted great influence and won high esteem as a jewel of nineteenth-century science.

Broca's work seemed particularly invulnerable to refutation. Had he not measured with the most scrupulous care and accuracy? (Indeed, he had. I have the greatest respect for Broca's meticulous procedure. His numbers are sound. But science is an inferential exercise, not a catalog of facts. Numbers, by themselves, specify nothing. All depends upon what you do with them.) Broca depicted himself as an apostle of objectivity, a man who bowed before facts and cast aside superstition and sentimentality. He declared that "there is no faith, however respectable, no interest, however legitimate, which must not accommodate itself to the progress of human knowledge and bend before truth." Women, like it or not, had smaller brains than men and, therefore, could not equal them in intelligence. This fact, Broca argued, may reinforce a common prejudice in male society, but it is also a scientific truth. L. Manouvrier, a black sheep in Broca's fold, rejected the inferiority of women and wrote with feeling about the burden imposed upon them by Broca's numbers:

> Women displayed their talents and their diplomas. They also invoked philosophical authorities. But they were opposed by *numbers* unknown to Condorcet or to John Stuart Mill. These numbers fell upon poor women like a sledge hammer, and they were accompanied by commentaries and sarcasms more ferocious than the most misogynist imprecations of certain church fathers. The theologians had asked if women had a soul. Several centuries later, some scientists were ready to refuse them a human intelligence.

Broca's argument rested upon two sets of data: the larger brains of men in modern societies, and a supposed increase in male superiority through time. His most extensive data came from autopsies performed personally in four Parisian hospitals. For 292 male brains, he calculated an average weight of 1,325 grams; 140 female brains averaged 1,144 grams for a difference of 181 grams, or 14 percent of the male weight. Broca understood, of course, that part of this difference could be attributed to the greater height of males. Yet he made no attempt to measure the effect of size alone and actually stated that it cannot account for the entire difference because we know, a priori, that women are not as intelligent as men (a premise that the data were supposed to test, not rest upon):

> We might ask if the small size of the female brain depends exclusively upon the small size of her body. Tiedemann has proposed this explanation. But we must not forget that women are, on the average, a little less intelligent than men, a difference which we should not exaggerate but which is, nonetheless, real. We are therefore permitted to suppose that the relatively small size of the female brain depends in part upon her physical inferiority and in part upon her intellectual inferiority.

In 1873, the year after Eliot published *Middlemarch*, Broca measured the cranial capacities of prehistoric skulls from L'Homme Mort cave. Here he found a difference of only 99.5 cubic centimeters between males and females, while modern populations range from 129.5 to 220.7. Topinard, Broca's chief disciple, explained the increasing discrepancy through time as a result of differing evolutionary pressures upon dominant men and passive women:

> The man who fights for two or more in the struggle for existence, who has all the responsibility and the cares of tomorrow, who is constantly active in combating the environment and human rivals, needs more brain than the woman whom he must protect and nourish, the sedentary woman, lacking any interior occupations, whose role is to raise children, love, and be passive.

In 1879, Gustave LeBon, chief misogynist of Broca's school, used these data to publish what must be the most vicious attack upon women in modern scientific literature (no one can top Aristotle). I do not claim his views were representative of Broca's school, but they were published in France's most respected anthropological journal. LeBon concluded:

> In the most intelligent races, as among the Parisians, there are a large number of women whose brains are closer in size to those of gorillas than to the most developed male brains. This inferiority is so obvious that no one can contest it for a moment; only its degree is worth discussion. All psychologists who have studied the intelligence of women, as well as poets and novelists, recognize today they represent the most inferior forms of human evolution and that they are closer to children and savages than to an adult, civilized man. They excel in fickleness, inconstancy, absence of thought and logic, and incapacity to reason. Without doubt there exist some distinguished women, very superior to the average man, but they are as exceptional as the birth of any monstrosity, as, for example, of a gorilla with two heads; consequently, we may neglect them entirely.

Nor did LeBon shrink from the social implications of his views. He was horrified by the proposal of some American reformers to grant women higher education on the same basis as men:

> A desire to give them the same education, and, as a consequence, to propose the same goals for them, is a dangerous chimera. . . . The day when, misunderstanding the inferior occupations which nature has given her, women leave the home and take part in our battles; on this day a social revolution will begin, and everything that maintains the sacred ties of the family will disappear.

Sound familiar?

I have reexamined Broca's data, the basis for all this derivative pronouncement, and I find his numbers sound but his interpretation ill-founded, to say the least. The data supporting his claim for increased difference through time can be easily dismissed. Broca based his contention on the samples from L'Homme Mort alone—only seven male and six female skulls in all. Never have so little data yielded such far-ranging conclusions.

In 1888, Topinard published Broca's more extensive data on the Parisian hospitals. Since Broca recorded height and age as well as brain size, we may use modern statistics to remove their effect. Brain weight decreases with age, and Broca's women were, on average, considerably older than his men. Brain weight increases with height, and his average man was almost half a foot taller than his average woman. I used multiple regression, a technique that allowed me to assess simultaneously the influence of height and age upon brain size. In an analysis of the data for women, I found that, at average male height and age, a woman's brain would weigh 1,212 grams. Correction for height and age reduces Broca's measured difference of 181 grams by more than a third, to 113 grams.

I don't know what to make of this remaining difference because I cannot assess other factors known to influence brain size in a major way. Cause of death has an important effect: degenerative disease often entails a substantial diminution of brain size. (This effect is separate from the decrease attributed to age alone.) Eugene Schreider, also working with Broca's data, found that men killed in accidents had brains weighing, on average, 60 grams more than men dying of infectious diseases. The best modern data I can find (from American hospitals) records a full 100-gram difference between death by degenerative arteriosclerosis and by violence or accident. Since so many of Broca's subjects were very elderly women, we may assume that lengthy degenerative disease was more common among them than among the men.

More importantly, modern students of brain size still have not agreed on a proper measure for eliminating the powerful effect of body size. Height is partly adequate, but men and women of the same height do not share the same body build. Weight is even worse than height, because most of its variation reflects nutrition rather than intrinsic size—fat versus skinny exerts little influence upon the brain. Manouvrier took up this subject in the 1880s and argued that muscular mass and force should be used. He tried to measure this elusive property in various ways and found a marked difference in favor of men, even in men and women of the same height. When he corrected for what he called "sexual mass," women actually came out slightly ahead in brain size.

Thus, the corrected 113-gram difference is surely too large; the true figure is probably close to zero and may as well favor women as men. And 113 grams, by the way, is exactly the average difference between a 5 foot 4 inch and a 6 foot 4 inch male in Broca's data. We would not (especially us short folks) want to ascribe greater intelligence to tall men. In short, who knows what to do with Broca's data? They certainly don't permit any confident claim that men have bigger brains than women.

To appreciate the social role of Broca and his school, we must recognize that his statements about the brains of women do not reflect an isolated prejudice toward a single disadvantaged group. They must be weighed in the context of a general theory that supported contemporary social distinctions as biologically ordained. Women, blacks, and poor people suffered the same disparagement, but women bore the brunt of Broca's argument because he had easier access to data on women's brains. Women were singularly denigrated but they also stood as surrogates for other disenfranchised groups. As one of

Broca's disciples wrote in 1881: "Men of the black races have a brain scarcely heavier than that of white women." This juxtaposition extended into many other realms of anthropological argument, particularly to claims that, anatomically and emotionally, both women and blacks were like white children—and that white children, by the theory of recapitulation, represented an ancestral (primitive) adult stage of human evolution. I do not regard as empty rhetoric the claim that women's battles are for all of us.

Maria Montessori did not confine her activities to educational reform for young children. She lectured on anthropology for several years at the University of Rome, and wrote an influential book entitled *Pedagogical Anthropology* (English edition, 1913). Montessori was no egalitarian. She supported most of Broca's work and the theory of innate criminality proposed by her compatriot Cesare Lombroso. She measured the circumference of children's heads in her schools and inferred that the best prospects had bigger brains. But she had no use for Broca's conclusions about women. She discussed Manouvrier's work at length and made much of his tentative claim that women, after proper correction of the data, had slightly larger brains than men. Women, she concluded, were intellectually superior, but men had prevailed heretofore by dint of physical force. Since technology has abolished force as an instrument of power, the era of women may soon be upon us: "In such an epoch there will really be superior human beings, there will really be men strong in morality and in sentiment. Perhaps in this way the reign of women is approaching, when the enigma of her anthropological superiority will be deciphered. Woman was always the custodian of human sentiment, morality and honor."

This represents one possible antidote to "scientific" claims the constitutional inferiority of certain groups. One may affirm the validity of biological distinctions but argue that the data have been misinterpreted by prejudiced men with a stake in the outcome, and that disadvantaged groups are truly superior. In recent years, Elaine Morgan has followed this strategy in her *Descent of Woman*, a speculative reconstruction of human prehistory from the woman's point of view—and as farcical as more famous tall tales by and for men.

I prefer another strategy. Montessori and Morgan followed Broca's philosophy to reach a more congenial conclusion. I would rather label the whole enterprise of setting a biological value upon groups for what it is: irrelevant and highly injurious. George Eliot well appreciated the special tragedy that biological labeling imposed upon members of disadvantaged groups. She expressed it for people like herself—women of extraordinary talent. I would apply it more widely—not only to those whose dreams are flouted but also to those who never realize that they may dream—but I cannot match her prose.

In conclusion, then, the rest of Eliot's prelude to *Middlemarch:*

The limits of variation are really much wider than anyone would imagine from the sameness of women's coiffure and the favorite love stories in prose and verse. Here and there a cygnet is reared uneasily among the ducklings in the brown pond, and never finds the living stream in fellowship with its own oary-footed kind. Here and there is born a Saint Theresa, foundress of nothing, whose loving heartbeats and sobs after an unattained goodness tremble off and are dispersed among hindrances instead of centering in some long-recognizable deed.

"What, Precisely, Is Thinking?" ...
Einstein's Answer

Gerald Holton

<hr>

How did Albert Einstein do his thinking? At first glance an answer seems impossible. His work was carried out at the very frontiers of physics and of human ability. And his mind was not open to easy study from the outside, even by those who worked with him—as was discovered by the physicist Banesh Hoffmann who, with Leopold Infeld, was Einstein's assistant in 1937. Hoffmann has given an account of what it was like when he and Infeld, having come to an impassable obstacle in their work, would seek out Einstein's help. At such a point, Hoffmann related,

> We would all pause and Einstein would stand up quietly and say, in his quaint English, "I will a little think." So saying, he would pace up and down and walk around in circles, all the time twirling a lock of his long grey hair around his forefinger. At these moments of high drama, Infeld and I would remain completely still, not daring to move or make a sound, lest we interrupt his train of thought.

Many minutes would pass this way, and then, all of a sudden,

> Einstein would visibly relax and a smile would light up his face . . . then he would tell us the solution to the problem, and almost always the solution worked. . . . The solution sometimes was so simple we could have kicked ourselves for not having been able to think of it by ourselves. But the magic was performed invisibly in the recesses of Einstein's mind, by a process that we could not fathom. From this point of view the whole thing was completely frustrating.[1]

But if not accessible from the outside, Einstein's mind was accessible from the inside, because like many of the best scientists, he was interested in the way the scientific imagination works, and wrote about it frankly. As far as

<hr>

[1] Quoted from a report by Banesh Hoffmann in *Einstein, the Man and His Achievement*, by G. J. Whitrow (New York: Dover, 1967), p. 75.

possible, we shall follow the description, quite accessible and in his own words, of how he wrestled with theories of fundamental importance. Needless to say, we shall not be under any illusion that by doing so we can imitate or even fully "explain" his detailed thought processes, nor will we forget that other scientists have other styles. But Einstein's humane and thoughtful description of scientific reasoning will serve as a reminder of how false the popular, hostile caricatures are that depict contemporary scientific thought. . . .

There are numerous sources to draw on, for Einstein wrote about his view of the nature of scientific discovery, in a generally consistent way, on many occasions, notably in the essays collected in the book *Ideas and Opinions* and in his letters. He was also intrigued enough by this problem to discuss it with researchers into the psychology of scientific ideas and with philosophers of science. Indeed, from his earliest student days, Einstein was deeply interested in the theory of knowledge (epistemology). He wrote, "The reciprocal relationship of epistemology and science is of noteworthy kind. They are dependent upon each other. Epistemology without contact with science becomes an empty scheme. Science without epistemology is—insofar as it is thinkable at all—primitive and muddled."[2]

There are two especially suitable routes to Einstein's thoughts. One is a set of pages near the beginning of the "Autobiographical Notes," which he wrote in 1946.[3] It is the only serious autobiographical essay he ever wrote, and he called it jokingly his own "obituary." It gives a fascinating picture of Einstein's contributions as he viewed them, looking back at the age of sixty-seven. The essay is chiefly an account of his intellectual development rather than an autobiography in the usual sense. We shall now use this remarkable document to learn from his own words, while avoiding the use of technical, philosophical terminology, as he himself avoided it. All quotations not otherwise identified are from the pages of this text.

The other path to an understanding of Einstein's way of thinking is found in some letters he wrote to an old friend after publication of the "Autobiographical Notes." These allow Einstein to rebut, so to speak, a few of the objections a reader of the autobiographical essay might have, and I discuss them therefore at the end of this chapter, where Einstein should have the final word.

The Courage to Think

It certainly is curious to start one's autobiography, not with where and when one was born, the names of one's parents, and similar personal

---

[2] Paul Arthur Schilpp, ed., *Albert Einstein: Philosopher-Scientist* (Evanston, Ill.: Library of Living Philosophers, Inc., 1949), pp. 683–84.
[3] Albert Einstein, "Autobiographical Notes" (in German and English), in Schilpp, pp. 1–95.

details, but to focus instead on a question which Einstein phrases simply: "What, precisely, is thinking?" Einstein explains why he has to start his "obituary" in this way: "For the essential in the being of a man of my type lies precisely in *what* he thinks and *how* he thinks, not in what he does or suffers."[4]

From this viewpoint, thinking is not a joy or a chore added to the daily existence. It is the essence of a person's very being, and the tool by which the transient sorrows, the primitive forms of feeling, and what he calls the other "merely personal" parts of existence can be mastered. For it is through such thought that one can lift oneself up to a level where one can think about "great, eternal riddles." It is a "liberation" which can yield inner freedom and security. When the mind grasps the "extra-personal" part of the world—that part which is not tied to shifting desires and moods—it gains knowledge which all men and women can share regardless of individual conditions customs and other differences.

This, of course, is precisely why the laws of nature, toward which these thoughts can be directed, are so powerful: their applicability in principle can be demonstrated by anyone, anywhere, at any time. The laws of nature are utterly shareable. Insofar as the conclusions are right, the laws discovered by a scientist are equally valid for different thinkers, or *invariant* with respect to the individual personal situations. Einstein's interest in this matter seems to be not unrelated to his work in the physics of relativity: The essence of relativity theory is precisely that it provides a tool for expressing the laws of nature in such a manner that they are invariant with respect to differently moving observers.

As his "Autobiographical Notes" show, Einstein was also aware that life cannot be all thought, that even the enjoyment of thought can be carried to a point where it may be "at the cost of other sides" of one's personality. But the danger which more ordinary persons face is not that they will abandon their very necessary personal ties, but that the society surrounding them will not say often enough what Einstein here suggests to his wide audience: that the purpose of thinking is more than merely solving problems and puzzles. It is instead, and most importantly, the necessary tool for permitting one's intellectual talent to come through, so that "gradually the major interest disengages itself . . . from the momentary and merely personal." Here Einstein is saying: Have the courage to take your own thoughts seriously, for they will shape you. And significantly, Einstein meant his whole analysis to apply to thinking on any topic, not only on scientific matters.

---

[4] Ibid., p. 33.

Thinking with Images

Having touched on the *why* of thinking, the autobiography takes up the *how* of thinking and strangely seems to be concerned with "pictures" (*Bilder*):

> What, precisely, is "thinking"? When, at the reception of sense-impressions, memory-pictures emerge, this is not yet "thinking." And when such pictures form series, each member of which calls forth another, this too is not yet "thinking." When, however, a certain picture turns up in many such series, then—precisely through such return—it becomes an ordering element for such series, in that it connects series which in themselves are unconnected. Such an element becomes an instrument, a concept.

Adhering to one of several contesting traditions in psychology and philosophy and perhaps particularly influenced by Helmholtz and Boltzmann,[5] Einstein holds that the repeated encounter with images (such as "memory pictures") in a different context leads to the formation of "concepts." Thus, a small child might form the concept "glass" when he or she experiences that a variety of differently shaped solids are hard, transparent, and break on being dropped.

A concept must of course eventually be put into a form where it can be communicated to others; but for private thought it is not necessary to wait for this stage. For some people, including such physicists as Faraday and Rutherford,[6] the most important part of thinking may occur without the use of words. Einstein writes: "I have no doubts but that our thinking goes on for the most part without use of signs (words) and beyond that to a considerable degree unconsciously." Such persons tend to think in terms of images to which words may or may not be assignable; Einstein tells of his pleasure in discovering, as a boy, his skill in contemplating relationships among geometrical "objects"— triangles and other nonverbal elements of the imagination. . . . Einstein explained in a letter to the mathematician Jacques Hadamar that in his thinking he used no words but "certain signs and more or less clear images which can be voluntarily produced and combined." Einstein's letter continued as follows:

> The psychical entities which seem to serve as elements in thought are certain signs and more or less clear images which can be "voluntarily" reproduced and combined. . . . But taken from a psychological viewpoint, this combinatory play seems to be the essential feature in productive thought— before there is any connection in words or other kinds of signs which can be communicated to others. The above-mentioned elements are, in my case,

---

[5] *Hermann Helmholtz* (1821–1894): German physicist; *Ludwig Boltzmann* (1844–1906): Austrian physicist. [Eds.]
[6] *Michael Faraday* (1791–1867): English physicist; *Ernest Rutherford* (1871–1937): English physicist. [Eds.].

of visual and some muscular type. Conventional words or other signs have to be sought for laboriously only in a secondary stage, when the mentioned associative play is sufficiently established and can be reproduced at will.[7]

Einstein's ability to visualize is evident in the brilliant use he made of "thought experiments" (*Gedankenexperimente*). His first came to him at the age of about sixteen, when he tried to imagine that he was pursuing a beam of light and wondered what the observable values of the electric and magnetic field vectors would be in the electromagnetic wave making up the light beam. For example, looking back along the beam over the space of one whole wavelength, one should see that the local magnitudes of the electric and magnetic field vectors increase point by point from, say, zero to full strength, and then decrease again to zero, one wavelength away. This seemed to him a paradoxical conclusion. Already at that age, he seems to have assumed that Maxwell's equations must remain unchanged in form for the observer moving along the beam;[8] but from those equations one did not expect to find such a stationary oscillatory pattern of electric and magnetic field vectors in free space. He realized later that in this problem "the germ of the special relativity theory was contained." (Among other examples of visualized *Gedankenexperimente*, Einstein related one which he said had led him to the general theory of relativity. . . .)

The Free Play with Concepts

Having stressed the role of images and memory pictures, including *Gedankenexperimente*, in thinking, and having defined "concepts" as the crystallized products, the unvarying elements found to be common to many series of such memory pictures, Einstein now makes a startling assertion: "All our thinking is of the nature of a free play with concepts." This sentence has to be unraveled for it deals with two opposite but equally indispensable elements in all human thought, the empirical and the rational.

Even if one grants that "free play" is still play within some set of rules— similar to tentatively trying out a word to see if it fits into a crossword puzzle—by no means all philosophers would agree with Einstein's position. Some would argue that the external world imposes itself strongly on us and gives us little leeway for play, let alone for choosing the rules of the game. In Einstein's youth, most of his contemporaries believed in Immanuel Kant's description of the boundaries of such "play," namely, that they were to be fixed by two intuitions which are present in one's mind already at birth (i.e.,

---

[7] Albert Einstein, *Ideas and Opinions*, new translations and revisions by Sonja Bergmann (New York: Crown, 1954), pp. 25–26.
[8] *James Clerk Maxwell* (1831–1879): Scottish physicist. [Eds.]

a priori): Newtonian absolute space and absolute time. Only a few disagreed, including Ernst Mach,[9] who called absolute space "a conceptual monstrosity, purely a thought-thing which cannot be pointed to in experience."

Thus Einstein was struggling anew with the old question: What precisely is the relation between our knowledge and the sensory raw material, "the only source of our knowledge"?[10] If we could be sure that there is one unchanging, external, "objective" world that is connected to our brains and our sensations in a reliable, causal way, then pure thought can lead to truths about physical science. But since we cannot be certain of this, how can we avoid falling constantly into error or fantasy? David Hume had shown that "habit may lead us to belief and expectation but not to the knowledge, and still less to the understanding, of lawful relations."[11] Einstein concluded that, "In error are those theorists who believe that theory comes inductively from experience."[12]

In fact, he was skeptical about both of the major opposing philosophies. He wrote that there is an "aristocratic illusion [of subjectivism or idealism] concerning the unlimited penetrating power of thought," just as there is a "plebian illusion of naive realism, according to which things are as they are perceived by us through our senses."[13] Einstein held that there is no "real world" which one can access directly—the whole concept of the "real world"[14] being justified only insofar as it refers to the mental connections that weave the multitude of sense impressions into some connected net. Sense impressions are "conditioned by an 'objective' and by a 'subjective' factor."[15] Similarly, reality itself is a relation between what is outside us and inside us. "The real world is not given to us, but put to us (by way of a riddle)."[16]

Since the world as dealt with by a scientist is more complex than was allowed for in the current philosophies, Einstein thought that the way to escape illusion was by avoiding being a captive of any one school of philosophy. He would take from any system the portions he found useful. Such a scientist, he realized "therefore must appear to the systematic epistemologist as a type of unscrupulous opportunist: he appears as a *realist* insofar as he seeks to describe the world independent of the acts of perception; as *idealist* insofar as he looks upon the concepts and theories as the free inventions of the human spirit (not logically derivable from what is empirically given); as *positivist* insofar as he considers his concepts and theories justified *only* to

---

[9] *Ernst Mach* (1838–1916): Austrian physicist, psychologist, and philosopher. [Eds.]
[10] Ibid., p. 22.
[11] Ibid. (David Hume [1711–1776]: Scottish philosopher and historian. [Eds.])
[12] Ibid., p. 301.
[13] Ibid., p. 20.
[14] Ibid., p. 291.
[15] Schilpp, p. 673.
[16] Ibid., p. 680.

the extent to which they furnish a logical representation of relations among sensory experiences. He may even appear as *Platonist* or *Pythagorean* insofar as he considers the viewpoint of logical simplicity as an indispensable and effective tool of his research."[17]

But what justifies this "free play with concepts"? There is only one justification: that it can result, perhaps after much labor, in a thought structure which gives us the testable realization of having achieved meaningful order over a large range of sense experiences that would otherwise seem separate and unconnected. In the important essay "Physics and Reality,"[18] which covers much of the same ground as the early pages of the "Autobiographical Notes," Einstein makes the same point with this fine image: "By means of such concepts and mental relations between them we are able to orient ourselves in the labyrinth of sense impressions."[19]

This important process is described by Einstein in a condensed paragraph of the "Autobiographical Notes." "Imagine," he says, "on one side the totality of sense experiences," such as the observation that the needle on a meter is seen to deflect. On the other side, he puts the "totality of concepts and propositions which are laid down in books," which comprises the distilled products of past progress such as the concepts of force or momentum, propositions or axioms that make use of such concepts (for example, the law of conservation of momentum), and more generally, any concepts of ordinary thinking (for example, "black" and "raven"). Investigating the relations that exist among the concepts and propositions is "the business of logical thinking," which is carried out along the "firmly laid-down rules" of logic. The rules of logic, like the concepts themselves, are of course not God-given but are the "creation of humans." However, once they are agreed upon and are part of a widely held convention—the rules of syllogism, for example—they tell us with (only seemingly) inescapable finality that *if* all ravens are black and a particular bird is a raven, then the bird is black. They allow us to deduce from the law of conservation of momentum that in a closed system containing only a neutron and proton, the momentum gained by one is accompanied by the loss experienced by the other. Without the use of logic to draw conclusions, no disciplined thinking, and hence no science, could exist.

But all such conclusions, Einstein warns, are empty of useful "meaning" or "content" until there is some definition by which the particular concept

---

[17] Ibid., p. 684. (The Greek philosopher Plato [c. 428–348 B.C.] regarded mathematics and its method far more highly than sense knowledge. Followers of Pythagoras [c. 580–500 B.C.], Greek philosopher and mathematician, supposed that the substances of all things were numbers and that all phenomena were sensuous apprehensions of mathematical ratios. [Eds.])

[18] Einstein, *Ideas and Opinions*, p. 290ff.

[19] Ibid., p. 291.

(e.g., "raven" or "neutron") is correlated with actual instances of the concept which have consequences in the world of experience rather than in the world of words and logical rules. Necessary though the correlation of connection between concepts and sense experience is, Einstein warns that it is "not itself of a logical nature." It is an act in which, Einstein holds, "intuition" is one guide, even if not an infallible one. Without it, one could not be led to the assertion that a particular bird, despite some differences in its exact size or degree of blackness from all other birds, does belong to the species raven; or that the start of a particular track, visible in the cloud chamber, is the place where a neutron has struck a proton.

One might wish that Einstein had used a notion more firm than the dangerous-sounding one of "intuition." But he saw no other way. He rejected the use of the word *abstraction* to characterize the transition from observation to concept, e.g., from individual black birds to the idea of "raven." He rejected it precisely because, he said, "I do not consider it justifiable to veil the logical independence of the concept from the sense experiences" (whereas the use of the term *abstraction* or *induction* might make it seem as if there *were* a logical dependence).

The danger is evidently that delusion or fantasy can and does make similar use of the elements of thinking: and since there are no hard, utterly reliable connections between the concepts, propositions, and experience, one cannot know with absolute certainty whether one has escaped the trap of false conclusion. That is why it was thought for so long that observations proved the earth was fixed and the sun went around the earth; that time had a universal meaning, the same for all moving observers; and that Euclidean geometry is the only one that has a place in the physical world. But this is just where Einstein's view is most helpful: Only those who think they *can* play freely with concepts can pull themselves out of such error. His message is even more liberal: The concepts themselves, in our thoughts and verbal expressions, are, "when viewed logically, the free creation of thought which cannot inductively be gained from sense experience." We must be continually aware that it is not necessity but habit which leads us to identify certain concepts (for example, "bread") with corresponding sense experience (feel, smell, taste, satisfaction); for, since this works well enough most of the time, "we do not become conscious of the gulf—logically unbridgeable—which separates the world of sense experience from the world of concepts and propositions." Einstein is perhaps so insistent on the point because he had to discover it the hard way: as a young man, he had to overcome the accepted meanings of such concepts as space, time, simultaneity, energy, etc., and to propose redefinitions that reshaped all our physics, and hence our very concept of reality itself. One might well add here that Einstein demanded the same freedom to challenge orthodoxy outside science. Thus, as a boy he rejected the malignant militarism he saw entrenched in the life of his native country.

Once a conceptual structure has tentatively been erected, how can one check whether it is scientifically "true"? It depends on how nearly the aim of making the system deal with a large amount of diverse sense experience has been achieved, and how economical or parsimonious the introduction of separate basic concepts or axioms into the system has been. Einstein doubted a physical theory, and would say that it failed to "go to the heart of the matter," if it had to be jerry-built with the aid of ad hoc hypotheses, each specially introduced to produce greater agreement between theory and experience (experiment). He also was rarely convinced by theories that dealt with only a small part of the range of physical phenomena, applicable only here or there under special circumstances. In this view, a really good theory, one that has high scientific "truth" value, is considered to be correct not merely when it does not harbor any logical contradictions, but when it allows a close check on the correspondence between the predictions of the theory and a large range of possible experimental experiences. He summarized all this in the following way: "One comes nearer to the most superior scientific goal, to embrace a maximum of experimental content through logical deduction from a minimum of hypotheses. . . . One must allow the theoretician his imagination, for there is no other possible way for reaching the goal. In any case, it is not an aimless imagination but a search for the logically simplest possibilities and their consequences."

This search may take "years of groping in the dark"; hence, the ability to hold onto a problem for a long time, and not to be destroyed by repeated failure, is necessary for any serious researcher. As Einstein once said, "Now I know why there are so many people who love chopping wood. In that activity one immediately sees the results." But for him, the goal of "embracing a maximum of experimental content . . . with a minimum of hypotheses" meant nothing less than endless devotion to the simplification and unification of our world picture, for example, by producing fusions in hitherto separate fundamental concepts such as space and time, mass and energy, gravitation and inertial mass, electric and magnetic fields, and inertial and accelerating systems.

Keeping Alive the Sense of Wonder

Embedded in Einstein's views on how to think scientifically about the deep problems, there is an engaging passage in the "Autobiographical Notes" in which Einstein speaks of the importance of the sense of marvel, of deep curiosity, of "wonder," such as his two experiences, when, at the age of four or five, he was shown a magnetic compass by his father, and when, at the age of twelve, a book on Euclidean geometry came into his hands. A person's thought-world develops in part by the mastering of certain new experiences which were so inexplicable, in terms of the previous stage of development, that a sense of wonder or enchantment was aroused. As we learn more, both through science and other approaches, we progressively find that the world around us, as it becomes more rational, also becomes more "disenchanted." But Einstein repeatedly insisted in other writings that there is a limit to this progressive disenchantment, and even the best scientist must not be so insensitive or falsely proud as to forget it. For, as Einstein said in a famous paragraph: "It is a fact that the totality of sense experiences is so constituted as to permit putting them in order by means of thinking—a fact which can only leave us astonished, but which we shall never comprehend. One can say: The eternally incomprehensible thing about the world is its comprehensibility."

He went on: "In speaking here of 'comprehensibility,' the expression is used in its most modest sense. It implies: the production of some sort of order among sense impressions, this order being produced by the creation of general concepts, by relations among these concepts, and by relations of some kind between the concepts and sense experience. It is in this sense that the world of our sense experiences is comprehensible. The fact that it is comprehensible is a wonder."[20]

That wonder [*Wunder*], that sense of awe, can only grow stronger, Einstein implied, the more successfully our scientific thoughts find order to exist among the separate phenomena of nature. This success aroused in him a "deep conviction of the rationality of the universe." To this conviction he gave the name "cosmic religious feeling," and he saw it as the "strongest and noblest motive for scientific research."[21] Indeed, "The most beautiful experience we can have is the mysterious. It is the fundamental emotion which stands at the cradle of true art and true science. Whoever does not know it and can no longer wonder, no longer marvel, is as good as dead. . . ."[22]

After the publication of such sentiments, Einstein received a worried letter from one of his oldest and best friends, Maurice Solovine. They had met in Bern in 1902 when Einstein was twenty-three years old, and they became close friends. Solovine was then a young philosophy student at the University of Bern, to which he had come from Romania, and, together with Conrad Habicht, who was also a student at the university, they banded together to meet regularly to read and discuss works in science and philosophy. With high irony they called themselves the "Olympia Academy." Their "dinners" were no banquets: They all lived on the edge of poverty, and Solovine tells us that their

---

[20] Ibid., p. 292 (but in corrected translation).
[21] Ibid., p. J9.
[22] Ibid., p. 11.

idea of a special dinner was two hard-boiled eggs each. But the talk was that much better, as they discussed works by Ernst Mach, J. S. Mill, David Hume, Plato, Henri Poincaré, Karl Pearson, Spinoza, Hermann Helmholtz, Ampère— and also those of Sophocles, Racine, and Dickens.[23] Many of Einstein's epistemological ideas might be traced back to these discussions.

Now, half a century later, Maurice Solovine was concerned. He asked Einstein how there could be a puzzle about the comprehensibility of our world. For us it is simply an undeniable necessity, which lies in our very nature. No doubt Solovine was bothered that Einstein's remarks seemed to allow into science, that most rational activity of mankind, a function for the human mind which is not rational in the sense of being coldly logical. But Einstein rejected as a "malady"[24] the kind of accusation that implied that he had become "metaphysical." Instead, he saw the opportunity of using *all* one's faculties and skills to do science as a sign of strength rather than of weakness.

Certainly, he did not propose to abandon rationality, nor to guess where one must puzzle things out in a careful, logical way. But he saw that there is, and has to be, a role for those other elements of thinking which properly used, can help scientific thought. Specifically, this could become necessary at two points in Einstein's scheme. One is the courageous use of an intuitive feeling for nature *when there is simply no other guide at all*—as when one has tentatively to propose an axiom that by definition is unproved (as Einstein did at the start of the first paper on relativity, where he simply proposed the principle of relativity and the principle of constancy of light velocity); or when one decides which sense experiences to select in order to make an operational definition of a concept. The other point is the sense of wonder at being able to discern something of the grand design of the world, a feeling that motivates and sustains many a scientist.

Einstein's reply (in his letter of 30 March 1952) to Solovine addresses this second point.

> You find it remarkable that the comprehensibility of the world (insofar as we are justified to speak of such a comprehensibility) seems to me a wonder or eternal secret. Now, *a priori*, one should, after all, expect a chaotic world that is in no way graspable through thinking. One could (even *should*) expect that the world turns out to be lawful only insofar as we make an ordering intervention. It would be a kind of ordering like putting into alphabetic order the words of a language. On the other hand, the kind of order

---

[23] *John Stuart Mill* (1806–1873): English philosopher and economist; *Henri Poincaré* (1854–1912): French mathematician; *Karl Pearson* (1857–1936): English statistician; *Baruch Spinoza* (1632–1677): Dutch philosopher; *André Ampère* (1775–1836): French physicist; *Sophocles* (c. 496–406 B.C.): Greek dramatist; *Jean Baptiste Racine* (1639–1699): French dramatist, *Charles Dickens* (1812–1870): English novelist. [Eds.]

[24] Ibid., p. 24.

which, for example, was created through [the discovery of] Newton's theory of gravitation is of quite a different character. Even if the axioms of the theory are put forward by human agents, the success of such an enterprise does suppose a high degree of, order in the objective world, which one had no justification whatever to expect *a priori*. Here lies the sense of "wonder" which increases even more with the development of our knowledge.

And here lies the weak point for the positivists and the professional atheists, who are feeling happy through the consciousness of having successfully made the world not only God-free, but even "wonder-free." The nice thing is that we must be content with the acknowledgment of the "wonder," without there being a legitimate way beyond it. I feel I must add this explicitly, so you wouldn't think that I—weakened by age—have become a victim of the clergy.

In one of Einstein's other letters to Maurice Solovine, Einstein goes over some of these questions—but this time with the aid of a diagram, as befits a person who prefers to think visually.[25] In this and all these writings, Einstein asks his reader to take the business of making progress in science into one's own hands; to insist on thinking one's own thoughts even if they are not blessed by consent from the crowd; to rebel against the presumed inevitability or orthodoxy of ideas that do not meet the test of an original mind; and to live and think in all segments of our rich world—at the level of everyday experience, the level of scientific reasoning, and the level of deeply felt wonder.

---

[25] The analysis is the subject of "Einstein's Model for Constructing a Scientific Theory," chapter 2 in G. Holton, *The Advancement of Science, and Its Burdens: The Jefferson Lecture and Other Essays* (New York: Cambridge University Press, 1986).

Feynman's Figurations

Martin Kemp

How are we to understand Richard Feynman's statement, repeated in various forms, that "nobody understands quantum mechanics"? As the great authority on quantum electrodynamics and an eloquent communicator of difficult physics to nonspecialist audiences, his aphorism cannot be taken at face value.

He could not have meant that it was impossible to comprehend the basic principles, nor was he intending to dismiss the analytical and predictive efficacy of the mathematics of quantum mechanics. Rather, his assertion has to be interpreted in the light of the gravitational pull of physical modeling and graphic picturing in his approach to the physics.

He was continually concerned about the way that physical behaviour could be expressed in algebraic conventions without concrete visualization: "Strange! I don't understand how it is that we can write mathematical expressions and calculate what the thing is going to do without being able to picture it."

As Freeman Dyson recalled, "he was a natural physicist, and he thought in terms of concrete objects. The mathematics was an encumbrance, something you had to stick on afterwards, more or less . . . as a necessary evil."

The now ubiquitous 'Feynman diagrams' achieved the graphic encoding of phenomena whose very nature means that they cannot be subject to direct picturing. In the 1949 paper that inaugurated his method, he provided the classic demonstration of the "fundamental interaction" in which electrons exchange a proton. The electrons are figured as solid lines, while the process of exchange of a 'virtual quantum' is represented by a wavy line, which graphically signals that the photon can be emitted from one electron and absorbed by the other, or if it travels backwards in time, in reverse. Either way, the result is the deflection of both electrons, denoted by their angular deviation.

Feynman diagrams look superficially like the simple graphics that physicists have used for centuries. But they are devices of exceptional power. Within their space–time coordinates, Feynman was able to sidestep the long-winded algebraic formulas that treated electrons and positrons separately. All the equations came together in one picture in a way that preceded and even directed calculation.

The diagrams rapidly and economically explained and predicted in ways that were both intuitive and analytical. Feynman himself described the intuitive element in a characteristically graphic way: "It's like asking a centipede which leg comes after which—it happens quickly, and I'm not exactly sure what flashes and things go on in the head. I do know it's a crazy mixture of partially solved equations and some kind of visual picture of what the equation is saying is happening, but not as well separated as the words I'm using."

The diagrams mirror his conviction that

"there is . . . a rhythm and a pattern between the phenomena of nature which is not apparent to the eye, but only to the eye of analysis".

Such a potent grammar of diagrams and matching equations provides a marvellous tool. Yet is it reasonable to wonder whether it also constrains what minds lesser than Feynman's permit themselves to envisage?

The Historical Structure of Scientific Discovery

Thomas Kuhn

My object in this article is to isolate and illuminate one small part of what I take to be a continuing historiographic revolution in the study of science.[1] The structure of scientific discovery is my particular topic, and I can best approach it by pointing out that the subject itself may well seem extraordinarily odd. Both scientists and, until quite recently, historians have ordinarily viewed discovery as the sort of event which, though it may have preconditions and surely has consequences, is itself without internal structure. Rather than being seen as a complex development extended both in space and time, discovering something has usually seemed to be a unitary event, one which, like seeing something, happens to an individual at a specifiable time and place.

This view of the nature of discovery has, I suspect, deep roots in the nature of the scientific community. One of the few historical elements recurrent in the textbooks from which the prospective scientist learns his field is the attribution of particular natural phenomena to the historical personages who first discovered them. As a result of this and other aspects of their training, discovery becomes for many scientists an important goal. To make a discovery is to achieve one of the closest approximations to a property right that the scientific career affords. Professional prestige is often closely associated with these acquisitions.[2] Small wonder, then, that acrimonious disputes about priority and independence in discovery have often marred the normally placid

---

[1] The larger revolution will be discussed in my forthcoming book, *The Structure of Scientific Revolution*, to be published in the fall by the University of Chicago Press. The central ideas in this paper have been abstracted from that source, particularly from its third chapter, "Anomaly and the Emergence of Scientific Discoveries" [2nd ed., 1970].

[2] For a brilliant discussion of these points, see R. K Merton, "Priorities in Scientific Discovery: A Chapter in the Sociology of Science," *American Sociological Review* 22 (1957): 635. Also very relevant, though it did not appear until this article had been prepared, is F. Reif, "The Competitive World of the Pure Scientist," *Science* 134 (1961): 1957.

tenor of scientific communication. Even less wonder that many historians of science have seen the individual discovery as an appropriate unit with which to measure scientific progress and have devoted much time and skill to determining what man made which discovery at what point in time. If the study of discovery has a surprise to offer, it is only that, despite the immense energy and ingenuity expended upon it, neither polemic nor painstaking scholarship has often succeeded in pinpointing the time and place at which a given discovery could properly be said to have "been made."

That failure, both of argument and of research, suggests the thesis that I now wish to develop. Many scientific discoveries, particularly the most interesting and important, are not the sort of event about which the questions "Where?" and, more particularly, "When?" can appropriately be asked. Even if all conceivable data were at hand, those questions would not regularly possess answers. That we are persistently driven to ask them nonetheless is symptomatic of a fundamental inappropriateness in our image of discovery. That inappropriateness is here my main concern, but I approach it by considering first the historical problem presented by the attempt to date and to place a major class of fundamental discoveries.

The troublesome class consists of those discoveries—including oxygen, the electric current, X rays, and the electron—which could not be predicted from accepted theory in advance and which therefore caught the assembled profession by surprise. That kind of discovery will shortly be my exclusive concern, but it will help first to note that there is another sort and one which presents very few of the same problems. Into this second class of discoveries fall the neutrino, radio waves, and the elements which filled empty places in the periodic table. The existence of all these objects had been predicted from theory before they were discovered, and the men who made the discoveries therefore knew from the start what to look for. That foreknowledge did not make their task less demanding or less interesting, but it did provide criteria which told them when their goal had been reached.[3] As a result, there have been few priority debates over discoveries of this second sort, and only a paucity of data can prevent the historian from ascribing them to a particular time and place. Those facts help to isolate the difficulties we encounter

[3] Not all discoveries fall so neatly as the preceding into one or the other of my two classes. For example, Anderson's work on the positron was done in complete ignorance of Dirac's electron theory from which the new particle's existence had already been very nearly predicted. On the other hand, the immediately succeeding work by Blackett and Occhialini made full use of Dirac's theory and therefore exploited experiment more fully and constructed a more forceful case for the positron's existence than Anderson had been able to do. On this subject see N. R. Hanson, "Discovering the Positron," *British Journal for the Philosophy of Science* 12 (1961): 194; 12 (1962): 299. Hanson suggests several of the points developed here. I am much indebted to Professor Hanson for a preprint of this material.

as we return to the troublesome discoveries of the first class. In the cases that most concern us here there are no benchmarks to inform either the scientist or the historian when the job of discovery has been done.

As an illustration of this fundamental problem and its consequences, consider first the discovery of oxygen. Because it has repeatedly been studied, often with exemplary care and skill, that discovery is unlikely to offer any purely factual surprises. Therefore it is particularly well suited to clarify points of principle.[4] At least three scientists—Carl Scheele, Joseph Priestley, and Antoine Lavoisier[5]—have a legitimate claim to this discovery, and polemicists have occasionally entered the same claim for Pierre Bayen.[6] Scheele's work, though it was almost certainly completed before the relevant researches of Priestley and Lavoisier, was not made public until their work was well known.[7] Therefore it had no apparent causal role, and I shall simplify my story by omitting it.[8] Instead, I pick up the main route to the discovery of oxygen with the work of Bayen, who, sometime before March 1774, discovered that red precipitate

---

[4] I have developed a less familiar example from the same viewpoint in "The Caloric Theory of Adiabatic Compression," *Isis* 49 (1958): 132. A closely similar analysis of the emergence of a new theory is included in the early pages of my essay "Energy Conservation as an Example of Simultaneous Discovery," in *Critical Problems in the History of Science*, ed. M. Clagett (Madison: University of Wisconsin Press, 1959), pp. 321–56. Reference to these papers may add depth and detail to the following discussion.

[5] *Carl Wilhelm Scheele* (1742-1786): Swedish chemist; *Joseph Priestley* (1733–1804): British chemist and clergyman; *Antoine-Laurent Lavoisier* (1743-1794): French chemist. *Pierre Bayen* (1725–1798), mentioned at the end of the sentence, was a French chemist [Eds.]

[6] The still classic discussion of the discovery of oxygen is A. N. Meldrum, *The Eighteenth Century Revolution in Science: The First Phase* (Calcutta, 1930), chap. 5. A more convenient and generally quite reliable discussion is included in J. B. Conant, *The Overthrow of the Phlogiston Theory: The Chemical Revolution of 1775–1789*. Harvard Case Histories in Experimental Science, case 2 (Cambridge: Harvard University Press, 1950). A recent and indispensable review, which includes an account of the development of the priority controversy, is M. Daumas, *Lavoisier, théoricien et expérimentateur* (Paris, 1955), chaps. 2 and 3. H. Guerlac has added much significant detail to our knowledge of the early relations between Priestley and Lavoisier in his "Joseph Priestley's First Papers on Gases and Their Reception in France," *Journal of the History of Medicine* 12 (1957): 1 and in his very recent monograph, *Lavoisier: The Crucial Year* (Ithaca: Cornell University Press, 1961). For Scheele see J. R. Partington, *A Short History of Chemistry*, 2d ed. (London, 1951), pp. 104–9.

[7] For the dating of Scheele's work, see A. E. Nordenskjöld, *Carl Wilhelm Scheele, Nachgelassene Briefe und Aufzeichnungen* (Stockholm, 1892).

[8] U. Backlund ("A Lost Letter from Scheele to Lavoisier," *Lychnos*, 1957–58, pp. 39-62) argues that Scheele communicated his discovery of oxygen to Lavoisier in a letter of 30 Sept. 1774. Certainly the letter is important, and it clearly demonstrates that Scheele was ahead of both Priestley and Lavoisier at the time it was written. But I think the letter is not quite so candid as Becklund supposes, and I fail to see how Lavoisier could have drawn the discovery of oxygen from it. Scheele describes a procedure for reconstituting common air, not for producing a new gas, and that, as we shall see, is almost the same information that Lavoisier received from Priestley at about the same time. In any case, there is no evidence that Lavoisier performed the sort of experiment that Scheele suggested.

of mercury (HgO) could, by heating, be made to yield a gas. That aeriform product Bayen identified as fixed air (CO_2), a substance made familiar to most pneumatic chemists by the earlier work of Joseph Black.[9] A variety of other substances were known to yield the same gas.

At the beginning of August 1774, a few months after Bayen's work had appeared, Joseph Priestley repeated the experiment, though probably independently. Priestley, however, observed that the gaseous product would support combustion and therefore changed the identification. For him the gas obtained on heating red precipitate was nitrous air (N_2O), a substance that he had himself discovered more than two years before.[10] Later in the same month Priestley made a trip to Paris and there informed Lavoisier of the new reaction. The latter repeated the experiment once more, both in November 1774 and in February 1775. But, because he used tests somewhat more elaborate than Priestley's, Lavoisier again changed the identification. For him, as of May 1775, the gas released by red precipitate was neither fixed air nor nitrous air. Instead, it was "[atmospheric] air itself entire without alteration . . . even to the point that . . . it comes out more pure."[11] Meanwhile, however, Priestley had also been at work, and, before the beginning of March 1775, he, too, had concluded that the gas must be "common air." Until this point all of the men who had produced a gas from red precipitate of mercury had identified it with some previously known species.[12]

The remainder of this story of discovery is briefly told. During March 1775 Priestley discovered that his gas was in several respects very much "better" than common air, and he therefore reidentified the gas once more, this time calling it "dephlogisticated air," that is, atmospheric air deprived of its normal complement of phlogiston.[13] This conclusion Priestley published in the *Philosophical Transactions,* and it was apparently that publication which led Lavoisier to reexamine his own results.[14] The reexamination

---

[9] P. Bayen, "Essai d'expériences chymiques, faites sur quelques précipités de mercure, dans la vue de découvrir leur nature, Seconde partie," *Observations sur la physique* 3 (1774): 280–95, particularly pp. 289–91. (*Joseph Black* [1728–1799]: Scottish physician and chemist. [Eds.])

[10] J. B. Conant, *The Overthrow of the Phlogiston Theory*, pp. 34–40.

[11] Ibid., p. 23. A useful translation of the full text is available in Conant.

[12] For simplicity I use the term *red precipitate* throughout. Actually, Bayen used the precipitate; Priestley used both the precipitate and the oxide produced by direct calcination of mercury; and Lavoisier used only the latter. The difference is not without importance, for it was not unequivocally clear to chemists that the two substances were identical.

[13] *phlogiston*, a New Latin coinage from the Greek word for inflammable, naming a substance formerly thought to escape when a material burns. Though a faulty theory, its investigation contributed to the discovery of oxygen. [Eds.]

[14] There has been some doubt about Priestley's having influenced Lavoisier's thinking at this point, but, when the latter returned to experimenting with the gas in February 1776, he recorded in his notebooks that he had obtained "l'air dephlogistique de M. Priestley" (M. Daumas, *Lavoisier*, p. 36).

began during February 1776 and within a year had led Lavoisier to the conclusion that the gas was actually a separable component of the atmospheric air which both he and Priestley had previously thought of as homogeneous. With this point reached, with the gas recognized as an irreducibly distinct species, we may conclude that the discovery of oxygen had been completed.

But to return to my initial question, when shall we say that oxygen was discovered and what criteria shall be used in answering that question? If discovering oxygen is simply holding an impure sample in one's hands, then the gas had been "discovered" in antiquity by the first man who ever bottled atmospheric air. Undoubtedly, for an experimental criterion, we must at least require a relatively pure sample like that obtained by Priestley in August 1774. But during 1774 Priestley was unaware that he had discovered anything except a new way to produce a relatively familiar species. Throughout that year his "discovery" is scarcely distinguishable from the one made earlier by Bayen, and neither case is quite distinct from that of the Reverend Stephen Hales, who had obtained the same gas more than forty years before.[15] Apparently to discover something one must also be aware of the discovery and know as well what it is that one has discovered.

But, that being the case, how much must one know? Had Priestley come close enough when he identified the gas as nitrous air? If not, was either he or Lavoisier significantly closer when he changed the identification to common air? And what are we to say about Priestley's next identification, the one made in March 1775? Dephlogisticated air is still not oxygen or even, for the phlogistic chemist, a quite unexpected sort of gas. Rather it is a particularly pure atmospheric air. Presumably, then, we wait for Lavoisier's work in 1776 and 1777, work which led him not merely to isolate the gas but to see what it was. Yet even that decision can be questioned, for in 1777 and to the end of his life Lavoisier insisted that oxygen was an atomic "principle of acidity" and that oxygen *gas* was formed only when that "principle" united with caloric, the matter of heat.[16] Shall we therefore say that oxygen had not yet been discovered in 1777? Some may be tempted to do so. But the principle of acidity was not banished from chemistry until after 1810 and caloric lingered on until the 1860s. Oxygen had, however, become a standard chemical substance long before either of those dates. Furthermore, what is perhaps the key point, it would probably have gained that status on the basis of Priestley's work alone without benefit of Lavoisier's still partial reinterpretation.

---

[15] J. R. Partington, *A Short History of Chemistry*, p. 91. (*Reverend Stephen Hales* [1677–1761]: British botanist and physiologist. [Eds.])

[16] For the traditional elements in Lavoisier's interpretations of chemical reactions, see H. Metzger, *La philosophie de la matière chez Lavoisier* (Paris, 1935), and Daumas, *Lavoisier,* chap. 7.

I conclude that we need a new vocabulary and new concepts for analyzing events like the discovery of oxygen. Though undoubtedly correct, the sentence "Oxygen was discovered" misleads by suggesting that discovering something is a single simple act unequivocally attributable, if only we knew enough, to an individual and an instant in time. When the discovery is unexpected, however, the latter attribution is always impossible and the former often is as well. Ignoring Scheele, we can, for example, safely say that oxygen had not been discovered before 1774; probably we would also insist that it had been discovered by 1774; probably we would also insist that it had been discovered by 1777 or shortly thereafter. But within those limits any attempt to date the discovery or to attribute it to an individual must inevitably be arbitrary. Furthermore, it must be arbitrary just because discovering a new sort of phenomenon is necessarily a complex process which involves recognizing both *that* something is and *what* it is. Observation and conceptualization, fact and the assimilation of fact to theory, are inseparably linked in the discovery of scientific novelty. Inevitably, that process extends over time and may often involve a number of people. Only for discoveries in my second category—those whose nature is known in advance—can discovering *that* and discovering *what* occur together and in an instant.

Two last, simpler, and far briefer examples will simultaneously show how typical the case of oxygen is and also prepare the way for a somewhat more precise conclusion. On the night of 13 March 1781, the astronomer William Herschel made the following entry in his journal: "In the quartile near Zeta Tauri . . . is a curious either nebulous star or perhaps a comet."[17] That entry is generally said to record the discovery of the planet Uranus, but it cannot quite have done that. Between 1690 and Herschel's observation in 1781 the same object had been seen and recorded at least seventeen times by men who took it to be a star. Herschel differed from them only in supposing that, because in his telescope it appeared especially large, it might actually be a *comet!* Two additional observations on 17 and 19 March confirmed that suspicion by showing that the object he had observed moved among the stars. As a result, astronomers throughout Europe were informed of the discovery, and the mathematicians among them began to compute the new comet's orbit. Only several months later, after all those attempts had repeatedly failed to square with observation, did the astronomer Lexell suggest that the object observed by Herschel might be a planet.[18] And only when additional computations, using a planet's rather than a comet's orbit, proved reconcilable with observation was

[17] P. Doig, *A Concise History of Astronomy* (London: Chapman, 1950), pp. 115–16. (*William Herschel* [1738–1822]: German-born English astronomer. [Eds.])
[18] *Anders Johan Lexell* (1740–1784): Swedish astronomer. [Eds.]

that suggestion generally accepted. At what point during 1781 do we want to say that the planet Uranus was discovered? And are we entirely and unequivocally clear that it was Herschel rather than Lexell who discovered it?

Or consider still more briefly the story of the discovery of X rays, a story which opens on the day in 1895 when the physicist Roentgen interrupted a well-precedented investigation of cathode rays because he noticed that a barium platinocyanide screen far from his shielded apparatus glowed when the discharge was in process.[19] Additional investigations—they required seven hectic weeks during which Roentgen rarely left the laboratory—indicated that the cause of the glow traveled in straight lines from the cathode ray tube, that the radiation cast shadows, that it could not be deflected by a magnet, and much else besides. Before announcing his discovery Roentgen had convinced himself that his effect was not due to cathode rays themselves but to a new form of radiation with at least some similarity to light. Once again the question suggests itself: When shall we say that X rays were actually discovered? Not, in any case, at the first instant, when all that had been noted was a glowing screen. At least one other investigator had seen that glow and, to his subsequent chagrin, discovered nothing at all. Nor, it is almost as clear, can the moment of discovery be pushed back to a point during the last week of investigation. By that time Roentgen was exploring the properties of the new radiation he had *already* discovered. We may have to settle for the remark that X rays emerged in Würzburg between 8 November and 28 December 1895.

The characteristics shared by these examples are, I think, common to all the episodes by which unanticipated novelties become subjects for scientific attention. I therefore conclude these brief remarks by discussing three such common characteristics, ones which may help to provide a framework for the further study of the extended episodes we customarily call "discoveries."

In the first place, notice that all three of our discoveries—oxygen, Uranus, and X rays—began with the experimental or observational isolation of an anomaly, that is, with nature's failure to conform entirely to expectation. Notice, further, that the process by which that anomaly was educed displays simultaneously the apparently incompatible characteristics of the inevitable and the accidental. In the case of X rays, the anomalous glow which provided Roentgen's first clue was clearly the result of an accidental disposition of his apparatus. But by 1895 cathode rays were a normal subject for research all over Europe; that research quite regularly juxtaposed cathode-ray tubes with sensitive screens and films; as a result Roentgen's accident was almost certain to occur elsewhere, as in fact it had. Those remarks, however, should make Roentgen's case look very much like those of Herschel

---

[19] L. W. Taylor, *Physics, the Pioneer Science* (Boston: Houghton Mifflin Co., 1941), p. 790. (*Wilhelm Konrad Roentgen* [1845–1923]: German physicist. [Eds.])

and Priestley. Herschel first observed his oversized and thus anomalous star in the course of a prolonged survey of the northern heavens. That survey was, except for the magnification provided by Herschel's instruments, precisely of the sort that had repeatedly been carried through before and that had occasionally resulted in prior observations of Uranus. And Priestley, too—when he isolated the gas that behaved almost but not quite like nitrous air and then almost but not quite like common air—was seeing something unintended and wrong in the outcome of a sort of experiment for which there was much European precedent and which had more than once before led to the production of the new gas.

These features suggest the existence of two normal requisites for the beginning of an episode of discovery. The first, which throughout this paper I have largely taken for granted, is the individual skill, wit, or genius to recognize that something has gone wrong in ways that may prove consequential. Not any and every scientist would have noted that no unrecorded star should be so large, that the screen ought not to have glowed, that nitrous air should not have supported life. But that requisite presupposes another which is less frequently taken for granted. Whatever the level of genius available to observe them, anomalies do not emerge from the normal course of scientific research until both instruments and concepts have developed sufficiently to make their emergence likely and to make the anomaly which results recognizable as a violation of expectation.[20] To say that an unexpected discovery begins only when something goes wrong is to say that it begins only when scientists know well both how their instruments and how nature should behave. What distinguished Priestley, who saw an anomaly, from Hales, who did not, is largely the considerable articulation of pneumatic techniques and expectations that had come into being during the four decades which separate their two isolations of oxygen.[21] The very number of claimants indicates that after 1770 the discovery could not have been postponed for long.

The role of anomaly is the first of the characteristics shared by our three examples. A second can be considered more briefly, for it has provided the main theme for the body of my text. Though awareness of anomaly

---

[20] Though the point cannot be argued here, the conditions which make the emergence of anomaly likely and those which make anomaly recognizable are to a very great extent the same. That fact may help us understand the extraordinarily large amount of simultaneous discovery in the sciences.

[21] A useful sketch of the development of pneumatic chemistry is included in Partington, *A Short History of Chemistry*, chap. 6.

marks the beginning of a discovery, it marks only the beginning. What necessarily follows, if anything at all is to be discovered, is a more or less extended period during which the individual and often many members of his group struggle to make the anomaly lawlike. Invariably that period demands additional observation or experimentation as well as repeated cogitation. While it continues, scientists repeatedly revise their expectations, usually their instrumental standards, and sometimes their most fundamental theories as well. In this sense discoveries have a proper internal history as well as prehistory and a posthistory. Furthermore, within the rather vaguely delimited interval of internal history, there is no single moment or day which the historian, however complete his data, can identify as the point at which the discovery was made. Often, when several individuals are involved, it is even impossible unequivocally to identify any one of them as the discoverer.

Finally, turning to the third of these selected common characteristics, note briefly what happens as the period of discovery draws to a close. A full discussion of that question would require additional evidence and a separate paper, for I have had little to say about the aftermath of discovery in the body of my text. Nevertheless, the topic must not be entirely neglected, for it is in part a corollary of what has already been said.

Discoveries are often described as mere additions or increments to the growing stockpile of scientific knowledge, and that description has helped make the unit discovery seem a significant measure of progress. I suggest, however, that it is fully appropriate only to those discoveries which, like the elements that filled missing places in the periodic table, were anticipated and sought in advance and which therefore demanded no adjustment, adaptation, and assimilation from the profession. Though the sorts of discoveries we have here been examining are undoubtedly additions to scientific knowledge, they are also something more. In a sense that I can now develop only in part, they also react back upon what has previously been known, providing a new view of some previously familiar objects and simultaneously changing the way in which even some traditional parts of science are practiced. Those in whose area of special competence the new phenomenon falls often see both the world and their work differently as they emerge from the extended struggle with anomaly which constitutes the discovery of that phenomenon.

William Herschel, for example, when he increased by one the time-honored number of planetary bodies, taught astronomers to see new things when they looked at the familiar heavens even with instruments more traditional than his own. That change in the vision of astronomers must be a principal reason why, in the half century after the discovery of Uranus, twenty additional circumsolar bodies were added to the traditional seven.[22] A similar transformation is even clearer in the aftermath of Roentgen's work. In the first place, established techniques for cathode-ray research had to be changed, for scientists found they had failed to control a relevant variable. Those changes included both the redesign of old apparatus and revised ways of asking old questions. In addition, those scientists most concerned experienced the same transformation of vision that we have just noted in the aftermath of the discovery of Uranus. X rays were the first new sort of radiation discovered since infrared and ultraviolet at the beginning of the century. But within less than a decade after Roentgen's work, four more were disclosed by the new scientific sensitivity (for example, to fogged photographic plates) and by some of the new instrumental techniques that had resulted from Roentgen's work and its assimilation.

Very often these transformations in the established techniques of scientific practice prove even more important than the incremental knowledge provided by the discovery itself. That could at least be argued in the cases of Uranus and of X rays; in the case of my third example, oxygen, it is categorically clear. Like the work of Herschel and Roentgen, that of Priestley and Lavoisier taught scientists to view old situations in new ways. Therefore, as we might anticipate, oxygen was not the only new chemical species to be identified in the aftermath of their work. But, in the case of oxygen, the readjustments demanded by assimilation were so profound that they played an integral and essential role—though they were not by themselves the cause—in the gigantic upheaval of chemical theory and practice which has since been known as the chemical revolution. I do not suggest that every unanticipated discovery has consequences for science so deep and so far-reaching as those which followed the discovery of oxygen. But I do suggest that every such discovery demands, from those most concerned, the sorts of readjustment that, when they are more obvious, we equate with scientific revolution. It is, I believe, just because they demand readjustments like these that the process of discovery is necessarily and inevitably one that shows structure and that therefore extends in time.

---

[22] R. Wolf, *Geschichte der Astronomie* (Munich, 1877), pp. 513–15, 683–93. The prephotographic discoveries of the asteroids [are] often seen as an effect of the invention of Bode's law. But that law cannot be the full explanation and may not even have played a large part. Piazzi's discovery of Ceres, in 1801, was made in ignorance of the current speculation about a missing planet in the "hole" between Mars and Jupiter. Instead, like Herschel, Piazzi was engaged on a star survey. More important, Bode's law was old by 1800 (ibid., p. 683), but only one man before that date seems to have thought it worthwhile to look for another planet. Finally, Bode's law, by itself, could only suggest the utility of looking for additional planets; it did not tell astronomers where to look. Clearly, however, the drive to look for additional planets dates from Herschel's work on Uranus.

The Spider and the Wasp

Alexander Petrunkevitch

In the feeding and safeguarding of their progeny insects and spiders exhibit some interesting analogies to reasoning and some crass examples of blind instinct. The case I propose to describe here is that of the tarantula spiders and their archenemy, the digger wasps of the genus Pepsis. It is a classic example of what looks like intelligence pitted against instinct—a strange situation in which the victim, though fully able to defend itself, submits unwittingly to its destruction.

Most tarantulas live in the tropics, but several species occur in the temperate zone and a few are common in the southern U.S. Some varieties are large and have powerful fangs with which they can inflict a deep wound. These formidable looking spiders do not, however, attack man; you can hold one in your hand, if you are gentle, without being bitten. Their bite is dangerous only to insects and small mammals such as mice; for man it is no worse than a hornet's sting.

Tarantulas customarily live in deep cylindrical burrows, from which they emerge at dusk and into which they retire at dawn. Mature males wander about after dark in search of females and occasionally stray into houses. After mating, the male dies in a few weeks, but a female lives much longer and can mate several years in succession. In a Paris museum is a tropical specimen which is said to have been living in captivity for 25 years.

A fertilized female tarantula lays from 200 to 400 eggs at a time; thus it is possible for a single tarantula to produce several thousand young. She takes no care of them beyond weaving a cocoon of silk to enclose the eggs. After they hatch, the young walk away, find convenient places in which to dig their burrows and spend the rest of their lives in solitude. The eyesight of tarantulas is poor, being limited to a sensing of change in the intensity of light and to the perception of moving objects. They apparently have little or no sense of hearing, for a hungry tarantula will pay no attention to a loudly chirping cricket placed in its cage unless the insect happens to touch one of its legs.

But all spiders, and especially hairy ones, have an extremely delicate sense of touch. Laboratory experiments prove that tarantulas can distinguish three types of touch: pressure against the body wall, stroking of the body hair, and riffling of certain very fine hairs on the legs called trichobothria. Pressure against the body, by the finger or the end of a pencil, causes the tarantula to move off slowly for a short distance. The touch excites no defensive response unless the approach is from above where the spider can see the motion, in which case it rises on its hind legs, lifts its front legs, opens its fangs and holds this threatening posture as long as the object continues to move.

The entire body of a tarantula, especially its legs, is thickly clothed with hair. Some of it is short and wooly, some long and stiff. Touching this body hair produces one of two distinct reactions. When the spider is hungry, it responds with an immediate and swift attack. At the touch of a cricket's antennae the tarantula seizes the insect so swiftly that a motion picture taken at the rate of 64 frames per second shows only the result and not the process of capture. But when the spider is not hungry, the stimulation of its hairs merely causes it to shake the touched limb. An insect can walk under its hairy belly unharmed.

The trichobothria, very fine hairs growing from dislike membranes on the legs, are sensitive only to air movement. A light breeze makes them vibrate slowly, without disturbing the common hair. When one blows gently on the trichobothria, the tarantula reacts with a quick jerk of its four front legs. If the front and hind legs are stimulated at the same time, the spider makes a sudden jump. This reaction is quite independent of the state of its appetite.

These three tactile responses—to pressure on the body wall, to moving of the common hair, and to flexing of the trichobothria—are so different from one another that there is no possibility of confusing them. They serve the tarantula adequately for most of its needs and enable it to avoid most annoyances and dangers. But they fail the spider completely when it meets its deadly enemy, the digger wasp Pepsis.

These solitary wasps are beautiful and formidable creatures. Most species are either a deep shiny blue all over, or deep blue with rusty wings. The largest have a wing span of about four inches. They live on nectar. When excited, they give off a pungent odor—a warning that they are ready to attack. The sting is much worse than that of a bee or common wasp, and the pain and swelling last longer. In the adult stage the wasp lives only a few months. The female produces but a few eggs, one at a time at intervals of two or three days. For each egg the mother must provide one adult tarantula, alive but paralyzed. The mother wasp attaches the egg to the paralyzed spider's abdomen. Upon hatching from the egg, the larva is many hundreds of times smaller than its living but helpless victim. It eats no other food and drinks no water. By the time it has finished its single Gargantuan meal and become ready for wasphood, nothing remains of the tarantula but its indigestible chitinous skeleton.

The mother wasp goes tarantula-hunting when the egg in her ovary is almost ready to be laid. Flying low over the ground late on a sunny afternoon, the wasp looks for its victim or for the mouth of a tarantula burrow, a round hole edged by a bit of silk. The sex of the spider makes no difference, but the mother is highly discriminating as to species. Each species of Pepsis requires a certain species of tarantula, and the wasp will not attack the wrong species. In a cage with a tarantula which is not its normal prey, the wasp avoids the spider and is usually killed by it in the night.

Yet when a wasp finds the correct species, it is the other way about. To identify the species the wasp apparently must explore the spider with her antennae. The tarantula shows an amazing tolerance to this exploration. The wasp crawls under it and walks over it without evoking any hostile response. The molestation is so great and so persistent that the tarantula often rises on all eight legs, as if it were on stilts. It may stand this way for several minutes. Meanwhile the wasp, having satisfied itself that the victim is of the right species, moves off a few inches to dig the spider's grave. Working vigorously with legs and jaws, it excavates a hole 8 to 10 inches deep with a diameter slightly larger than the spider's girth. Now and again the wasp pops out of the hole to make sure that the spider is still there.

When the grave is finished, the wasp returns to the tarantula to complete her ghastly enterprise. First she feels it all over once more with her antennae. Then her behavior becomes more aggressive. She bends her abdomen, protruding her sting, and searches for the soft membrane at the point where the spider's legs join its body—the only spot where she can penetrate the horny skeleton. From time to time, as the exasperated spider slowly shifts ground, the wasp turns on her back and slides along with the aid of her wings, trying to get under the tarantula for a shot at the vital spot. During all this maneuvering, which can last for several minutes, the tarantula makes no move to save itself. Finally the wasp corners it against some obstruction and grasps one of its legs in her powerful jaws. Now at last the harassed spider tries a desperate but vain defense. The two contestants roll over and over on the ground. It is a terrifying sight and the outcome is always the same. The wasp finally manages to thrust her sting into the soft spot and holds it there for a few seconds while she pumps in the poison. Almost immediately the tarantula falls paralyzed on its back. Its legs stop twitching; its heart stops beating. Yet it is not dead, as is shown by the fact that if taken from the wasp it can be restored to some sensitivity by being kept in a moist chamber for several months.

After paralyzing the tarantula, the wasp cleans herself by dragging her body along the ground and rubbing her feet, sucks the drop of blood oozing from the wound in the spider's abdomen, then grabs a leg of the flabby, helpless animal in her jaws and drags it down to the bottom of the grave. She stays there for many minutes, sometimes for several hours, and what she does all that time in the dark we do not know. Eventually she lays her egg and attaches it to the side of the spider's abdomen with a sticky secretion. Then she emerges, fills the grave with soil carried bit by bit in her jaws, and finally tramples the ground all around to hide any trace of the grave from prowlers. Then she flies away, leaving her descendant safely started in life.

In all this the behavior of the wasp evidently is qualitatively different from that of the spider. The wasp acts like an intelligent animal. This is not to say that instinct plays no part or that she reasons as man does. But her actions are to the point; they are not automatic and can be modified to fit the situation. We do not know for certain how she identifies the tarantula—probably it is by some olfactory or chemo-tactile sense—but she does it purposefully and does not blindly tackle a wrong species.

On the other hand, the tarantula's behavior shows only confusion. Evidently the wasp's pawing gives it no pleasure, for it tries to move away. That the wasp is not simulating sexual stimulation is certain because male and female tarantulas react in the same way to its advances. That the spider is not anesthetized by some odorless secretion is easily shown by blowing lightly at the tarantula and making it jump suddenly. What, then, makes the tarantula behave as stupidly as it does?

No clear, simple answer is available. Possibly the stimulation by the wasp's antennae is masked by a heavier pressure on the spider's body, so that it reacts as when prodded by a pencil. But the explanation may be much more complex. Initiative in attack is not in the nature of tarantulas; most species fight only when cornered so that escape is impossible. Their inherited patterns of behavior apparently prompt them to avoid problems rather than attack them. For example, spiders always weave their webs in three dimensions, and when a spider finds that there is insufficient space to attach certain threads in the third dimension, it leaves the place and seeks another, instead of finishing the web in a single plane. This urge to escape seems to arise under all circumstances, in all phases of life, and to take the place of reasoning. For a spider to change the pattern of its web is as impossible as for an inexperienced man to build a bridge across a chasm obstructing his way.

In a way the instinctive urge to escape is not only easier but often more efficient than reasoning. The tarantula does exactly what is most efficient in all cases except in an encounter with a ruthless and determined attacker dependent for the existence of her own species on killing as many tarantulas as she can lay eggs. Perhaps in this case the spider follows its usual pattern of trying to escape, instead of seizing and killing the wasp, because it is not aware of its danger. In any case, the survival of the tarantula species as a whole is protected by the fact that the spider is much more fertile than the wasp.

Paradoxes and Predicaments in Learning to Design

Donald Schon

So far, we have considered the dialogue of Quist and Petra for what it reveals about the design process. What would we notice if we took it as an example of design *education*?

Petra, who has been trying to do something on her own, has got stuck. She seems unclear just what she should be doing, or she has ideas about it that are incongruent with Quist's. Quist, after listening to her "big problems," takes charge of the desk crit. Using the drawing/talking language to make his process accessible to Petra, he demonstrates the kind of process he believes she should be carrying out, punctuating his demonstration with reflections on designing.

What does Petra make of all this? Quist does not ask her, and she does not tell him. If she remains confused about the meaning of "designing," in spite of Quist's demonstrations and reflections, neither we nor Quist can know it from the data available. But there is considerable evidence that many students at Petra's stage of development *are* thoroughly confused about designing: indeed, they sometimes find the whole experience of the studio mysterious.

In Petra's studio, for example, in spite of the students' general admiration for Quist as practitioner and teacher, fully half the group find it hard to grasp what he means by "thinking architecturally." Judith, a colleague of Petra's, has a jury in which the critic finally tells her:

Unless you can begin to think of the problem architecturally, you aren't going to find any way to proceed.

And Judith herself says, in a later interview,

I began to realize that my approach wasn't architectural at all.

In another studio, the studio master, Leftwich, says of a student,

Lauda is the hardest guy to deal with. Intelligent, articulate, comes up with something that works, but architecturally, it's horrible. Now, what do I do? In a way, it's the kind of case which precipitates the weakest responses, because he has not internalized some of the covert things . . . I think he should do something else. He is bright but totally unvisual. Within the frame of reference of a designing architect, he is totally misplaced . . . I wouldn't know what to do with him.*

Leftwich argues that, because Lauda has not picked up the "covert things," he does not know what to do with him. As for Lauda, he accepts but is rather bewildered by the demand that he perform according to standards that he finds alien and mysterious:

I think that at times, Leftwich assumed a greater awareness on my part than I had . . . I wasn't doing it around my own standards. My standards were far surpassed. . . . That's probably the key thing.

So he says,

I want to go out and learn first. I want to know what it is we are arguing about.

In yet another studio, a student who has not been singled out by his teachers as a problem makes this poignant observation:

What we have is a very Kafkaesque situation where you really don't know where you are, and you have no basis for evaluation. You hang on the inflection of the tone of voice in your crit to discover if something is really wrong.

So, in addition to the features of design education I have already mentioned—the student trying to do something on her own, being unclear about just what she is supposed to do, and getting stuck; the studio master offering demonstration, instruction, and reflection—we must add, at least in the early phase of the studio, the student's experience of mystery and confusion. These phenomena are not unique to Quist's dialogue with Petra or even to Quist's studio as a whole. They are characteristic of architectural studios. To make sense of them, we must begin with a certain paradox inherent in design education.

The Paradox of Learning to Design

Initially, the student does not and cannot understand what designing means. He finds the artistry of thinking like an architect to be elusive, obscure, alien, and mysterious. Moreover, even if he were able to give a plausible verbal description of designing—to intellectualize about it—he would still be unable to meet the requirement that he demonstrate an understanding of designing *in the doing*.

*"Leftwich" and "Lauda" are fictitious names assigned by Florian Von Buttlar to a master and a student in a design studio where he observed as part of the Harvard/M.I.T. Review of Architectural Education.

From his observation of the students' performance, the studio master realizes that they do not at first understand the essential things. He sees, further, that he cannot explain these things with any hope of being understood, at least at the outset, because they can be grasped only through the experience of actual designing. Indeed, many studio masters believe, along with Leftwich, that there are essential "covert things" that can never be explained; either the student gets them in the doing, or he does not get them at all. Hence the Kafkaesque situation in which the student must "hang on the inflection of the tone of voice . . . to discover if something is really wrong."

The design studio shares in a general paradox attendant on the teaching and learning of any really new competence or understanding; for the student seeks to learn things whose meaning and importance she cannot grasp ahead of time. She is caught in the paradox Plato describes so vividly in his dialogue the *Meno*. There, just as Socrates induces Meno to admit that he hasn't the least idea what virtue is, Meno bursts out with this question:

> But how will you look for something when you don't in the least know what it is? How on earth are you going to set up something you don't know as the object of your search? To put it another way, even if you come right up against it, how will you know that what you have found is the thing you didn't know? [Plato, 1956, p. 128.]

Like Meno, the design student knows she needs to look for something but does not know what that something is. She seeks to learn it, moreover, in the sense of coming to know it *in action*. Yet, at the beginning, she can neither do it nor recognize it when she sees it. Hence, she is caught up in a self-contradiction: "looking for something" implies a capacity to recognize the thing one looks for, but the student lacks at first the capacity to recognize the object of her search. The instructor is caught up in the same paradox: he cannot tell the student what she needs to know, even if he has words for it, because the student would not at that point understand him.

The logical paradox of the *Meno* accurately describes the experience of learning to design. It captures the very feelings of mystery, confusion, frustration, and futility that many students experience in their early months or years of architectural study. Yet most students do attempt to carry out the paradoxical task.

The student discovers that she is expected to learn, by doing, both what designing is and how to do it. The studio seems to rest on the assumption that it is only in this way that she can learn. Others may help her, but they can do so only as she begins to understand for herself the process she finds initially mysterious. And although they may help her, *she* is the essential self-educator. In this respect, the studio tradition of design education is consistent with an older and broader tradition of educational thought and practice, according to which the most important things—artistry, wisdom, virtue—can only be learned for oneself.

In the *Meno*, to return to that deceptively simple text, Plato has Socrates argue that one person cannot teach virtue to another. The evidence is that good men, who have certainly wished to teach virtue to their sons, have manifestly failed to do so.

> *Socrates:* . . . there are plenty of good statesmen here in Athens and have been as good in the past. The question is, have they also been good teachers of their own virtue? That is the point we are discussing . . . whether virtue can be taught. It amounts to the question whether the good men of this and former times have known how to hand on to someone else the goodness that was in themselves, or whether, on the contrary, it is not something that can be handed over, or that one man can receive from another [Plato, 1956, p. 148].

And in answer to this question, having considered the cases of a number of celebrated statesmen and their sons, Socrates finally concludes,

> I am afraid it is something that cannot be done by teaching [p. 149].

How, then, do human beings become good? For that some do, Socrates leaves no doubt. On this point, the *Meno* offers two perhaps conflicting and certainly disconnected answers. In the final section of the dialogue, Socrates concludes that virtue is a matter of "divine dispensation":

> If all we have said in this discussion and the questions we have asked have been right, virtue will be acquired neither by nature nor by teaching. Whoever has it gets it by divine dispensation, without taking thought, unless he be the kind of statesmen who can create another like himself [pp. 156–157].

But earlier in his discussion of the implications of his paradox, Socrates suggests a different view:

> One thing I am ready to fight for as long as I can, in word and act: that is, that we shall be better, braver, and more active men if we believe it right to look for what we don't know than if we believe there is no point in looking because what we don't know we can never discover [p. 139].

Indeed, in his parable of the slave boy from whom he elicits the statement of a geometrical theorem, Socrates goes so far as to suggest the nature of the process by which we may "look for what we don't know." It is, in its essence, a process of *recollection*; the learner "spontaneously recovers knowledge that is in him but forgotten."

This knowledge will not come from teaching but from questioning. He [the slave boy] will recover it for himself [p. 138].

And the beginning of this process of recovery depends on Socrates, the epistemological gadfly and midwife, who goads the boy into discovering that he does not know what he thought he knew:

Socrates: Do you suppose, then, that he would have attempted to look for, or learn, what he thought he knew (although he did not), before he was thrown into perplexity, became aware of this ignorance, and felt a desire to know?
Meno: No.
Socrates: Then the numbing process was good for him?
Meno: I agree [p. 135].

Perhaps we can reconcile the two Platonic views of the process by which human beings learn something new. The earlier view is the general one: we can learn something new by recovering forgotten knowledge with the help of a Socratic gadfly whose questioning numbs us into perplexity. When it comes to really important things like virtue, however, the recovery of forgotten knowledge also depends on a talent given, as though by divine dispensation, to only a few.

Some contemporary authors have tried to dissolve the paradox of the *Meno* by arguments similar to Plato's. Just as Plato argued that the slave boy had once known and then forgotten the geometrical theorem and could therefore, when properly numbed and awakened, *recognize* it, so other writers have attributed to those who seek to learn something new an implicit capacity to recognize it when they find it.

Polanyi proposed that we already know *tacitly* the things we seek to learn. Socrates's dialogue with the slave boy is, for Polanyi, a parable of reflection on tacit knowledge:

The *Meno* shows conclusively that if all knowledge is explicit, that is, capable of being clearly stated, then we cannot know a problem or look for its solution. And the *Meno* also shows, therefore, that if problems nevertheless exist, and discoveries can be made by solving them, we can know things, and important things, that we cannot tell.

The kind of tacit knowledge that solves the paradox of the *Meno* consists in the intimation of something hidden which we may yet discover [Polanyi, 1967, pp. 22–23].

Herbert Simon (1969), who thinks of designing as converting a situation from its actual state to a preferred one, proposes to solve the paradox of the *Meno* by distinguishing between "state" and "process." Surely, he argues, we can describe the change of state that occurs when we solve a problem—climb a hill or win a game of chess—even though we cannot at first describe the process that would produce it. Problem solving is a search for the values of the process variables that would produce a desired change of state; we regulate our search for the former by our capacity to recognize the latter.

Israel Scheffler has suggested in informal conversation that the paradox of the *Meno* can be dissolved by distinguishing between "inside" and "outside" views of the activity we are trying to learn. As he sees it, the architectural students know, from the very beginning of their studies, that they want a diploma; and they want to be on the inside of the practice they see at first only from the outside. Extending Scheffler's view, we might say that the students can recognize, from the very beginning, the external signs of a competent design performance. The problem they try to solve in the studio is to learn the internal cues that correspond to these external signs. They try to discover what it feels like to do the things they have seen the studio master do. And they regulate their search by the external signs of competence they already know how to recognize.

Each of these proposals—based, as it is, on a distinction between tacit and explicit, state and process, or outside and inside—captures something important about the process of learning to design.

If we were to apply Polanyi's view to the experience of students in the design studio, we would say, correctly, that learning to design sometimes takes the form of making explicit what one already knows how to do. As Petra says, "Intuitively you look at the shape and you know it is wrong, but it's hard to get down to the reason." And students do seem to experience, at one time or another, Polanyi's "intimation of something hidden." However, most students do not *begin* with a tacit knowledge of competent designing. If anything, they are more likely at the outset to be able to give verbal descriptions of designing that they cannot produce. Only later, when they have learned some aspects of designing, can they advance their learning by reflecting on the tacit knowledge implicit in their own performance.

Simon's resolution of the paradox holds for a limited number of design problems where the student *can* recognize the change of state that would constitute a solution—for example, "In a space of a given size and shape, arrange certain specified items of furniture so that the space holds the furniture comfortably and allows for its ordinary use." But not all design problems are of this kind; indeed, the most important ones are not. At the beginning of her dialogue with Quist, Petra has not yet arrived at a satisfactory formulation of the problem to be solved—"the problem of this problem," as Quist calls it. She does not begin with a capacity to recognize either the problem or its solution. In the course of the dialogue, however, it is quite possible that she begins to understand the problem of establishing the global configuration of the buildings on the site and to identify a direction in which to search for solutions to it. It is by learning to work on the problem that she may also learn to recognize when she has solved it. About this kind of learning, however, Simon's account tells us nothing.

Scheffler is clearly right when he says that the first-year design students know they want to get a diploma and become insiders to the profession. But this does not cut very deeply into the paradox of learning to design, for many students who hold such aspirations still haven't the faintest idea what it means to think like an architect. It is true that students do often come to recognize and appreciate the qualities of competent designing, which they then try to learn to produce. One way of learning to design does seem to consist in coordinating the inner feelings of performance with the external signs of competent designing. What is important, however, is that students must *come* to be able to do this. In our effort to account for this way of learning, we cannot avoid the problem of explaining how, in the first place, they come to recognize good designing when they see it.

In the early stages of the design studio, most students do experience the paradox of the *Meno*; they feel like people looking for something they could not recognize even if they stumbled across it. Hence, their initial learning process bears a double burden: they must learn both to execute design performances and to recognize their competent execution. But these two components of the learning task support each other: as a student begins to perform, she also begins to recognize competent performance and to regulate her search by reference to the qualities she recognizes. *How* she comes to be able to do this is quite another matter, to which we will return in our discussion of the dialogue between student and coach.

In 1952 a Socratic figure of our own times, Carl Rogers, presented some personal reflections on teaching and learning to a group of teachers assembled at Harvard University. What he said on that occasion closely parallels the line of thought I have been developing here:

a. My experience has been that I cannot teach another person how to teach. To attempt it is for me, in the long run, futile.

b. It seems to me that anything that can be taught to another is relatively inconsequential and has little or no significant influence on behavior. That sounds so ridiculous that I can't help but question it at the same time I present it.

c. I realize increasingly that I am only interested in learnings which significantly influence behavior. Quite possibly this is simply a personal idiosyncrasy.

d. I have come to feel that only learning which significantly influences behavior is self-discovered, self-appropriated learning.

e. Such self-discovered learning, truth that has been personally appropriated and assimilated in experience, cannot be directly communicated to another. As soon as an individual tries to communicate such experience directly, often with a quite natural enthusiasm, it becomes teaching, and its results are inconsequential. It was some relief recently to discover that Sören Kierkegaard, the Danish philosopher, has found this, too, in his own experience, and stated it very clearly a century ago. It made it seem less absurd.

f. As a consequence of the above, I realize that I have lost interest in being a teacher.

g. When I try to teach, as I do sometimes, I am appalled by the results, which seem a little more than inconsequential, because sometimes the teaching appears to succeed. When this happens, I find that the results are damaging. It seems to cause the individual to distrust his own experience and to stifle significant learning. Hence I have come to feel that the outcomes of teaching are either unimportant or hurtful.

h. When I look back at the results of my past teaching, the real results seem the same—either damage was done, or nothing significant occurred. This is frankly troubling.

i. As a consequence, I realize that I am only interested in being a learner, preferably learning things that matter, that have some significant influence on my own behavior.

j. I find it very rewarding to learn, in groups, in relationship with one person as in therapy, or by myself.

k. I find that one of the best, but most difficult, ways for me to learn is to drop my own defensiveness, at least temporarily, and to try to understand the way in which this experience seems and feels to the other person.

l. I find that another way of learning for me is to state my own uncertainties, to try to clarify my puzzlement, and thus get closer to the meaning that my experience actually seems to have.

m. The whole train of experiencing, and the meanings that I have thus far discovered in it, seem to have launched me on a process which is both fascinating and at times a little frightening. It seems to mean letting my experience carry me on, in a direction which appears to be forward, toward that I can but dimly define, as I try to understand at least the current meaning of that experience. The sensation is that of floating with a complex stream of experience, with the fascinating possibility of trying to comprehend its ever-changing reality [Rogers, 1969, p. 277].

In the remaining few moments of his talk, Rogers drew some further inferences. If others' experience agreed with his own, he thought, we would do away with teaching, examinations, grades, credits, "the exposition of conclusions," and the whole apparatus of formal education.

His words had a profound effect on the assembled teachers. As he describes it,

> Feelings ran high. It seemed I was threatening their jobs. I was obviously saying things I didn't mean, etc., etc. And occasionally a quiet voice of appreciation arose from a teacher who had felt these things but never dared to say them . . . I refused to defend myself by replying to the questions and attacks which came from every quarter. I endeavored to accept and empathize with the indignation, the frustration, criticisms which they felt. I pointed out that I had merely expressed some very personal views of my own. After much storm, members of the group began expressing, more and more frankly, their own significant feelings about teaching—often feelings divergent from mine, often feelings divergent from each other. It was a very thought-provoking session. I question whether any participant in that session has ever forgotten it [Rogers, 1969, p. 277].

There is something odd about Rogers's account. He tells the teachers that, having come to believe in the futility of trying to teach anything of significance for behavior, he has lost interest in being a teacher. Yet clearly he believes that his conduct of the session contributed to a climate of self-expression and self-discovery that few of the participants will ever forget. From the evidence of this example, I would say, not that Rogers has lost all interest in being a teacher, but that he has *reframed teaching* in a way that gives central importance to his own role as a learner. He elicits self-discovery in others, first by modeling for others, as a learner, the open expression of his own deepest reflections (however absurd they may seem) and then, when others criticize him, by refusing to become defensive. As he expresses his own uncertainties and convictions, emphasizes the "merely personal" nature of his views, and invites and listens to the reactions of others, he seeks to be literally thought-provoking. He believes that the very expression of thoughts and feelings usually withheld, manifestly divergent from one another, has the potential to promote self-discovery.

Like Socrates in the *Meno*, Rogers believes that the most important things cannot be taught but must be discovered and appropriated for oneself. Like Socrates, he attributes to himself and others a capacity for self-discovery and functions as a paradoxical teacher who does not teach but serves as gadfly and midwife to others' self-discovery—provoking in his interlocutors, like Socrates, a storm of anger and confusion.

More recently still, a friend of mine, Professor Thomas Cowan of the University of Pennsylvania, put the same point of view very succinctly in a letter to me, as follows:

I like old Carl Gustav Jung best on education. You know that, unlike Freud, for whom psychoanalysis is a branch of the healing arts, Jung always insisted that it is a propadeutic, a branch of education. For him, education is what one does to and for oneself. Hence, the universal irrelevance of all systems of education. . . . This view forced me to distinguish education from training: education—the self-learning process: training—what others make you do. . . . What are education systems (so-called) *really* doing? For example, law school, I discovered, primarily trains students to listen . . . to think and talk the way the rest of the profession does. What is its educational function, then? To drive you mad with its incessant drill to educate yourself. The process is or appears terribly wasteful, yet some do get educated. If the teacher had a big stick and hit you over the head every time you tried to get him to educate you, the thing would be done in less than a semester. It seems to me that this is the Zen method of education, so of course I can't claim to have invented it [personal communication, 1979].

The Predicament of Learning to Design

The paradox of learning a really new competence is this: that a student cannot at first understand what he needs to learn, can learn it only by educating himself, and can educate himself only by beginning to do what he does not yet understand.

In the architectural studio, the paradox inherent in learning to design places the student in a predicament. He is expected to plunge into designing, trying from the very outset to do what he does not yet know how to do, in order to get the sort of experience that will help him learn what designing means. He cannot make an informed choice to take this plunge because he does not yet grasp its essential meanings, and his instructors cannot convey these to him until he has had the requisite experience. Thus, he must jump in without knowing—indeed, in order to discover—what he needs to learn.

It is as though the studio master had said to him, "I can tell you that there is something you need to know, and with my help you may be able to learn it. But I cannot tell you what it is in a way you can now understand. I can only arrange for you to have the right sorts of experiences for yourself. You must be willing, therefore, to have these experiences. Then you will be able to make an informed choice about whether you wish to continue. If you are unwilling to step into this new experience without knowing ahead of time what it will be like, I cannot help you. You must trust me."

As Quist said in an interview, the studio master asks his students to make a "willing suspension of disbelief":

It has to be a kind of contract between the two. The teacher must be open to challenge and must be able to defend his position. The student, in turn, must be willing to suspend his disbelief, to give the teacher's suggestion a chance—to try the suggestion out. The student must be willing to trust that the faculty member has a programmatic intention which will be preempted or ruined by his requiring full justification and explanation before anything is done. . . . A good student is capable of the willing suspension of disbelief.

Quist's phrase originated with Samuel Taylor Coleridge, who used it to describe the stance essential to an understanding of poetry (Coleridge, 1817/1983). In order to allow a poem to do its work, Coleridge thought, the reader must enter into a kind of contract with the poet, willingly suspending his disbelief in utterances that seem false or even absurd. The reader is not asked to will "belief," because he cannot be expected to make an informed choice to believe until he understands, which depends, in turn, on his having the right sort of experience. Disbelief must be suspended until the reader (or student) has access to the information on which to base a good decision. But in order to get that information, he must commit to the enterprise that yields the experience.

What makes this situation into a predicament for the student is that he or she is likely to find the costs of commitment greater than its expected rewards. Perhaps the least of these costs is the opportunity cost of remaining in the studio. More important is the sense of being at risk. Swimming in unfamiliar waters, the student risks the loss of his sense of competence, control, and confidence. He must temporarily abandon much that he already values. If he comes to the studio with knowledge he considers useful, he may be asked to unlearn it. If he comes with a perspective on what is valuable for design, he may be asked to put it aside. Later in his studio education, or after it, he may judge for himself what he wishes to keep, discard, or combine, but he is at first unable to make such a judgment. And he may fear that, by a kind of insidious coercion, he may permanently lose what he already knows and values.

He becomes dependent on his instructors. He must look to them for help in acquiring understanding, direction, and competence. As he willingly suspends disbelief, he also suspends autonomy—as though he were becoming a child again. In such a predicament, he is more or less vulnerable to anxiety, depending on the strengths and weaknesses he brings to the studio. If he is easily threatened by the temporary surrender of his sense of competence, then the risk of loss will seem to be high. If he comes with a distrust of those in authority, a readiness to see them as manipulating him, especially if he is unaware of his dispositions to perceive, then the willing suspension of disbelief may seem difficult or even impossible.

The studio master has a predicament complementary to the student's. He knows that he cannot at first communicate to the student what he understands about designing. He knows that the student, like a postulant asked to make a leap of faith in order to attain understanding, can get good reasons for acting only by beginning to act. However much the master may dislike asking the student to give up his autonomy, he must invite him to enter into a temporary relationship of trust and dependency.

To be sure, the learning contract between student and instructor is seldom made explicit. Quist is exceptional in the degree to which he reflects on it. More frequently, the two parties simply find themselves in the relationship described by the contract. And if they should happen to think about it later on, their attempts to talk about it will be embedded in the complex, multileveled discourse in which the main work of the studio consists.

Communication Between Student and Studio Master

We can think of this process as one of sending and receiving messages. However, it is not a kind of telegraphy in which meaningful signals are directly transmitted from one participant to the other.* Rather, each participant must construct for himself the meaning of the other's messages and must design messages whose meanings the other can decipher. When the process works well, it is a kind of reciprocal construction that results in convergence of meaning: So much the studio shares with all human communication.

But communication between student and studio master is in several ways problematic.

Messages often refer both to the process of designing and to the process of learning to design. An event like Petra's desk crit, pertaining to both processes, holds a potential for two-tiered confusion.

Messages are conveyed primarily through actions—the studio master's demonstrations and the student's efforts at design. This is useful, because successful communication is measured, after all, not by the student's ability to talk about design but by her ability to do it. Nevertheless, communication through action poses problems. The student must construct the meanings of the studio master's actions even though his meanings are likely to conflict with her own (the likelihood of their conflict underlies the need for an initial suspension of disbelief); and the student's own action-messages make her vulnerable to feelings of confusion and failure.

The studio master wants to convey essential things, some of which go beyond statable rules even if he is good at reflecting on his own tacit knowledge. He

---

*Michael Reddy (1979) has described this way of looking at interpersonal Communication in terms of the "conduit metaphor."

can alert his students to the desirability of attending to the situation's surprising back talk, for example, but he cannot give them rules for doing so. His feeling for drawing—to represent contours of the site, cross-sectional views of buildings, or perspective—cannot be conveyed by a verbal description of rules for drawing. This is true, first, because drawing depends on seeing, and words are very poor approximations to visual things, but also because skillful drawing depends on a feeling for the use of line that is not reducible to verbally described procedures. And designing, like other forms of artistry, demands authenticity. A designer must *mean* what she does. If she works from a generative metaphor, for example, she must take it seriously, enter into it, and treat it as her own. The studio master cannot give rules for authenticity; even if he could imagine them, the student would still need to apply them in an authentic way!

Not everything important about designing escapes verbal description. There are many things the studio master can put into words. But his attempts to clarify, specify, and differentiate meanings are vulnerable to the very ambiguities he would like to dispel.

Quist, for example, devotes much effort to demonstrating and describing the variety of design domains that ought to be considered in spinning out and evaluating the consequences of a designer's moves. He advises Petra to see the cafeteria not only as a "formal function" but also in terms of access to summer and winter sun, and he treats the gallery not only as circulation but as a way of marking differences in level. Nowhere, however, does he make explicit reference to the system of design domains on which he draws. And even if he were to do so, some students would find it confusing. A student like Lauda can understand designing only in terms of structure and technology; Judith, in terms of program and use. For them, other domains are vague and nonexistent.

When Quist tells Petra that she must "draw and draw" in order to calibrate her grid, he means drawing in the sense of drawing experiment. She must draw in order to discover the consequences of the various possible grids. Students who understood drawing only as the visual presentation of an idea, however, would probably take Quist's advice to mean that their delineations lacked polish. Quist uses *metaphor* to mean the image generative of a design. But a student like Judith, for whom the term seems to mean embellishment of an existing design, can say that in order to please her instructors she will "put in some metaphors."

The subprocesses of design—making a site plan, for example, or analyzing a program—can be demonstrated and described. But designing is a holistic process, and the studio master cannot explain "thinking architecturally" by listing component design skills. A student cannot understand and acquire each component skill, in the sense in which "thinking architecturally" requires it, until he has experienced that component in the context of a whole process. Hence, he may be confused about what he has learned—or he may believe he has learned more than the studio master thinks he has.

There are potential sources of unclarity in the studio master's implicit claims about his approach to design. Quist makes clearly positive judgments about nooks and soft back areas, and he expresses negative judgments by such terms as "screwy," "no good," and "spoils the whole idea." Suppose, however, that Petra had happened not to share his judgments. In the one case where she raises a question of this kind—the calibration of the grid—he invites her to look at it in section. But if she were to persist in her point of view, would he try to argue her out of it or simply give up, as though she had missed the point of a joke? Certainly, Quist acts as though his judgments had objective validity. The site *is* screwy, he seems to say; the auditorium *is* too much of a hard-edged block. But students like Petra, exposed to many different schools of contemporary architecture, may wonder. When Quist expresses such judgments, is he also conveying the message that they are normatively binding on everyone? Or is he saying only that she must invest her design with values of her own, regardless of their fit with his? Are the differences among schools of architecture objectively grounded, or are they matters of taste or ideology? On such issues even Quist is silent. As one student says, "One of the things that really bug me about architectural education is that a lot of things are really implicit, remain under the surface and are not talked about."

The studio master's silence about his implicit claims becomes a projective test for the student. Petra is free to think, for example:

"These things are obvious to everyone but me."
"Quist cannot say what he means."
"What he means is inexpressible in words."
"I have not learned to ask the right questions."

The issue becomes crucial just at the point when a student, seeking to interpret an instructor's criticism of her work, cannot grasp the view of designing that underlies the criticism. Then her questions about the error she has failed to see may be joined to confusion about the perspective that allows the studio master to see it and the ambiguity of his implicit claims to objectivity. How she resolves these questions has much to do with her further learning.

The architectural studio rests on an implicit response to the paradox and predicament of learning to design: the student must begin to design before she knows what she is doing, so that the studio master's demonstrations and descriptions can take on meanings useful to her further designing. But this "virtuous circle" depends on the capacity of student and studio master to communicate effectively with each other, in spite of the potential for vagueness, ambiguity, or obscurity inherent in the things about which they try to communicate.

Imelda

Richard Selzer

I

I heard the other day that Hugh Franciscus had died. I knew him once. He was the Chief of Plastic Surgery when I was a medical student at Albany Medical College. Dr. Franciscus was the archetype of the professor of surgery—tall, vigorous, muscular, as precise in his technique as he was impeccable in his dress. Each day a clean lab coat monkishly starched, that sort of thing. I doubt that he ever read books. One book only, that of the human body, took the place of all others. He never raised his eyes from it. He read it like a printed page as though he knew that in the calligraphy there just beneath the skin were all the secrets of the world. Long before it became visible to anyone else, he could detect the first sign of granulation at the base of a wound, the first blue line of new epithelium at the periphery that would tell him that a wound would heal, or the barest hint of necrosis that presaged failure. This gave him the appearance of a prophet. "This skin graft will take," he would say, and you must believe beyond all cyanosis, exudation and inflammation that it would.

He had enemies, of course, who said he was arrogant, that he exalted activity for its own sake. Perhaps. But perhaps it was no more than the honesty of one who knows his own worth. Just look at a scalpel, after all. What a feeling of sovereignty, megalomania even, when you know that it is you and you alone who will make certain use of it. It was said, too, that he was a ladies' man. I don't know about that. It was all rumor. Besides, I think he had other things in mind than mere living. Hugh Franciscus was a zealous hunter. Every fall during the season he drove upstate to hunt deer. There was a glass-front case in his office where he showed his guns. How could he shoot a deer? we asked. But he knew better. To us medical students he was someone heroic, someone made up of several gods, beheld at a distance, and always from a lesser height. If he had grown accustomed to his miracles, we had not. He had no close friends on the staff. There was something a little sad in that. As though once long ago he had been flayed by friendship and now the

311

slightest breeze would hurt. Confidences resulted in dishonor. Perhaps the person in whom one confided would scorn him, betray. Even though he spent his days among those less fortunate, weaker than he—the sick, after all—Franciscus seemed aware of an air of personal harshness in his environment to which he reacted by keeping his own counsel, by a certain remoteness. It was what gave him the appearance of being haughty. With the patients he was forthright. All the facts laid out, every question anticipated and answered with specific information. He delivered good news and bad with the same dispassion.

I was a third-year student, just turned onto the wards for the first time, and clerking on Surgery. Everything—the operating room, the morgue, the emergency room, the patients, professors, even the nurses—was terrifying. One picked one's way among the mines and booby traps of the hospital, hoping only to avoid the hemorrhage and perforation of disgrace. The opportunity for humiliation was everywhere.

It all began on Ward Rounds. Dr. Franciscus was demonstrating a cross-leg flap graft he had constructed to cover a large fleshy defect in the leg of a merchant seaman who had injured himself in a fall. The man was from Spain and spoke no English. There had been a comminuted fracture of the femur, much soft tissue damage, necrosis. After weeks of debridement and dressings, the wound had been made ready for grafting. Now the patient was in his fifth postoperative day. What we saw was a thick web of pale blue flesh arising from the man's left thigh, and which had been sutured to the open wound on the right thigh. When the surgeon pressed the pedicle with his finger, it blanched; when he let up, there was a slow return of the violaceous color.

"The circulation is good," Franciscus announced. "It will get better." In several weeks, we were told, he would divide the tube of flesh at its site of origin, and tailor it to fit the defect to which, by then, it would have grown more solidly. All at once, the webbed man in the bed reached out, and gripping Franciscus by the arm, began to speak rapidly, pointing to his groin and hip. Franciscus stepped back at once to disengage his arm from the patient's grasp.

"Anyone here know Spanish? I didn't get a word of that."

"The cast is digging into him up above," I said. "The edges of the plaster are rough. When he moves, they hurt."

Without acknowledging my assistance, Dr. Franciscus took a plaster shears from the dressing cart and with several large snips cut away the rough edges of the cast.

"*Gracias, gracias.*" The man in the bed smiled. But Franciscus had already moved on to the next bed. He seemed to me a man of immense strength and ability, yet without affection for the patients. He did not want to be touched by them. It was less kindness that he showed them than a reassurance that he would never give up, that he would bend every effort. If anyone could, he would solve the problems of their flesh.

Ward Rounds had disbanded and I was halfway down the corridor when I heard Dr. Franciscus' voice behind me.

"You speak Spanish." It seemed a command.

"I lived in Spain for two years," I told him.

"I'm taking a surgical team to Honduras next week to operate on the natives down there. I do it every year for three weeks, somewhere. This year, Honduras. I can arrange the time away from your duties here if you'd like to come along. You will act as interpreter. I'll show you how to use the clinical camera. What you'd see would make it worthwhile."

So it was that, a week later, the envy of my classmates, I joined the mobile surgical unit—surgeons, anesthetists, nurses and equipment—aboard a Military Air Transport plane to spend three weeks performing plastic surgery on people who had been previously selected by an advance team. Honduras. I don't suppose I shall ever see it again. Nor do I especially want to. From the plane it seemed a country made of clay—burnt umber, raw sienna, dry. It had a deadweight quality, as though the ground had no buoyancy, no air sacs through which a breeze might wander. Our destination was Comayagua, a town in the Central Highlands. The town itself was situated on the edge of one of the flatlands that were linked in a network between the granite mountains. Above, all was brown, with only an occasional Spanish cedar tree; below, patches of luxuriant tropical growth. It was a day's bus ride from the airport. For hours, the town kept appearing and disappearing with the convolutions of the road. At last, there it lay before us, panting and exhausted at the bottom of the mountain.

That was all I was to see of the countryside. From then on, there was only the derelict hospital of Comayagua, with the smell of spoiling bananas and the accumulated odors of everyone who had been sick there for the last hundred years. Of the two, I much preferred the frank smell of the sick. The heat of the place was incendiary. So hot that, as we stepped from the bus, our own words did not carry through the air, but hung limply at our lips and chins. Just in front of the hospital was a thirsty courtyard where mobs of waiting people squatted or lay in the meager shade, and where, on dry days, a fine dust rose through which untethered goats shouldered. Against the walls of this courtyard, gaunt, dejected men stood, their faces, like their country, preternaturally solemn, leaden. Here no one looked up at the sky. Every head was bent beneath a wide-brimmed straw hat. In the days that followed, from the doorway of the dispensary, I would watch the brown mountains sliding about, drinking the hospital into their shadow as the afternoon grew later and later, flattening us by their very altitude.

The people were mestizos, of mixed Spanish and Indian blood. They had flat, broad, dumb museum feet. At first they seemed to me indistinguishable the one from the other, without animation. All the vitality, the hidden sexuality, was in their black hair. Soon I was to know them by the fissures with which each face was graven. But, even so, compared to us, they were masked, shut away. My job was to follow Dr. Franciscus around, photograph the patients before and after surgery, interpret and generally act as aide-de-camp. It was exhilarating. Within days I had decided that I was not just useful, but essential. Despite that we spent all day in each other's company, there were no overtures of friendship from Dr. Franciscus. He knew my place, and I knew it, too. In the afternoon he examined the patients scheduled for the next day's surgery. I would call out a name from the doorway to the examining room. In the courtyard someone would rise. I would usher the patient in, and nudge him to the examining table where Franciscus stood, always, I thought, on the verge of irritability. I would read aloud the case history, then wait while he carried out his examination. While I took the "before" photographs, Dr. Franciscus would dictate into a tape recorder:

"Ulcerating basal cell carcinoma of the right orbit—six by eight centimeters—involving the right eye and extending into the floor of the orbit. Operative plan: wide excision with enucleation of the eye. Later, bone and skin grafting." The next morning we would be in the operating room where the procedure would be carried out.

We were more than two weeks into our tour of duty—a few days to go—when it happened. Earlier in the day I had caught sight of her through the window of the dispensary. A thin, dark Indian girl about fourteen years old. A figurine, orange-brown, terra-cotta, and still attached to the unshaped clay from which she had been carved. An older, sun-weathered woman stood behind and somewhat to the left of the girl. The mother was short and dumpy. She wore a broad-brimmed hat with a high crown, and a shapeless dress like a cassock. The girl had long, loose black hair. There were tiny gold hoops in her ears. The dress she wore could have been her mother's. Far too big, it hung from her thin shoulders at some risk of slipping down her arms. Even with her in it, the dress was empty, something hanging on the back of a door. Her breasts made only the smallest imprint in the cloth, her hips none at all. All the while, she pressed to her mouth a filthy, pink, balled-up rag as though to stanch a flow or buttress against pain. I knew that what she had come to show us, what we were there to see, was hidden beneath that pink cloth. As I watched, the woman handed down to her a gourd from which the girl drank, lapping like a dog. She was the last patient of the day. They had been waiting in the courtyard for hours.

"Imelda Valdez," I called out. Slowly she rose to her feet, the cloth never leaving her mouth, and followed her mother to the examining-room door. I shooed them in.

"You sit up there on the table," I told her. "Mother, you stand over there, please." I read from the chart:

"This is a fourteen-year-old girl with a complete, unilateral, left-sided cleft lip and cleft palate. No other diseases or congenital defects. Laboratory tests, chest X ray—negative."

"Tell her to take the rag away," said Dr. Franciscus. I did, and the girl shrank back, pressing the cloth all the more firmly.

"Listen, this is silly," said Francsicus. "Tell her I've got to see it. Either she behaves, or send her away."

"Please give me the cloth," I said to the girl as gently as possible. She did not. She could not. Just then, Franciscus reached up and, taking the hand that held the rag, pulled it away with a hard jerk. For an instant the girl's head followed the cloth as it left her face, one arm still upflung against showing. Against all hope, she would hide herself. A moment later, she relaxed and sat still. She seemed to me then like an animal that looks outward at the infinite, at death, without fear, with recognition only.

Set as it was in the center of the girl's face, the defect was utterly hideous— a nude rubbery insect that had fastened there. The upper lip was widely split all the way to the nose. One white tooth perched upon the protruding upper jaw projected through the hole. Some of the bones seemed to have been gnawed away as well. Above the thing, clear almond eyes and long black hair reflected the light. Below, a slender neck where the pulse trilled visibly. Under our gaze the girl's eyes fell to her lap where her hands lay palms upward, half open. She was a beautiful bird with a crushed beak. And tense with the expectation of more shame.

"Open your mouth," said the surgeon. I translated. She did so, and the surgeon tipped back her head to see inside.

"The palate, too. Complete," he said. There was a long silence. At last he spoke.

"What is your name?" The margins of the wound melted until she herself was being sucked into it.

"Imelda." The syllables leaked through the hole with a sloth and a whistle.

"Tomorrow," said the surgeon, "I will fix your lip. *Mañana*."

It seemed to me that Hugh Franciscus, in spite of his years of experience, in spite of all the dreadful things he had seen, must have been awed by the sight of this girl. I could see it flit across his face for an instant. Perhaps it was her small act of concealment, that he had had to demand that she show him the lip, that he had had to force her to show it to him. Perhaps it was

315

her resistance that intensified the disfigurement. Had she brought her mouth to him willingly, without shame, she would have been for him neither more nor less than any other patient.

He measured the defect with calipers, studied it from different angles, turning her head with a finger at her chin.

"How can it ever be put back together?" I asked.

"Take her picture," he said. And to her, "Look straight ahead." Through the eye of the camera she seemed more pitiful than ever, her humiliation more complete.

"Wait!" The surgeon stopped me. I lowered the camera. A strand of her hair had fallen across her face and found its way to her mouth, becoming stuck there by saliva. He removed the hair and secured it behind her ear.

"Go ahead," he ordered. There was the click of the camera. The girl winced.

"Take three more, just in case."

When the girl and her mother had left, he took paper and pen and with a few lines drew a remarkable likeness of the girl's face.

"Look," he said. "If this dot is A, and this one B, this, C and this, D, the incisions are made to A to B, then C to D. CD must equal AB. It is all equilateral triangles." All well and good, but then came X and Y and rotation flaps and the rest.

"Do you see?" he asked.

"It is confusing," I told him.

"It is simply a matter of dropping the upper lip into a normal position, then crossing the gap with two triangular flaps. It is geometry," he said.

"Yes," I said. "Geometry." And relinquished all hope of becoming a plastic surgeon.

II

In the operating room the next morning the anesthesia had already been administered when we arrived from Ward Rounds. The tube emerging from the girl's mouth was pressed against her lower lip to be kept out of the field of surgery. Already, a nurse was scrubbing the face which swam in a reddish-brown lather. The tiny gold earrings were included in the scrub. Now and then, one of them gave a brave flash. The face was washed for the last time, and dried. Green towels were placed over the face to hide everything but the mouth and nose. The drapes were applied.

"Calipers!" The surgeon measured, locating the peak of the distorted Cupid's bow.

"Marking pen!" He placed the first blue dot at the apex of the bow. The nasal sills were dotted; next, the inferior philtral dimple, the vermilion line. The A flap and the B flap were outlined. On he worked, peppering the lip and nose, making sense out of chaos, realizing the lip that lay waiting in that deep essential pink, that only he could see. The last dot and line were placed. He was ready.

"Scalpel!" He held the knife above the girl's mouth.

"O.K. to go ahead?" he asked the anesthetist.

"Yes."

He lowered the knife.

"No! Wait!" The anesthetist's voice was tense, staccato. "Hold it!"

The surgeon's hand was motionless.

"What's the matter?"

"Something's wrong. I'm not sure. God, she's hot as a pistol. Blood pressure is way up. Pulse one eighty. Get a rectal temperature." A nurse fumbled beneath the drapes. We waited. The nurse retrieved the thermometer.

"One hundred seven . . . no . . . eight." There was disbelief in her voice.

"Malignant hyperthermia," said the anesthetist. "Ice! Ice! Get lots of ice!" I raced out the door, accosted the first nurse I saw.

"Ice!" I shouted. "*Hielo!* Quickly! *Hielo!*" The woman's expression was blank. I ran to another. "*Hielo! Hielo!* For the love of God, ice."

"*Hielo?*" She shrugged. "*Nada.*" I ran back to the operating room.

"There isn't any ice," I reported. Dr. Franciscus had ripped off his rubber gloves and was feeling the skin of the girl's abdomen. Above the mask his eyes were the eyes of a horse in battle.

"The EKG is wild . . . "

"I can't get a pulse . . . "

"What the hell . . . "

The surgeon reached for the girl's groin. No femoral pulse.

"EKG flat. My God! She's dead!"

"She can't be."

"She is."

The surgeon's fingers pressed the groin where there was no pulse to be felt, only his own pulse hammering at the girl's flesh to be let in.

III

It was noon, four hours later, when we left the operating room. It was a day so hot and humid I felt steamed open like an envelope. The woman was sitting on a bench in the courtyard in her dress like a cassock. In one hand she held the piece of cloth the girl had used to conceal her mouth. As we watched, she folded it once neatly, and then again, smoothing it, cleaning the cloth which might have been the head of the girl in her lap that she stroked and consoled.

"I'll do the talking here," he said. He would tell her himself, in whatever Spanish he could find. Only if she did not understand was I to speak for him.

317

I watched him brace himself, set his shoulders. How could he tell her? I wondered. What? But I knew he would tell her everything, exactly as it had happened. As much for himself as for her, he needed to explain. But suppose she screamed, fell to the ground, attacked him, even? All that hope of love . . . gone. Even in his discomfort I knew that he was teaching me. The way to do it was professionally. Now he was standing above her. When the woman saw that he did not speak, she lifted her eyes and saw what he held crammed in his mouth to tell her. She knew, and rose to her feet.

"*Señora,*" he began, "I am sorry." All at once he seemed to me shorter than he was, scarcely taller than she. There was a place at the crown of his head where the hair had grown thin. His lips were stones. He could hardly move them. The voice dry, dusty.

"No one could have known. Some bad reaction to the medicine for sleeping. It poisoned her. High fever. She did not wake up." The last, a whisper. The woman studied his lips as though she were deaf. He tried, but could not control a twitching at the corner of his mouth. He raised a thumb and forefinger to press something back into his eyes.

"*Muerte,*" the woman announced to herself. Her eyes were human, deadly.

"*Si, muerte.*" At that moment he was like someone cast, still alive, as an effigy for his own tomb. He closed his eyes. Nor did he open them until he felt the touch of the woman's hand on his arm, a touch from which he did not withdraw. Then he looked and saw the grief corroding her face, breaking it down, melting the features so that eyes, nose, mouth ran together in a distortion, like the girl's. For a long time they stood in silence. It seemed to me that minutes passed. At last her face cleared, the features rearranged themselves. She spoke, the words coming slowly to make certain that he understood her. She would go home now. The next day her sons would come for the girl, to take her home for burial. The doctor must not be sad. God has decided. And she was happy now that the harelip had been fixed so that her daughter might go to Heaven without it. Her bare feet retreating were the felted pads of a great bereft animal.

IV

The next morning I did not go to the wards, but stood at the gate leading from the courtyard to the road outside. Two young men in striped ponchos lifted the girl's body wrapped in a straw mat onto the back of a wooden cart. A donkey waited. I had been drawn to this place as one is drawn, inexplicably, to certain scenes of desolation—executions, battlefields. All at once, the woman looked up and saw me. She had taken off her hat. The heavy-hanging coil of her hair made her head seem larger, darker, noble. I pressed some money into her hand.

"For flowers," I said. "A priest." Her cheeks shook as though minutes ago a stone had been dropped into her naval and the ripples were just now reaching her head. I regretted having come to that place.

"*Si, si,*" the woman said. Her own face was stitched with flies. "The doctor is one of the angels. He has finished the work of God. My daughter is beautiful."

What could she mean! The lip had not been fixed. The girl had died before he would have done it.

"Only a fine line that God will erase in time," she said.

I reached into the cart and lifted a corner of the mat in which the girl had been rolled. Where the cleft had been there was now a fresh line of tiny sutures. The Cupid's bow was delicately shaped, the vermilion border aligned. The flattened nostril had now the same rounded shape as the other one. I let the mat fall over the face of the dead girl, but not before I had seen the touching place where the finest black hairs sprang from the temple.

"*Adiós, adiós . . .*" And the cart creaked away to the sound of hooves, a tinkling bell.

V

There are events in a doctor's life that seem to mark the boundary between youth and age, seeing and perceiving. Like certain dreams, they illuminate a whole lifetime of past behavior. After such an event, a doctor is not the same as he was before. It had seemed to me then to have been the act of someone demented, or at least insanely arrogant. An attempt to reorder events. Her death had come to him out of order. It should have come after the lip had been repaired, not before. He could have told the mother that, no, the lip had not been fixed. But he did not. He said nothing. It had been an act of omission, one of those strange lapses to which all of us are subject and which we live to regret. It must have been then, at that moment, that the knowledge of what he would do appeared to him. The words of the mother had not consoled him; they had hunted him down. He had not done it for her. The dire necessity was his. He would not accept that Imelda had died before he could repair her lip. People who do such things break free from society. They follow their own lonely path. They have a secret which they can never reveal. I must never let on that I knew.

VI

How often I have imagined it. Ten o'clock at night. The hospital of Comayagua is all but dark. Here and there lanterns tilt and skitter up and down the corridors. One of these lamps breaks free from the others and descends the stone steps to the underground room that is the morgue of the hospital. This room wears the expression as if it had waited all night for someone to come. No silence so deep as this place with its cargo of newly dead. Only the slow drip of water over stone. The door closes gassily and clicks shut. The lock is turned. There are four tables, each with a body encased in a paper shroud. There is no mistaking her. She is the smallest. The surgeon takes a knife from his pocket and slits open the paper shroud, that part in which the girl's head is enclosed. The wound seems to be living on long after she has died. Waves of heat emanate from it, blurring his vision. All at once, he turns to peer over his shoulder. He sees nothing, only a wooden crucifix on the wall.

He removes a package of instruments from a satchel and arranges them on a tray. Scalpel, scissors, forceps, needle holder. Sutures and gauze sponges are produced. Stealthy, hunched, engaged, he begins. The dots of blue dye are still there upon her mouth. He raises the scalpel, pauses. A second glance into the darkness. From the wall a small lizard watches and accepts. The first cut is made. A sluggish flow of dark blood appears. He wipes it away with a sponge. No new blood comes to take its place. Again and again he cuts, connecting each of the blue dots until the whole of the zigzag slice is made, first on one side of the cleft, then on the other. Now the edges of the cleft are lined with fresh tissue. He sets down the scalpel and takes up scissors and forceps, undermining the little flaps until each triangle is attached only at one side. He rotates each flap into its new position. He must be certain that they can be swung without tension. They can. He is ready to suture. He fits the tiny curved needle into the jaws of the needle holder. Each suture is placed precisely the same number of millimeters from the cut edge, and the same distance apart. He ties each knot down until the edges are apposed. Not too tightly. These are the most meticulous sutures of his life. He cuts each thread close to the knot. It goes well. The vermilion border with its white skin roll is exactly aligned. One more stitch and the Cupid's bow appears as if by magic. The man's face shines with moisture. Now the nostril is incised around the margin, released, and sutured into a round shape to match its mate. He wipes the blood from the face of the girl with gauze that he has dipped in water. Crumbs of light are scattered on the girl's face. The shroud is folded once more about her. The instruments are handed into the satchel. In a moment the morgue is dark and a lone lantern ascends the stairs and is extinguished.

VII

Six weeks later I was in the darkened amphitheater of the Medical School. Tiers of seats rose in a semicircle above the small stage where Hugh Franciscus stood presenting the case material he had encountered in Honduras. It was the highlight of the year. The hall was filled. The night before he had arranged the slides in the order in which they were to be shown. I was at the controls of the slide projector.

"Next slide!" he would order from time to time in that military voice which had called forth blind obedience from generations of medical students, interns, residents and patients.

"This is a fifty-seven-year-old man with a severe burn contracture of the neck. You will notice the rigid webbing that has fused the chin to the presternal tissues. No motion of the head on the torso is possible. . . . Next slide!"

"Click," went the projector.

"Here he is after the excision of the scar tissue and with the head in full extension for the first time. The defect was then covered. . . . Next slide!"

"Click."

". . . with full-thickness drums of skin taken from the abdomen with the Padgett dermatome. Next slide!"

"Click."

And suddenly there she was, extracted from the shadows, suspended above and beyond all of us like a resurrection. There was the oval face, the long black hair unbraided, the tiny gold hoops in her ears. And that luminous gnawed mouth. The whole of her life seemed to have been summed up in this photograph. A long silence followed that was the surgeon's alone to break. Almost at once, like the anesthetist in the operating room in Comayagua, I knew that something was wrong. It was not that the man would not speak as that he could not. The audience of doctors, nurses and students seemed to have been infected by the black, limitless silence. My own pulse doubled. It was hard to breathe. Why did he not call out for the next slide? Why did he not save himself? Why had he not removed this slide from the ones to be shown? All at once I knew that he had used his camera on her again. I could see the long black shadows of her hair flowing into the darker shadows of the morgue. The sudden blinding flash . . . The next slide would be the one taken in the morgue. He would be exposed.

In the dim light reflected from the slide, I saw him gazing up at her, seeing not the colored photograph, I thought, but the negative of it where the ghost of the girl was. For me, the amphitheater had become Honduras. I saw again that courtyard littered with patients. I could see the dust in the beam of light from the projector. It was then that I knew that she was his measure of perfection and pain—the one lost, the other gained. He, too, had heard the click of the camera, had seen her wince and felt his mercy enlarge. At last he spoke.

"Imelda." It was the one word he had heard her say. At the sound of his voice I removed the next slide from the projector. "Click" . . . and she was gone. "Click" again, and in her place the man with the orbital cancer. For a long moment Franciscus looked up in my direction, on his face an expression that I have given up trying to interpret. Gratitude? Sorrow? It made me think of the gaze of the girl when at last she understood that she must hand over to him the evidence of her body.

"This is a sixty-two-year-old man with a basal cell carcinoma of the temple eroding into the bony orbit . . ." he began as though nothing had happened.

At the end of the hour, even before the lights went on, there was loud applause. I hurried to find him among the departing crowd. I could not. Some weeks went by before I caught sight of him. He seemed vaguely convalescent, as though a fever had taken its toll before burning out.

Hugh Franciscus continued to teach for fifteen years, although he operated a good deal less, then gave it up entirely. It was as though he had grown tired of blood, of always having to be involved with blood, of having to draw it, spill it, wipe it away, stanch it. He was a quieter, softer man, I heard, the ferocity diminished. There were no more expeditions to Honduras or anywhere else.

I, too, have not been entirely free of her. Now and then, in the years that have passed, I see that donkey-cart cortège, or his face bent over hers in the morgue. I would like to have told him what I now know, that his unrealistic act was one of goodness, one of those small, persevering acts done, perhaps, to ward off madness. Like lighting a lamp, boiling water for tea, washing a shirt. But, of course, it's too late now.

Technology

Steps Toward a Small Theory of the Visible

John Berger

When I say the first line of the Lord's Prayer: "Our father who art in heaven . . ." I imagine this heaven is invisible, unenterable but intimately close. There is nothing baroque about it, no swirling infinite space or stunning foreshortening. To find it—if one had the grace—it would only be necessary to lift up something as small and as at hand as a pebble or a salt-cellar on the table. Perhaps Cellini knew this.

"Thy kingdom come . . ." The difference is infinite between heaven and earth, yet the distance as minimal. Simone Weil wrote concerning this sentence: "Here our desire pierces through time to find eternity behind it and this happens when we know how to turn whatever happens, no matter what it is, into an object of desire."

Her words might also be a prescription for the art of painting.

Today images abound everywhere. Never has so much been depicted and watched. We have glimpses at any moment of what things look like on the other side of the planet, or the other side of the moon. Appearances registered, and transmitted with lightning speed.

Yet with this, something has innocently changed. They used to be called *physical* appearances because they belonged to solid bodies. Now appearances are volatile. Technological innovation has made it easy to separate the apparent from the existent. And this is precisely what the present system's mythology continually needs to exploit. It turns appearances into refractions, like mirages: refractions not of light but of appetite, in fact a single appetite, the appetite for more.

Consequently—and oddly, considering the physical implications of the notion of *appetite*—the existent, the body, disappears. We live within a spectacle of empty clothes and unworn masks.

Consider any newsreader on any television channel in any country. These speakers are the mechanical epitome of the *disembodied*. It took the system many years to invent them and to teach them to talk as they do.

No bodies and no Necessity—for Necessity is the condition of the existent. It is what makes reality real. And the system's mythology requires only the not-yet-real, the virtual, the next purchase. This produces in the spectator, not, as claimed, a sense of freedom (the so-called freedom of choice) but a profound isolation.

Until recently, history, all the accounts people gave of their lives, all proverbs, fables, parables, confronted the same thing: the everlasting, fearsome, and occasionally beautiful, struggle of living with Necessity, which is the enigma of existence—that which followed from the Creation, and which subsequently has always continued to sharpen the human spirit. Necessity produces both tragedy and comedy. It is what you kiss or bang your head against.

Today, in the system's spectacle, it exists no more. Consequently no experience is communicated. All that is left to share is the spectacle, the game that nobody plays and everybody can watch. As has never happened before, people have to try to place their own existence and their own pains single-handed in the vast arena of time and the universe.

I had a dream in which I was a strange dealer: a dealer in looks or appearances. I collected and distributed them. In the dream I had just discovered a secret! I discovered it on my own, without help or advice.

The secret was to get inside whatever I was looking at—a bucket of water, a cow, a city (like Toledo) seen from above, an oak tree, and, once inside, to arrange its appearances for the better. *Better* did not mean making the thing seem more beautiful or more harmonious; nor did it mean making it more typical, so that the oak tree might represent all oak trees; it simply meant making it more itself so that the cow or the city or the bucket of water became more evidently unique!

The *doing* of this gave me pleasure and I had the impression that the small changes I made from the inside gave pleasure to others.

The secret of how to get inside the object so as to rearrange how it looked was as simple as opening the door of a wardrobe. Perhaps it was merely a question of being there when the door swung open on its own. Yet when I woke up, I couldn't remember how it was done and I no longer knew how to get inside things.

The history of painting is often presented as a history of succeeding styles. In our time art dealers and promoters have used this battle of styles to make brand-names for the market. Many collectors—and museums—buy names rather than works.

Maybe it's time to ask a naive question: what does all painting from the Palaeolithic period until our century have in common? Every painted image announces: *I have seen this*, or, when the making of the image was incorporated into a tribal ritual: *We have seen this.* The *this* refers to the sight represented. Non-figurative art is no exception. A late canvas by Rothko represents an illumination or a coloured glow which derived from the painter's experience with the visible. When he was working, he judged his canvas according to something else that he *saw*.

Painting is, first, an affirmation of the visible which surrounds us and which continually appears and disappears. Without the disappearing, there would perhaps be no impulse to paint, for then the visible itself would possess the surety (the permanence) which painting strives to find. More directly than any other art, painting is an affirmation of the existent, of the physical world into which mankind has been thrown.

Animals were the first subject in painting. And right from the beginning and then continuing through Sumerian, Assyrian, Egyptian and early Greek art, the depiction of these animals was extraordinarily true. Many millennia had to pass before an equivalent "life-likeness" was achieved in the depiction of the human body. At the beginning, the existent was what confronted man.

The first painters were hunters whose lives, like everybody else's in the tribe, depended upon their close knowledge of animals. Yet the act of painting was not the same as the act of hunting: the relation between the two was magical.

In a number of early cave paintings there are stencil representations of the human hand beside the animals. We do not know what precise ritual this served. We do know that painting was used to confirm a magical "companionship" between prey and hunter, or, to put it more abstractly, between the existent and human ingenuity. Painting was the means of making this companionship explicit and therefore (hopefully) permanent.

This may still be worth thinking about, long after painting has lost its herds of animals and its ritual function. I believe it tells us something about the nature of the act.

The impulse to paint comes neither from observation nor from the soul (which is probably blind) but from an encounter: the encounter between painter and model—even if the model is a mountain or a shelf of empty medicine bottles. Mont St Victoire as seen from Aix (seen from elsewhere it has a very different shape) was Cézanne's companion.

When a painting is lifeless it is the result of the painter not having the nerve to get close enough for a collaboration to start. He stays at a *copying* distance. Or, as in mannerist periods like today, he stays at an art-historical distance, playing stylistic tricks which the model knows nothing about.

To go in close means forgetting convention, reputation, reasoning, hierarchies and self. It also means risking incoherence, even madness. For it can happen that one gets too close and then the collaboration breaks down and the painter dissolves into the model. Or the animal devours or tramples the painter into the ground.

Every authentic painting demonstrates a collaboration. Look at Petrus Christus's portrait of a young girl in the Staatliche Museum of Berlin, or the stormy seascape in the Louvre by Courbet, or the mouse with an aubergine painted by Tchou-Ta in the seventeenth century, and it is impossible to deny the participation of the model. Indeed, the paintings are *not* first and foremost about a young woman, a rough sea or a mouse with a vegetable; they are about this participation. "The brush," wrote Shitao, the great seventeenth-century Chinese landscape painter, "is for saving things from chaos."

It is a strange area into which we are wandering and I'm using words strangely. A rough sea on the northern coast of France, one autumn day in 1870, *participating in being seen* by a man with a beard who, the following year, will be put in prison! Yet there is no other way of getting close to the actual practice of this silent art, which stops everything moving.

The *raison d'être* of the visible is the eye; the eye evolved and developed where there was enough light for the visible forms of life to become more and more complex and varied. Wild flowers, for example, are the colours they are in order to be seen. That an empty sky appears blue is due to the structure of our eyes and the nature of the solar system. There is a certain ontological basis for the collaboration between model and painter. Silesius, a seventeenth-century doctor of medicine in Wrocklau, wrote about the interdependence of the seen and the seeing in a mystical way.

> *La rose qui contemple ton oeil de chair*
> *A fleuri de la sorte en Dieu dans l'éternel*

How did you become what you visibly are: asks the painter.

I am as I am. I'm waiting, replies the mountain or the mouse or the child.

What for?

For you, if you abandon everything else.

For how long?

For as long as it takes.

There are other things in life.

Find them and be more normal.

And if I don't?

I'll give you what I've given nobody else, but it's worthless, it's simply the answer to your useless question.

Useless?

I am as I am.

No promise more than that?

None. I can wait for ever.
I'd like a normal life.
Live it and don't count on me.
And if I do count on you?
Forget everything and in me you'll find—me!

The collaboration which sometimes follows is seldom based on good will: more usually on desire, rage, fear, pity or longing. The modern illusion concerning painting (which post-modernism has done nothing to correct) is that the artist is a creator. Rather he is a receiver. What seems like creation is the act of giving form to what he has received.

Bogena and Robert and his brother Witek came to spend the evening because it was the Russian new year. Sitting at the table whilst they spoke Russian, I tried to draw Bogena. Not for the first time. I always fail because her face is very mobile and I can't forget her beauty. And to draw well you have to forget that. It was long past midnight when they left. As I was doing my last drawing Robert said: This is your last chance tonight, just draw her, John, draw her and be a man!

When they had gone, I took the least bad drawing and started working on it with colours—acrylic. Suddenly like a weather vane swinging round because the wind has changed, the portrait began to look like something. Her "likeness" now was in my head—and all I had to do was to draw it out, not look for it. The paper tore. I rubbed on paint sometimes as thick as ointment. At four in the morning the face began to lend itself to, to smile at, its own representation.

The next day the frail piece of paper, heavy with paint, still looked good. In the daylight there were a few nuances of tone to change. Colours applied at night sometimes tend to be too desperate—like shoes pulled off without being untied. Now it was finished.

From time to time during the day I went to look at it and I felt elated. Because I had done a small drawing I was pleased with? Scarcely. The elation came from something else. It came from the face's *appearing*—as if out of the dark. It came from the fact that Bogena's face had made a present of *what it could leave behind of itself.*

What is a likeness? When a person dies, they leave behind, for those who knew them, an emptiness, a space: the space has contours and is different for each person mourned. This space with its contours is the person's *likeness* and is what the artist searches for when making a living portrait. A likeness is something left behind invisibly.

Soutine was among the great painters of the twentieth century. It has taken fifty years for this to become clear, because his art was both traditional and uncouth, and this mixture offended all fashionable tastes. It was as if his painting had a heavy broken accent and so was considered inarticulate: at best exotic, and at worst barbarian. Now his devotion to the existent becomes more and more exemplary. Few other painters have revealed more graphically than he the collaboration, implicit in the act of painting, between model and painter. The poplars, the carcasses, the children's faces on Soutine's canvases clung to his brush.

Shitao—to quote him again—wrote:

Painting is the result of the receptivity of ink: the ink is open to the brush: the brush is open to the hand: the hand is open to the heart: all this is the same way as the sky engenders what the earth produces: everything is the result of receptivity.

It is usually said about the late work of Titian or Rembrandt or Turner that their handling of paint became *freer*. Although, in a sense, true, this may give a false impression of *wilfulness*. In fact these painters in their old age simply became more receptive, more open to the appeal of the "model" and its strange energy. It is as if their own bodies fall away.

When once the principle of collaboration has been understood, it becomes a criterion for judging works of any style, irrespective of their freedom of handling. Or rather (because *judgment* has little to do with art) it offers us an insight for seeing more clearly why painting moves us.

Rubens painted his beloved Hélène Fourment many times. Sometimes she collaborated, sometimes not. When she didn't, she remains a painted ideal: when she did, we too wait for her. There is a painting of roses in a vase by Morandi (1949) in which the flowers wait like cats to be let into this vision. (This is very rare for most flower paintings remain pure spectacle.) There is a portrait of a man painted on wood two millennia ago, whose participation we still feel. There are dwarfs painted by Velázquez, dogs by Titian, houses by Vermeer in which we recognise, as energy, the will-to-be-seen.

More and more people go to museums to look at paintings and do not come away disappointed. What fascinates them? To answer: Art, or the history of art, or art appreciation, misses, I believe, the essential.

In art museums we come upon the visible of other periods and it offers us company. We feel less alone in the face of what we ourselves see each day appearing and disappearing. So much continues to look the same: teeth, hands, the sun, women's legs, fish . . . in the realm of the visible all epochs coexist and are fraternal, whether separated by centuries or millennia. And when the painted image is not a copy but the result of a dialogue, the painted thing speaks if we listen.

In matters of seeing, Joseph Beuys was the great prophet of the second half of our century, and his life's work was a demonstration of, and an appeal for, the kind of collaboration I'm talking about. Believing that everybody is potentially an artist, he took objects and arranged them in such a way that they beg the spectator to collaborate with them, not this time by painting, but by listening to what their eyes tell them and remembering.

I know of few things more sad (sad, not tragic) than an animal who has lost its sight. Unlike humans, the animal has no supporting language left which can describe the world. If on a familiar terrain, the blind animal manages to find its way about with its nose. But it has been deprived of the existent and with this deprivation it begins to diminish until it does little but sleep, therein perhaps hunting for a dream of that which once existed.

The Marquise de Sorcy de Thélusson, painted in 1790 by David, looks at me. Who could have foreseen in her time the solitude in which people today live? A solitude confirmed daily by networks of bodiless and false images concerning the world. Yet their falseness is not an error. If the pursuit of profit is considered as the only means of salvation for mankind, turnover becomes the absolute priority, and, consequently, the existent has to be disregarded or ignored or suppressed.

Today, to try to paint the existent is an act of resistance instigating hope.

Creation Myth:
Xerox PARC, Apple, and the
Truth about Innovation

Malcolm Gladwell

In late 1979, a twenty-four-year-old entrepreneur paid a visit to a research center in Silicon Valley called Xerox PARC. He was the co-founder of a small computer startup down the road, in Cupertino. His name was Steve Jobs.

Xerox PARC was the innovation arm of the Xerox Corporation. It was, and remains, on Coyote Hill Road, in Palo Alto, nestled in the foothills on the edge of town, in a long, low concrete building, with enormous terraces looking out over the jewels of Silicon Valley. To the northwest was Stanford University's Hoover Tower. To the north was Hewlett-Packard's sprawling campus. All around were scores of the other chip designers, software firms, venture capitalists, and hardware-makers. A visitor to PARC, taking in that view, could easily imagine that it was the computer world's castle, lording over the valley below—and, at the time, this wasn't far from the truth. In 1970, Xerox had assembled the world's greatest computer engineers and programmers, and for the next ten years they had an unparalleled run of innovation and invention. If you were obsessed with the future in the seventies, you were obsessed with Xerox PARC—which was why the young Steve Jobs had driven to Coyote Hill Road.

Apple was already one of the hottest tech firms in the country. Everyone in the Valley wanted a piece of it. So Jobs proposed a deal: he would allow Xerox to buy a hundred thousand shares of his company for a million dollars—its highly anticipated I.P.O. was just a year away—if PARC would "open its kimono." A lot of haggling ensued. Jobs was the fox, after all, and PARC was the henhouse. What would he be allowed to see? What wouldn't he be allowed to see? Some at PARC thought that the whole idea was lunacy, but, in the end, Xerox went ahead with it. One PARC scientist recalls Jobs as "rambunctious"—a fresh-cheeked, caffeinated version of today's austere digital emperor. He was given a couple of tours, and he ended up standing in front of a Xerox Alto, PARC's prized personal computer.

333

An engineer named Larry Tesler conducted the demonstration. He moved the cursor across the screen with the aid of a "mouse." Directing a conventional computer, in those days, meant typing in a command on the keyboard. Tesler just clicked on one of the icons on the screen. He opened and closed "windows," deftly moving from one task to another. He wrote on an elegant word-processing program, and exchanged e-mails with other people at PARC, on the world's first Ethernet network. Jobs had come with one of his software engineers, Bill Atkinson, and Atkinson moved in as close as he could, his nose almost touching the screen. "Jobs was pacing around the room, acting up the whole time," Tesler recalled. "He was very excited. Then, when he began seeing the things I could do onscreen, he watched for about a minute and started jumping around the room, shouting, 'Why aren't you doing anything with this? This is the greatest thing. This is revolutionary!'"

Xerox began selling a successor to the Alto in 1981. It was slow and underpowered—and Xerox ultimately withdrew from personal computers altogether. Jobs, meanwhile, raced back to Apple, and demanded that the team working on the company's next generation of personal computers change course. He wanted menus on the screen. He wanted windows. He wanted a mouse. The result was the Macintosh, perhaps the most famous product in the history of Silicon Valley.

"If Xerox had known what it had and had taken advantage of its real opportunities," Jobs said, years later, "it could have been as big as I.B.M. plus Microsoft plus Xerox combined—and the largest high-technology company in the world."

This is the legend of Xerox PARC. Jobs is the Biblical Jacob and Xerox is Esau, squandering his birthright for a pittance. In the past thirty years, the legend has been vindicated by history. Xerox, once the darling of the American high-technology community, slipped from its former dominance. Apple is now ascendant, and the demonstration in that room in Palo Alto has come to symbolize the vision and ruthlessness that separate true innovators from also-rans. As with all legends, however, the truth is a bit more complicated.

After Jobs returned from PARC, he met with a man named Dean Hovey, who was one of the founders of the industrial-design firm that would become known as IDEO. "Jobs went to Xerox PARC on a Wednesday or a Thursday, and I saw him on the Friday afternoon," Hovey recalled. "I had a series of ideas that I wanted to bounce off him, and I barely got two words out of my mouth when he said, 'No, no, no, you've got to do a mouse.' I was, like, 'What's a mouse?' I didn't have a clue. So he explains it, and he says, 'You know, [the Xerox mouse] is a mouse that cost three hundred dollars to build and it breaks within two weeks. Here's your design spec: Our mouse needs to be manufacturable for less than fifteen bucks. It needs to not fail for a couple of years, and I want to be able to use it on Formica and my bluejeans.' From that meeting, I went to Walgreens, which is still there, at the corner of Grant and El Camino in Mountain View, and I wandered around and bought all the underarm deodorants that I could find, because they had that ball in them. I bought a butter dish. That was the beginnings of the mouse."

I spoke with Hovey in a ramshackle building in downtown Palo Alto, where his firm had started out. He had asked the current tenant if he could borrow his old office for the morning, just for the fun of telling the story of the Apple mouse in the place where it was invented. The room was the size of someone's bedroom. It looked as if it had last been painted in the Coolidge Administration. Hovey, who is lean and healthy in a Northern California yoga-and-yogurt sort of way, sat uncomfortably at a rickety desk in a corner of the room. "Our first machine shop was literally out on the roof," he said, pointing out the window to a little narrow strip of rooftop, covered in green outdoor carpeting. "We didn't tell the planning commission. We went and got that clear corrugated stuff and put it across the top for a roof. We got out through the window."

He had brought a big plastic bag full of the artifacts of that moment: diagrams scribbled on lined paper, dozens of differently sized plastic mouse shells, a spool of guitar wire, a tiny set of wheels from a toy train set, and the metal lid from a jar of Ralph's preserves. He turned the lid over. It was filled with a waxlike substance, the middle of which had a round indentation, in the shape of a small ball. "It's epoxy casting resin," he said. "You pour it, and then I put Vaseline on a smooth steel ball, and set it in the resin, and it hardens around it." He tucked the steel ball underneath the lid and rolled it around the tabletop. "It's a kind of mouse."

The hard part was that the roller ball needed to be connected to the housing of the mouse, so that it didn't fall out, and so that it could transmit information about its movements to the cursor on the screen. But if the friction created by those connections was greater than the friction between the tabletop and the roller ball, the mouse would skip. And the more the mouse was used the more dust it would pick up off the tabletop, and the more it would skip. The Xerox PARC mouse was an elaborate affair, with an array of ball bearings supporting the roller ball. But there was too much friction on the top of the ball, and it couldn't deal with dust and grime.

At first, Hovey set to work with various arrangements of ball bearings, but nothing quite worked. "This was the 'aha' moment," Hovey said, placing his fingers loosely around the sides of the ball, so that they barely touched its surface. "So the ball's sitting here. And it rolls. I attribute that not to the table but to the oldness of the building. The floor's not level. So I started playing with it, and that's when I realized: I *want* it to roll. I don't want it to be supported by all kinds of ball bearings. I want to just barely touch it."

The trick was to connect the ball to the rest of the mouse at the two points where there was the least friction—right where his fingertips had been, dead center on either side of the ball. "If it's right at midpoint, there's no force causing it to rotate. So it rolls."

Hovey estimated their consulting fee at thirty-five dollars an hour; the whole project cost perhaps a hundred thousand dollars. "I originally pitched Apple on doing this mostly for royalties, as opposed to a consulting job," he recalled. "I said, 'I'm thinking fifty cents apiece,' because I was thinking that they'd sell fifty thousand, maybe a hundred thousand of them." He burst out laughing, because of how far off his estimates ended up being. "Steve's pretty savvy. He said no. Maybe if I'd asked for a nickel, I would have been fine."

Here is the first complicating fact about the Jobs visit. In the legend of Xerox PARC, Jobs stole the personal computer from Xerox. But the striking thing about Jobs's instructions to Hovey is that he *didn't* want to reproduce what he saw at PARC. "You know, there were disputes around the number of buttons—three buttons, two buttons, one-button mouse," Hovey went on. "The mouse at Xerox had three buttons. But we came around to the fact that learning to mouse is a feat in and of itself, and to make it as simple as possible, with just one button, was pretty important."

So was what Jobs took from Xerox the *idea* of the mouse? Not quite, because Xerox never owned the idea of the mouse. The PARC researchers got it from the computer scientist Douglas Engelbart, at Stanford Research Institute, fifteen minutes away on the other side of the university campus. Engelbart dreamed up the idea of moving the cursor around the screen with a stand-alone mechanical "animal" back in the mid-nineteen-sixties. His mouse was a bulky, rectangular affair, with what looked like steel roller-skate wheels. If you lined up Engelbart's mouse, Xerox's mouse, and Apple's mouse, you would not see the serial reproduction of an object. You would see the evolution of a concept.

The same is true of the graphical user interface that so captured Jobs's imagination. Xerox PARC's innovation had been to replace the traditional computer command line with onscreen icons. But when you clicked on an icon you got a pop-up menu: this was the intermediary between the user's intention and the computer's response. Jobs's software team took the graphical interface a giant step further. It emphasized "direct manipulation." If you wanted to make a window bigger, you just pulled on its corner and made it bigger; if you wanted to move a window across the screen, you just grabbed it and moved it. The Apple designers also invented the menu bar, the pull-down menu, and the trash can—all features that radically simplified the original Xerox PARC idea.

The difference between direct and indirect manipulation—between three buttons and one button, three hundred dollars and fifteen dollars, and a roller ball supported by ball bearings and a free-rolling ball—is not trivial. It is the difference between something intended for experts, which is what Xerox PARC had in mind, and something that's appropriate for a mass audience, which is what Apple had in mind. PARC was building a personal computer. Apple wanted to build a *popular* computer.

In a recent study, "The Culture of Military Innovation," the military scholar Dima Adamsky makes a similar argument about the so-called Revolution in Military Affairs. R.M.A. refers to the way armies have transformed themselves with the tools of the digital age—such as precision-guided missiles, surveillance drones, and real-time command, control, and communications technologies—and Adamsky begins with the simple observation that it is impossible to determine who invented R.M.A. The first people to imagine how digital technology would transform warfare were a cadre of senior military intellectuals in the Soviet Union, during the nineteen-seventies. The first country to come up with these high-tech systems was the United States. And the first country to use them was Israel, in its 1982 clash with the Syrian Air Force in Lebanon's Bekaa Valley, a battle commonly referred to as "the Bekaa Valley turkey shoot." Israel coordinated all the major innovations of R.M.A. in a manner so devastating that it destroyed nineteen surface-to-air batteries and eighty-seven Syrian aircraft while losing only a handful of its own planes.

That's three revolutions, not one, and Adamsky's point is that each of these strands is necessarily distinct, drawing on separate skills and circumstances. The Soviets had a strong, centralized military bureaucracy, with a long tradition of theoretical analysis. It made sense that they were the first to understand the military implications of new information systems. But they didn't do anything with it, because centralized military bureaucracies with strong intellectual traditions aren't very good at connecting word and deed.

The United States, by contrast, has a decentralized, bottom-up entrepreneurial culture, which has historically had a strong orientation toward technological solutions. The military's close ties to the country's high-tech community made it unsurprising that the U.S. would be the first to invent precision-guidance and next-generation command-and-control communications. But those assets also meant that Soviet-style systemic analysis wasn't going to be a priority. As for the Israelis, their military culture grew out of a background of resource constraint and constant threat. In response, they became brilliantly improvisational and creative. But, as Adamsky points out, a military built around urgent, short-term "fire extinguishing" is not going to be distinguished by reflective theory. No one stole the revolution. Each party viewed the problem from a different perspective, and carved off a different piece of the puzzle.

In the history of the mouse, Engelbart was the Soviet Union. He was the visionary, who saw the mouse before anyone else did. But visionaries are limited by their visions. "Engelbart's self-defined mission was not to produce a product, or even a prototype; it was an open-ended search for knowledge," Matthew Hiltzik writes, in "Dealers of Lightning" (1999), his wonderful history of Xerox PARC. "Consequently, no project in his lab ever seemed to come to an end." Xerox PARC was the United States: it was a place where things got made. "Xerox created this perfect environment," recalled Bob Metcalfe, who worked there through much of the nineteen-seventies, before leaving to found the networking company 3Com. "There wasn't any hierarchy. We built our own tools. When we needed to publish papers, we built a printer. When we needed to edit the papers, we built a computer. When we needed to connect computers, we figured out how to connect them. We had big budgets. Unlike many of our brethren, we didn't have to teach. We could just research. It was heaven."

But heaven is not a good place to commercialize a product. "We built a computer and it was a beautiful thing," Metcalfe went on. "We developed our computer language, our own display, our own language. It was a gold-plated product. But it cost sixteen thousand dollars, and it needed to cost three thousand dollars." For an actual product, you need threat and constraint—and the improvisation and creativity necessary to turn a gold-plated three-hundred-dollar mouse into something that works on Formica and costs fifteen dollars. Apple was Israel.

Xerox *couldn't* have been I.B.M. and Microsoft combined, in other words. "You can be one of the most successful makers of enterprise technology products the world has ever known, but that doesn't mean your instincts will carry over to the consumer market," the tech writer Harry McCracken recently wrote. "They're really different, and few companies have ever been successful in both." He was talking about the decision by the networking giant Cisco System, this spring, to shut down its Flip camera business, at a cost of many hundreds of millions of dollars. But he could just as easily have been talking about the Xerox of forty years ago, which was one of the most successful makers of enterprise technology the world has ever known. The fair question is whether Xerox, through its research arm in Palo Alto, found a better way to be Xerox—and the answer is that it did, although that story doesn't get told nearly as often.

One of the people at Xerox PARC when Steve Jobs visited was an optical engineer named Gary Starkweather. He is a solid and irrepressibly cheerful man, with large, practical hands and the engineer's gift of pretending that what is impossibly difficult is actually pretty easy, once you shave off a bit here, and remember some of your high-school calculus, and realize that the thing that you thought should go in left to right should actually go in right to left. Once, before the palatial Coyote Hill Road building was constructed, a group that Starkweather had to be connected to was moved to another building, across the Foothill Expressway, half a mile away. There was no way to run a cable under the highway. So Starkweather fired a laser through the air between the two buildings, an improvised communications system that meant that, if you were driving down the Foothill Expressway on a foggy night and happened to look up, you might see a mysterious red beam streaking across the sky. When a motorist drove into the median ditch, "we had to turn it down," Starkweather recalled, with a mischievous smile.

Lasers were Starkweather's specialty. He started at Xerox's East Coast research facility in Webster, New York, outside Rochester. Xerox built machines that scanned a printed page of type using a photographic lens, and then printed a duplicate. Starkweather's idea was to skip the first step—to run a document from a computer directly into a photocopier, by means of a laser, and turn the Xerox machine into a printer. It was a radical idea. The printer, since Gutenberg, had been limited to the function of re-creation: if you wanted to print a specific image or letter, you had to have a physical character or mark corresponding to that image or letter. What Starkweather wanted to do was take the array of bits and bytes, ones and zeros that constitute digital images, and transfer them straight into the guts of a copier. That meant, at least in theory, that he could print anything.

"One morning, I woke up and I thought, Why don't we just print something out directly?" Starkweather said. "But when I flew that past my boss he thought it was the most brain-dead idea he had ever heard. He basically told me to find something else to do. The feeling was that lasers were too expensive. They didn't work that well. Nobody wants to do this, computers aren't powerful enough. And I guess, in my naïveté, I kept thinking, He's just not right—there's something about this I really like. It got to be a frustrating situation. He and I came to loggerheads over the thing, about late 1969, early 1970. I was running my experiments in the back room behind a black curtain. I played with them when I could. He threatened to lay off my people if I didn't stop. I was having to make a decision: do I abandon this, or do I try and go up the ladder with it?"

Then Starkweather heard that Xerox was opening a research center in Palo Alto, three thousand miles away from its New York headquarters. He went to a senior vice-president of Xerox, threatening to leave for I.B.M. if he didn't get a transfer. In January of 1971, his wish was granted, and, within ten months, he had a prototype up and running.

Starkweather is retired now, and lives in a gated community just north of Orlando, Florida. When we spoke, he was sitting at a picnic table, inside a screened-in porch in his back yard. Behind him, golfers whirred by in carts. He was wearing white chinos and a shiny black short-sleeved shirt, decorated with fluorescent images of vintage hot rods. He had brought out two large plastic bins filled with the artifacts of his research, and he spread the contents on the table: a metal octagonal disk, sketches on lab paper, a black plastic laser housing that served as the innards for one of his printers.

"There was still a tremendous amount of opposition from the Webster group, who saw no future in computer printing," he went on. "They said, 'I.B.M. is doing that. Why do we need to do that?' and so forth. Also, there were two or three competing projects, which I guess I have the luxury of calling ridiculous. One group had fifty people and another had twenty. I had two." Starkweather picked up a picture of one of his in-house competitors, something called an "optical carriage printer." It was the size of one of those modular Italian kitchen units that you see advertised in fancy design magazines. "It was an unbelievable device," he said, with a rueful chuckle. "It had a ten-inch drum, which turned at five thousand r.p.m., like a super washing machine. It had characters printed on its surface. I think they only ever sold ten of them. The problem was that it was spinning so fast that the drum would blow out and the characters would fly off. And there was only this one lady in Troy, New York, who knew how to put the characters on so that they would stay.

"So we finally decided to have what I called a fly-off. There was a full page of text—where some of them were non-serif characters, Helvetica, stuff like that—and then a page of graph paper with grid lines, and pages with pictures and some other complex stuff—and everybody had to print all six pages. Well, once we decided on those six pages, I knew I'd won, because I knew there wasn't anything I couldn't print. Are you kidding? If you can translate it into bits, I can print it. Some of these other machines had to go through hoops just to print a curve. A week after the fly-off, they folded those other projects. I was the only game in town." The project turned into the Xerox 9700, the first high-speed, cut-paper laser printer in the world.

In one sense, the Starkweather story is of a piece with the Steve Jobs visit. It is an example of the imaginative poverty of Xerox management. Starkweather had to hide his laser behind a curtain. He had to fight for his transfer to PARC. He had to endure the indignity of the fly-off, and even then Xerox management remained skeptical. The founder of PARC, Jack Goldman, had to bring in a team from Rochester for a personal demonstration. After that, Starkweather and Goldman had an idea for getting the laser printer to market quickly: graft a laser onto a Xerox copier called the 7000. The 7000 was an older model, and Xerox had lots of 7000s sitting around that had just come off lease.

Goldman even had a customer ready: the Lawrence Livermore laboratory was prepared to buy a whole slate of the machines. Xerox said no. Then Starkweather wanted to make what he called a photo-typesetter, which produced camera-ready copy right on your desk. Xerox said no. "I wanted to work on higher-performance scanners," Starkweather continued. "In other words, what if we print something other than documents? For example, I made a high-resolution scanner and you could print on glass plates." He rummaged in one of the boxes on the picnic table and came out with a sheet of glass, roughly six inches square, on which a photograph of a child's face appeared. The same idea, he said, could have been used to make "masks" for the semi-conductor industry—the densely patterned screens used to etch the designs on computer chips. "No one would ever follow through, because Xerox said, 'Now you're in Intel's market, what are you doing that for?' They just could not seem to see that they were in the information business. This"—he lifted up the plate with the little girl's face on it—"is a copy. It's just not a copy of an office document." But he got nowhere. "Xerox had been infested by a bunch of spreadsheet experts who thought you could decide every product based on metrics. Unfortunately, creativity wasn't on a metric."

A few days after that afternoon in his back yard, however, Starkweather e-mailed an addendum to his discussion of his experiences at PARC. "Despite all the hassles and risks that happened in getting the laser printer going, in retrospect the journey was that much more exciting," he wrote. "Often difficulties are just opportunities in disguise." Perhaps he felt that he had painted too negative a picture of his time at Xerox, or suffered a pang of guilt about what it must have been like to be one of those Xerox executives on the other side of the table. The truth is that Starkweather was a difficult employee. It went hand in hand with what made him such an extraordinary innovator. When his boss told him to quit working on lasers, he continued in secret. He was disruptive and stubborn and independent-minded—and he had a thousand ideas, and sorting out the good ideas from the bad wasn't always easy. Should Xerox have put out a special order of laser printers for Lawrence Livermore, based on the old 7000 copier? In "Fumbling the Future: How Xerox Invented, Then Ignored, the First Personal Computer" (1988)—a book dedicated to the idea that Xerox was run by the blind—Douglas Smith and Robert Alexander admit that the proposal was hopelessly impractical: "The scanty Livermore proposal could not justify the investment required to start a laser printing business. . . . How and where would Xerox manufacture the laser printers? Who would sell and service them? Who would buy them and why?" Starkweather, and his compatriots at Xerox PARC, weren't the source of disciplined strategic insights. They were wild geysers of creative energy.

The psychologist Dean Simonton argues that this fecundity is often at the heart of what distinguishes the truly gifted. The difference between Bach and his forgotten peers isn't necessarily that he had a better ratio of hits to misses. The difference is that the mediocre might have a dozen ideas, while Bach, in his lifetime, created more than a thousand full-fledged musical compositions. A genius is a genius, Simonton maintains, because he can put together such a staggering number of insights, ideas, theories, random observations, and unexpected connections that he almost inevitably ends up with something great. "Quality," Simonton writes, is "a probabilistic function of quantity."

Simonton's point is that there is nothing neat and efficient about creativity. "The more successes there are," he says, "the more failures there are as well"—meaning that the person who had far more ideas than the rest of us will have far more bad ideas than the rest of us, too. This is why managing the creative process is so difficult. The making of the classic Rolling Stones album "Exile on Main Street" was an ordeal, Keith Richards writes in his new memoir, because the band had too many ideas. It had to fight from under an avalanche of mediocrity: "Head in the Toilet Blues," "Leather Jackets," "Windmill," "I Was Just a Country Boy," "Bent Green Needles," "Labour Pains," and "Pommes de Terre"—the last of which Richards explains with the apologetic, "Well, we were in France at the time."

At one point, Richards quotes a friend, Jim Dickinson, remembering the origins of the song "Brown Sugar":

I watched Mick write the lyrics. . . . He wrote it down as fast as he could move his hand. I'd never seen anything like it. He had one of those yellow legal pads, and he'd write a verse a page, just write a verse and then turn the page, and when he had three pages filled, they started to cut it. It was amazing.

Richards goes on to marvel, "It's unbelievable how prolific he was." Then he writes, "Sometimes you'd wonder how to turn the fucking tap off. The odd times he would come out with so many lyrics, you're crowding the airwaves, boy." Richards clearly saw himself as the creative steward of the Rolling Stones (only in a rock-and-roll band, by the way, can someone like Keith Richards perceive himself as the responsible one), and he came to understand that one of the hardest and most crucial parts of his job was to "turn the fucking tap off," to rein in Mick Jagger's incredible creative energy.

The more Starkweather talked, the more apparent it became that his entire career had been a version of this problem. Someone was always trying to turn his tap off. But someone *had* to turn his tap off: the interests of the innovator aren't perfectly aligned with the interests of the corporation. Starkweather saw ideas on their own merits. Xerox was a multinational corporation, with shareholders, a huge sales force, and a vast corporate customer base, and it needed to consider every new idea within the context of what it already had.

Xerox's managers didn't always make the right decisions when they said no to Starkweather. But he got to PARC, didn't he? And Xerox, to its great credit, *had* a PARC—a place where, a continent away from the top managers, an engineer could sit and dream, and get every purchase order approved, and fire a laser across the Foothill Expressway if he was so inclined. Yes, he had to pit his laser printer against lesser ideas in the contest. But he won the contest. And, the instant he did, Xerox cancelled the competing projects and gave him the green light.

"I flew out there and gave a presentation to them on what I was looking at," Starkweather said of his first visit to PARC. "They really liked it, because at the time they were building a personal computer, and they were beside themselves figuring out how they were going to get whatever was on the screen onto a sheet of paper. And when I showed them how I was going to put prints on a sheet of paper it was a marriage made in heaven." The reason Xerox invented the laser printer, in other words, is that it invented the personal computer. Without the big idea, it would never have seen the value of the small idea. If you consider innovation to be efficient and ideas precious, that is a tragedy: you give the crown jewels away to Steve Jobs, and all you're left with is a printer. But in the real, messy world of creativity, giving away the thing you don't really understand for the thing that you do is an inevitable tradeoff.

"When you have a bunch of smart people with a broad enough charter, you will always get something good out of it," Nathan Myhrvold, formerly a senior executive at Microsoft, argues. "It's one of the best investments you could possibly make—but only if you chose to value it in terms of successes. If you chose to evaluate it in terms of how many times you failed, or times you could have succeeded and didn't, then you are bound to be unhappy. Innovation is an unruly thing. There will be some ideas that don't get caught in your cup. But that's not what the game is about. The game is what you catch, not what you spill."

In the nineteen-nineties, Myhrvold created a research laboratory at Microsoft modelled in part on what Xerox had done in Palo Alto in the nineteen-seventies, because he considered PARC a triumph, not a failure. "Xerox did research outside their business model, and when you do that you should not be surprised that you have a hard time dealing with it—any more than if some bright guy at Pfizer wrote a word processor. Good luck to Pfizer getting into the word-processing business. Meanwhile, the thing that they invented that was similar to their own business—a really big machine that spit paper out—they made a lot of money on it." And so they did. Gary Starkweather's laser printer made billions for Xerox. It paid for every other single project at Xerox PARC, many times over.

In 1988, Starkweather got a call from the head of one of Xerox's competitors, trying to lure him away. It was someone whom he had met years

343

ago. "The decision was painful," he said. "I was a year from being a twenty-five-year veteran of the company. I mean, I'd done enough for Xerox that unless I burned the building down they would never fire me. But that wasn't the issue. It's about having ideas that are constantly squashed. So I said, 'Enough of this,' and I left."

He had a good many years at his new company, he said. It was an extraordinarily creative place. He was part of decision-making at the highest level. "Every employee from technician to manager was hot for the new, exciting stuff," he went on. "So, as far as buzz and daily environment, it was far and away the most fun I've ever had." But it wasn't perfect. "I remember I called in the head marketing guy and I said, 'I want you to give me all the information you can come up with on when people buy one of our products—what software do they buy, what business are they in—so I can see the model of how people are using the machines.' He looked at me and said, 'I have no idea about that.'" Where was the rigor? Then Starkweather had a scheme for hooking up a high-resolution display to one of his new company's computers. "I got it running and brought it into management and said, 'Why don't we show this at the tech expo in San Francisco? You'll be able to rule the world.' They said, 'I don't know. We don't have room for it.' It was that sort of thing. It was like me saying I've discovered a gold mine and you saying we can't afford a shovel."

He shrugged a little wearily. It was ever thus. The innovator says go. The company says stop—and maybe the only lesson of the legend of Xerox PARC is that what happened there happens, in one way or another, everywhere. By the way, the man who hired Gary Starkweather away to the company that couldn't afford a shovel? His name was Steve Jobs.

Small Change:
Why the Revolution
Will Not Be Tweeted

Malcolm Gladwell

At four-thirty in the afternoon on Monday, February 1, 1960, four college students sat down at the lunch counter at the Woolworth's in downtown Greensboro, North Carolina. They were freshmen at North Carolina A. & T., a black college a mile or so away.

"I'd like a cup of coffee, please," one of the four, Ezell Blair, said to the waitress.

"We don't serve Negroes here," she replied.

The Woolworth's lunch counter was a long L-shaped bar that could seat sixty-six people, with a standup snack bar at one end. The seats were for whites. The snack bar was for blacks. Another employee, a black woman who worked at the steam table, approached the students and tried to warn them away. "You're acting stupid, ignorant!" she said. They didn't move. Around five-thirty, the front doors to the store were locked. The four still didn't move. Finally, they left by a side door. Outside, a small crowd had gathered, including a photographer from the Greensboro *Record*. "I'll be back tomorrow with A. & T. College," one of the students said.

By next morning, the protest had grown to twenty-seven men and four women, most from the same dormitory as the original four. The men were dressed in suits and ties. The students had brought their schoolwork, and studied as they sat at the counter. On Wednesday, students from Greensboro's "Negro" secondary school, Dudley High, joined in, and the number of protesters swelled to eighty. By Thursday, the protesters numbered three hundred, including three white women, from the Greensboro campus of the University of North Carolina. By Saturday, the sit-in had reached six hundred. People spilled out onto the street. White teen-agers waved Confederate flags. Someone threw a firecracker. At noon, the A. & T. football team arrived. "Here comes the wrecking crew," one of the white students shouted.

By the following Monday, sit-ins had spread to Winston-Salem, twenty-five miles away, and Durham, fifty miles away. The day after that, students at Fayetteville State Teachers College and at Johnson C. Smith College, in Charlotte, joined in, followed on Wednesday by students at St. Augustine's College and Shaw University, in Raleigh. On Thursday and Friday, the protest crossed state lines, surfacing in Hampton and Portsmouth, Virginia, in Rock Hill, South Carolina, and in Chattanooga, Tennessee. By the end of the month, there were sit-ins throughout the South, as far west as Texas. "I asked every student I met what the first day of the sitdowns had been like on his campus," the political theorist Michael Walzer wrote in *Dissent*. "The answer was always the same: 'It was like a fever. Everyone wanted to go.'" Some seventy thousand students eventually took part. Thousands were arrested and untold thousands more radicalized. These events in the early sixties became a civil-rights war that engulfed the South for the rest of the decade—and it happened without e-mail, texting, Facebook, or Twitter.

The world, we are told, is in the midst of a revolution. The new tools of social media have reinvented social activism. With Facebook and Twitter and the like, the traditional relationship between political authority and popular will has been upended, making it easier for the powerless to collaborate, coördinate, and give voice to their concerns. When ten thousand protesters took to the streets in Moldova in the spring of 2009 to protest against their country's Communist government, the action was dubbed the Twitter Revolution, because of the means by which the demonstrators had been brought together. A few months after that, when student protests rocked Tehran, the State Department took the unusual step of asking Twitter to suspend scheduled maintenance of its Web site, because the Administration didn't want such a critical organizing tool out of service at the height of the demonstrations. "Without Twitter the people of Iran would not have felt empowered and confident to stand up for freedom and democracy," Mark Pfeifle, a former national-security adviser, later wrote, calling for Twitter to be nominated for the Nobel Peace Prize. Where activists were once defined by their causes, they are now defined by their tools. Facebook warriors go online to push for change. "You are the best hope for us all," James K. Glassman, a former senior State Department official, told a crowd of cyber activists at a recent conference sponsored by Facebook, A. T. & T., Howcast, MTV, and Google. Sites like Facebook, Glassman said, "give the U.S. a significant competitive advantage over terrorists. Some time ago, I said that Al Qaeda was 'eating our lunch on the Internet.' That is no longer the case. Al Qaeda is stuck in Web 1.0. The Internet is now about interactivity and conversation."

These are strong, and puzzling, claims. Why does it matter who is eating whose lunch on the Internet? Are people who log on to their Facebook page really the best hope for us all? As for Moldova's so-called Twitter Revolution, Evgeny Morozov, a scholar at Stanford who has been the most persistent of digital evangelism's critics, points out that Twitter had scant internal significance in Moldova, a country where very few Twitter accounts exist. Nor does it seem to have been a revolution, not least because the protests—as Anne Applebaum suggested in the *Washington Post*—may well have been a bit of stagecraft cooked up by the government. (In a country paranoid about Romanian revanchism, the protesters flew a Romanian flag over the Parliament building.) In the Iranian case, meanwhile, the people tweeting about the demonstrations were almost all in the West. "It is time to get Twitter's role in the events in Iran right," Golnaz Esfandiari wrote, this past summer, in *Foreign Policy*. "Simply put: There was no Twitter Revolution inside Iran." The cadre of prominent bloggers, like Andrew Sullivan, who championed the role of social media in Iran, Esfandiari continued, misunderstood the situation. "Western journalists who couldn't reach—or didn't bother reaching?—people on the ground in Iran simply scrolled through the English-language tweets post with tag #iranelection," she wrote. "Through it all, no one seemed to wonder why people trying to coordinate protests in Iran would be writing in any language other than Farsi."

Some of this grandiosity is to be expected. Innovators tend to be solipsists. They often want to cram every stray fact and experience into their new model. As the historian Robert Darnton has written, "The marvels of communication technology in the present have produced a false consciousness about the past—even a sense that communication has no history, or had nothing of importance to consider before the days of television and the Internet." But there is something else at work here, in the outsized enthusiasm for social media. Fifty years after one of the most extraordinary episodes of social upheaval in American history, we seem to have forgotten what activism is.

Greensboro in the early nineteen-sixties was the kind of place where racial insubordination was routinely met with violence. The four students who first sat down at the lunch counter were terrified. "I suppose if anyone had come up behind me and yelled 'Boo,' I think I would have fallen off my seat," one of them said later. On the first day, the store manager notified the police chief, who immediately sent two officers to the store. On the third day, a gang of white toughs showed up at the lunch counter and stood ostentatiously behind the protesters, ominously muttering epithets such as "burr-head nigger." A local Ku Klux Klan leader made an appearance. On Saturday, as tensions grew, someone called in a bomb threat, and the entire store had to be evacuated.

The dangers were even clearer in the Mississippi Freedom Summer Project of 1964, another of the sentinel campaigns of the civil-rights movement. The Student Nonviolent Coordinating Committee recruited hundreds of Northern, largely white unpaid volunteers to run Freedom Schools, register black voters, and raise civil-rights awareness in the Deep South. "No one should go *anywhere* alone, but certainly not in an automobile and certainly not at night," they were instructed. Within days of arriving in Mississippi, three volunteers— Michael Schwerner, James Chaney, and Andrew Goodman —were kidnapped and killed, and, during the rest of the summer, thirty-seven black churches were set on fire and dozens of safe houses were bombed; volunteers were beaten, shot at, arrested, and trailed by pickup trucks full of armed men. A quarter of those in the program dropped out. Activism that challenges the status quo— that attacks deeply rooted problems—is not for the faint of heart.

What makes people capable of this kind of activism? The Stanford sociologist Doug McAdam compared the Freedom Summer dropouts with the participants who stayed, and discovered that the key difference wasn't, as might be expected, ideological fervor. "*All* of the applicants—participants and withdrawals alike—emerge as highly committed, articulate supporters of the goals and values of the summer program," he concluded. What mattered more was an applicant's degree of personal connection to the civil-rights movement. All the volunteers were required to provide a list of personal contacts—the people they wanted kept apprised of their activities—and participants were far more likely than dropouts to have close friends who were also going to Mississippi. High-risk activism, McAdam concluded, is a "strong-tie" phenomenon.

This pattern shows up again and again. One study of the Red Brigades, the Italian terrorist group of the nineteen-seventies, found that seventy percent of recruits had at least one good friend already in the organization. The same is true of the men who joined the mujahideen in Afghanistan. Even revolutionary actions that look spontaneous, like the demonstrations in East Germany that led to the fall of the Berlin Wall, are, at core, strong-tie phenomena. The opposition movement in East Germany consisted of several hundred groups, each with roughly a dozen members. Each group was in limited contact with the others: at the time, only thirteen percent of East Germans even had a phone. All they knew was that on Monday nights, outside St. Nicholas Church in downtown Leipzig, people gathered to voice their anger at the state. And the primary determinate of who showed up was "critical friends"—the more friends you had who were critical of the regime the more likely you were to join the protest.

So one crucial fact about the four freshmen at the Greensboro lunch counter —David Richmond, Franklin McCain, Ezell Blair, and Joseph McNeil—was their relationship with one another. McNeil was a roommate of Blair's in A. & T.'s Scott Hall dormitory. Richmond roomed with McCain one floor up, and Blair, Richmond, and McCain had all gone to Dudley High School. The four would smuggle beer into the dorm and talk late into the night in Blair and McNeil's room. They would all have remembered the murder of Emmett Till in 1955, the Montgomery bus boycott that same year, and the showdown in Little Rock in 1957. It was McNeil who brought up the idea of a sit-in at Woolworth's. They'd discussed it for nearly a month. Then McNeil came in to the dorm room and asked the others if they were ready. There was a pause, and McCain said, in a way that works only with people who talk late into the night with one another, "Are you guys chicken or not?" Ezell Blair worked up the courage the next day to ask for a cup of coffee because he was flanked by his roommates and two good friends from high school.

The kind of activism associated with social media isn't like this at all. The platforms of social media are built around weak ties. Twitter is a way of following (or being followed by) people you may never have met. Facebook is a tool for efficiently managing your acquaintances, for keeping up with the people you would not otherwise be able to stay in touch with. That's why you can have a thousand "friends" on Facebook, as you never could in real life.

This is in many ways a wonderful thing. There is strength in weak ties, as the sociologist Mark Granovetter has observed. Our acquaintances—not our friends—are our greatest source of new ideas and information. The Internet lets us exploit the power of these kinds of distant connections with marvellous efficiency. It's terrific at the diffusion of innovation, interdisciplinary collaboration, seamlessly matching up buyers and sellers, and the logical functions of the dating world. But weak ties seldom lead to high-risk activism.

In a new book called "The Dragonfly Effect: Quick, Effective, and Powerful Ways to Use Social Media to Drive Social Change," the business consultant Andy Smith and the Stanford Business School professor Jennifer Aaker tell the story of Sameer Bhatia, a young Silicon Valley entrepreneur who came down with acute myelogenous leukemia. It's a perfect illustration of social media's strengths. Bhatia needed a bone-marrow transplant, but he could not find a match among his relatives and friends. The odds were best with a donor of his ethnicity, and there were few South Asians in the national bone-marrow database. So Bhatia's business partner sent out an e-mail explaining Bhatia's plight to more than four hundred of their acquaintances, who forwarded the e-mail to their personal contacts; Facebook pages and YouTube videos were devoted to the Help Sameer campaign. Eventually, nearly twenty-five thousand new people were registered in the bone-marrow database, and Bhatia found a match.

But how did the campaign get so many people to sign up? By not asking too much of them. That's the only way you can get someone you don't really know to do something on your behalf. You can get thousands of people to sign up for a donor registry, because doing so is pretty easy. You have to send in a cheek swab and—in the highly unlikely event that your bone marrow is a good match for someone in need—spend a few hours at the hospital. Donating bone marrow isn't a trivial matter. But it doesn't involve financial or personal risk; it doesn't mean spending a summer being chased by armed men in pickup trucks. It doesn't require that you confront socially entrenched norms and practices. In fact, it's the kind of commitment that will bring only social acknowledgment and praise.

The evangelists of social media don't understand this distinction; they seem to believe that a Facebook friend is the same as a real friend and that signing up for a donor registry in Silicon Valley today is activism in the same sense as sitting at a segregated lunch counter in Greensboro in 1960. "Social networks are particularly effective at increasing motivation," Aaker and Smith write. But that's not true. Social networks are effective at increasing *participation*—by lessening the level of motivation that participation requires. The Facebook page of the Save Darfur Coalition has 1,282,339 members, who have donated an average of nine cents apiece. The next biggest Darfur charity on Facebook has 22,073 members, who have donated an average of thirty-five cents. Help Save Darfur has 2,797 members, who have given, on average, fifteen cents. A spokesperson for the Save Darfur Coalition told *Newsweek*, "We wouldn't necessarily gauge someone's value to the advocacy movement based on what they've given. This is a powerful mechanism to engage this critical population. They inform their community, attend events, volunteer. It's not something you can measure by looking at a ledger." In other words, Facebook activism succeeds not by motivating people to make a real sacrifice but by motivating them to do the things that people do when they are not motivated enough to make a real sacrifice. We are a long way from the lunch counters of Greensboro.

The students who joined the sit-ins across the South during the winter of 1960 described the movement as a "fever." But the civil-rights movement was more like a military campaign than like a contagion. In the late nineteen-fifties, there had been sixteen sit-ins in various cities throughout the South, fifteen of which were formally organized by civil-rights organizations like the N.A.A.C.P. and CORE. Possible locations for activism were scouted. Plans were drawn up. Movement activists held training sessions and retreats for would-be protesters. The Greensboro Four were a product of this ground-work: all were members of the N.A.A.C.P. Youth Council. They had close ties with the head of the local N.A.A.C.P. chapter. They had been briefed on the earlier wave of sit-ins in Durham, and had been part of series of movement meetings in activist churches. When the sit-in movement spread from Greensboro throughout the South, it did not spread indiscriminately. It spread to those cities which had preëxisting "movement centers"—a core of dedicated and trained activists ready to turn the "fever" into action.

The civil-rights movement was high-risk activism. It was also, crucially, strategic activism: a challenge to the establishment mounted with precision and discipline. The N.A.A.C.P. was a centralized organization, run from

New York according to highly formalized operating procedures. At the Southern Christian Leadership Conference, Martin Luther King, Jr., was the unquestioned authority. At the center of the movement was the black church, which had, as Aldon D. Morris points out in his superb 1984 study, "The Origins of the Civil Rights Movement," a carefully demarcated division of labor, with various standing committees and disciplined groups. "Each group was task-oriented and coordinated its activities through authority structures," Morris writes. "Individuals were held accountable for their assigned duties, and important conflicts were resolved by the minister, who usually exercised ultimate authority over the congregation."

This is the second crucial distinction between traditional activism and its online variant: social media are not about this kind of hierarchical organization. Facebook and the like are tools for building *networks*, which are the opposite, in structure and character, of hierarchies. Unlike hierarchies, with their rules and procedures, networks aren't controlled by a single central authority. Decisions are made through consensus, and the ties that bind people to the group are loose.

This structure makes networks enormously resilient and adaptable in low-risk situations. Wikipedia is a perfect example. It doesn't have an editor sitting in New York, who directs and corrects each entry. The effort of putting together each entry is self-organized. If every entry in Wikipedia were to be erased tomorrow, the content would swiftly be restored, because that's what happens when a network of thousands spontaneously devote their time to a task.

There are many things, though, that networks don't do well. Car companies sensibly use a network to organize their hundreds of suppliers, but not to design their cars. No one believes that the articulation of a coherent design philosophy is best handled by a sprawling, leaderless organizational system. Because networks don't have a centralized leadership structure and clear lines of authority, they have real difficulty reaching consensus and setting goals. They can't think strategically; they are chronically prone to conflict and error. How do you make difficult choices about tactics or strategy or philosophical direction when everyone has an equal say?

The Palestine Liberation Organization originated as a network, and the international-relations scholars Mette Eilstrup-Sangiovanni and Calvert Jones argue in a recent essay in *International Security* that this is why it ran into such trouble as it grew: "Structural features typical of networks—the absence of central authority, the unchecked autonomy of rival groups, and the inability to arbitrate quarrels through formal mechanisms—made the P.L.O. excessively vulnerable to outside manipulation and internal strife."

In Germany in the nineteen-seventies, they go on, "the far more unified and successful left-wing terrorists tended to organize hierarchically, with professional management and clear divisions of labor. They were concentrated geographically in universities, where they could establish central leadership, trust, and camaraderie through regular, face-to-face meetings." They seldom betrayed their comrades in arms during police interrogations. Their counterparts on the right were organized as decentralized networks, and had no such discipline. These groups were regularly infiltrated, and members, once arrested, easily gave up their comrades. Similarly, Al Qaeda was most dangerous when it was a unified hierarchy. Now that it has dissipated into a network, it has proved far less effective.

The drawbacks of networks scarcely matter if the network isn't interested in systemic change—if it just wants to frighten or humiliate or make a splash—or if it doesn't need to think strategically. But if you're taking on a powerful and organized establishment you have to be a hierarchy. The Montgomery bus boycott required the participation of tens of thousands of people who depended on public transit to get to and from work each day. It lasted a *year.* In order to persuade those people to stay true to the cause, the boycott's organizers tasked each local black church with maintaining morale, and put together a free alterative private carpool service, with forty-eight dispatchers and forty-two pickup stations. Even the White Citizens Council, King later said, conceded that the carpool system moved with "military precision." By the time King came to Birmingham, for the climactic showdown with Police Commissioner Eugene (Bull) Connor, he had a budget of a million dollars, and a hundred full-time staff members on the ground, divided into operational units. The operation itself was divided into steadily escalating phases, mapped out in advance. Support was maintained through consecutive mass meetings rotating from church to church around the city.

Boycotts and sit-ins and nonviolent confrontations—which were the weapons of choice for the civil-rights movement—are high-risk strategies. They leave little room for conflict and error. The moment even one protestor deviates from the script and responds to provocation, the moral legitimacy of the entire protest is compromised. Enthusiasts for social media would no doubt have us believe that King's task in Birmingham would have been made infinitely easier had he been able to communicate with his followers through Facebook, and contented himself with tweets from a Birmingham jail. But networks are messy: think of the ceaseless pattern of correction and revision, amendment and debate, that characterizes Wikipedia. If Martin Luther King, Jr., had tried to do a wiki-boycott in Montgomery, he would have been steamrollered by the white power structure. And of what use would a digital communication tool be in a town where ninety-eight per cent of the black community could be reached every Sunday morning in church? The things King needed in Birmingham—discipline and strategy—were things that online social media cannot provide.

The bible of the social-media movement is Clay Shirky's "Here Comes Everybody." Shirky, who teaches at New York University, sets out to demonstrate the organizing power of the Internet, and he begins with the story of Evan, who worked on Wall Street, and his friend Ivanna, after she left her smart phone, an expensive Sidekick, on the back seat of a New York City taxicab. The telephone company transferred the data on Ivanna's lost phone to a new phone, whereupon she and Evan discovered that the Sidekick was now in the hands of a teenager from Queens, who was using it to take photographs of herself and her friends.

When Evan e-mailed the teenager, Sasha, asking for the phone back, she replied that his "white ass" didn't deserve to have it back. Miffed, he set up a Web page with her picture and a description of what had happened. He forwarded the link to his friends, and they forwarded it to their friends. Someone found the MySpace page of Sasha's boyfriend, and a link to it found its way onto the site. Someone found her address online and took a video of her home while driving by; Evan posted the video on the site. The story was picked up by the news filter Digg. Evan was now up to ten e-mails a minute. He created a bulletin board for his readers to share their stories, but it crashed under the weight of responses. Evan and Ivanna went to the police, but the police filed the report under "loss" rather than "stolen," which essentially closed the case. "By this point millions of readers were watching," Shirky writes, "and dozens of mainstream news outlets had covered the story." Bowing to the pressure, the N.Y.P.D. reclassified the item as "stolen." Sasha was arrested, and Evan got his friend's Sidekick back.

Shirky's argument is that this is the kind of thing that could never have happened in the pre-Internet age—and he's right. Evan could never have tracked down Sasha. The story of the Sidekick would never have been publicized. An army of people could never have been assembled to wage this fight. The police wouldn't have bowed to the pressure of a lone person who had misplaced something as trivial as a cell phone. The story, to Shirky, illustrates "the ease and speed with which a group can be mobilized for the right kind of cause" in the Internet age.

Shirky considers this model of activism an upgrade. But it is simply a form of organizing which favors the weak-tie connections that give us access to information over the strong-tie connections that help us persevere in the face of danger. It shifts our energies from organizations that promote strategic and disciplined activity and toward those which promote resilience and adaptability. It makes it easier for activists to express themselves, and harder for that expression to have any impact. The instruments of social media are well suited to making the existing social order more efficient. They are not a natural enemy of the status quo. If you are of the opinion that all the world needs is a little buffing around the edges, this should not trouble you. But if you think that there are still lunch counters out there that need integrating it ought to give you pause.

Shirky ends the story of the lost Sidekick by asking, portentously, "What happens next?"—no doubt imagining future waves of digital protesters. But he has already answered the question. What happens next is more of the same. A networked, weak-tie world is good at things like helping Wall Streeters get phones back from teenage girls. *Viva la revolución.*

Tethering

Sherry Turkle

In the mid-1990s, a group of young researchers at the MIT Media Lab carried computers and radio transmitters in their backpacks, keyboards in their pockets, and wore digital displays embedded in their eyeglass frames. Always on the Internet, they called themselves "cyborgs." The cyborgs seemed at a remove from their bodies. When their burdensome technology cut into their skin, causing lesions and then scar tissue, they were indifferent. When their encumbrances led them to be taken for the physically disabled, they patiently provided explanations. They were learning to walk and talk as new creatures, learning to inhabit their own bodies all over again, and yet in a way, they were fading away, bleeding out onto the Net. Their experiment was both a re-embodiment (prosthetic consummation), and a disembodiment (disappearance of their bodies into still-nascent computational spaces).

Within a few years, the cyborgs had a new institutional identity as the Media Lab's "Wearable Computing Group." In only a short time, what was novel in their practice had been reduced to how the cyborgs were harbingers of the "cool" clothing of embedded technologies while the rest of us clumsily juggled cell phones, laptops, and PDAs. Yet the legacy of the cyborgs goes beyond the idea that communications technologies might be wearable (or totable). Core elements of their experience have become generalized in global culture: the experience of living on the Net, newly free in some ways, newly yoked and tethered in others.

Today, the near-ubiquity of handheld and palm-size computing and cellular technologies (including voice, text-messaging, e-mail, and Web access) have made connectivity a new commonplace. The marketplace boasts of bicycle helmets through which one can take cell calls and ski jackets equipped with interactive GPS (Global Positioning Systems). When digital technologies first came onto the consumer market in the form of personal computers, they could be understood as objects onto which one could project personality. The technology—in large part because it was programmable, plastic—constituted a "second self."[1] In the early twenty-first century, such language does not go

---

[1] Sherry Turkle, *The Second Self: Computers and the Human Spirit* [1984] 2nd ed., with new introduction, epilogue, and notes (Cambridge, MA: MIT Press, 2005).

far enough; our new intimacy with machines, and in particular, communications technologies, compels us to speak of a new state of the self, itself.

For the most part, our everyday language for talking about technology's effects assumes a life both on and off the screen; it assumes the existence of separate worlds, plugged and unplugged. ("Wearable" computers can be donned and doffed, although they anticipate, like training wheels, the prosthetics and implants that may make us more fully cyborg.) But some of today's locutions suggest a new placement of the subject, such as when we say, "I'll be on my cell," by which we mean, "You can reach me; my cell phone will be on, and I will be wired into (social) existence through it." On my cell, online, on the Web, on instant messaging—these phrases suggest a *tethered* self. Tethering refers to how we connect to always-on communications devices and to the people and things we reach through them, who/which in a certain sense now live through them, always ready-to-mind and hand.

Already, tethering retrains the body. The gestures of privacy one learned when intimacies were shared in face-to-face conversations protected the face itself. In a café, one leaned in toward the person with whom one was speaking, lending an ear while veiling the shared gaze. With always-on cell phones come new behaviors. Each speaker talks out loud, often when walking, behaving as though no one around is listening. What sustains a sense of intimacy when people have personal cell phone conversations in public spaces is this presumption, perhaps the sustaining myth, that they are operating in a social environment that not only treats them as anonymous, but as disembodied, privileged with a certain suggested absence. Holding a cell phone (or the behavior of "speaking into air" that indicates a cell phone with an earphone microphone) marks them as tethered. They are transported to the space of the new ether; "T"-ethered, virtualized.

The tethered self and the social fact of the call set the stage for new relationships and draw the curtains on others. A train station is no longer a communal public space, but a space of social collection: tethered selves come together, but do not speak to each other. In the sociology of social collection each person in the station is more likely to be having an encounter with someone miles away than with the person in the next chair. Each inhabits a private media bubble. Increasingly, what people want out of public spaces is a place to be private with technology. People speak aloud into invisible microphones; they appear to talk to themselves, share intimacies with the air, seemingly unconcerned by their physical surroundings. Of course they are not alone. They are with their cell phones and all that the phones connect them to. We are witnessing a new form of sociality in which the isolation of our physical bodies does not indicate our state of connectedness but may be its precondition. Our state of connectedness is determined by our proximity to available communications technology, and we display our cell phones as a signal that we may need to be left undisturbed. Our devices become a badge of our networks, a sign that we indeed have networks, have places to go and people to see. Whether or not our devices are in use, without them we feel disconnected, adrift.

The tethered self is already split and compartmentalized when the call comes in. New body gestures (the phone flipped open, brought to the ear, the head tossed back or bent over the phone to hear the incoming signal) make the self ready to become who the call requires it to be. A hand motion (a finger placed in the ear not at the phone to better wall off the sounds of physical reality) can signal an identity shift. Our multiple social roles existed prior to the technology. The technology makes them more visible, makes it possible for us to rapidly "cycle through" our various roles and to do so in the presence of new social actors and audiences. So, in the past, I did not have to perform my role as mother in the presence of my professional colleagues. Now an important call from my fourteen-year-old daughter instantaneously produces me as mother. What the tethering of selves changes is not my several roles but the social location of their display and the fact that I cycle through their performance so quickly that they become almost simultaneous. But compartmentalization had its comforts; with its demise comes new psychological challenges, in particular, the erosion of the boundary between work and personal life.

The expression "phoning it in" used to be a pejorative. Now, as pure description, it is a measure of status; it suggests you are important enough to deliver your work remotely. The location of the working body is symbolically significant, but with high status and connectivity come multiple patterns for its deployment, most of which feature travel. In one pattern, the traveling body is in intensive contact with others, but spreads itself around the world. In another pattern, the traveling body is in retreat, fleeing face-to-face contact to maximize privacy and creativity. However the traveling body chooses to use its time, the mobile self is always tethered, always kept in touch through technical means. The new glamour that technology confers is the luxury of bringing your community with you wherever you are. You, your clients, your boss, your loved ones are potentially always together "on your cell." Advertisements for wireless technology typically feature a handsome man with a sleek computer sitting on a beach. The ad copy makes it clear that he is important and he is working. The new disembodiment does not ask you to deny your body its pleasures but to love your body, indeed, to put it somewhere beautiful, warm, and exotic while it works.

Our tethering devices provide us with much that is useful: addresses and phone links, access to family, friends, and professional acquaintances, a place to keep our calendar, to-do lists, mail, music, photographs, financial records, and documents. More than the sum of their parts, these constitute a subjectivity, a projection of self in digital space. They enable us to store, display, perform, and manipulate aspects of identity. Powerful, evocative objects for adults, they are even more intense and compelling for adolescents, located at that point in development when identity play is at the center of life.

Teenagers define themselves through music, and handheld digital technology now puts them in communication with hitherto unimagined libraries of sound. Creating and manipulating personal music playlists is a new mode of personal expression. The playlist itself becomes a way of capturing one of one's variable personae at a particular moment in time. Music is now shared actively, virally; songs proliferate by being copied onto discs or by the reinscription of their code in the memory of MP3 players. The bonds teens forge through music are not only generational but local in the new, virtual sense—bonds to people all over the world who have copied their songs. Devices that connect teens to their music—and those that connect them to their friends—are experienced less as objects than as portals.

Telephones have always made an offer that adolescence cannot refuse, the offer to be in contact with peers. Today, cell phones take what telephones have offered teens for half a century and raise it to a higher power. Cell phones can send text and photographs; they enable the volley of instant messaging; contact can be continual. Cells are to teens what Blackberries are to businessmen: an identity accessory. In Japan, adolescent desires to express individual differences are perhaps behind the mania to elaborately decorate and dress one's cell phone—with a special carrying case, charms, tokens, jewelry, as well as personalized displays and ring tones—that is finding its way across the Pacific. The experiences of today's adolescents with always-on communication devices provide our first view of tethering in developmental terms.

One of the classic conflicts of adolescence is that it is a time when one wants both to be part of the group and to assert individual identity. The adolescent feels both sustained and constrained by peers. Certainly, the norms of always-on communication support the demands of the group: the mores among urban teens have it that within a group of friends, one stays available by cell. Confidences are shared; likewise moments of triumph and anxiety. But it is part of the social contract that one needs good cause to claim time "offline." The pressure to be always-on can be a burden. Teenagers who need uninterrupted time for schoolwork sometimes resort to using their parents' Internet accounts to hide out from their friends. Other fallout for teenagers from the always-on communications culture may be more enduring and less easily managed.

The process of separation in which adolescents work out their identity for themselves was mythologized by Mark Twain as the Huck Finn experience, the on-the-Mississippi moment of escape from an adult world. This moment, really the ongoing drama of a rite of passage, is now transformed by technology. In the mythic archetype, the adults in the child's world were internalized before the threshold of independence was crossed. In the tethered variant, the past may not need to be brought within in quite the same way but can be brought along in an intermediate space; everyone is on speed dial. By definition, the mobile phone is with you whenever you have a feeling, enabling a new coupling of: "I have a feeling. / Get me my friend." One is left to speculate about a possible emotional corollary: "I need to have a feeling. / Get me my friend." In either case, what is not being cultivated is the ability to be alone and to manage and contain one's emotions. Someone is always on call: friend or parent.

Children are usually given cell phones by their parents in early adolescence. In return, they make a promise to answer their parents' calls. On the one hand, this arrangement gives the child permission to have experiences—trips to the museum, to movies, to the beach—that would not be permitted without the phone-tethering to parents. On the other, the child does not have the experience of being alone, with only him or herself to count on. There is a point for an urban child, usually between the ages of eleven and fourteen, when there is a "first time" to navigate the city alone. It is a rite of passage that communicates, "You are on your own and responsible. If you are frightened, you have to experience those feelings." The cell phone buffers this moment; the parent is "on tap." With the parent-on-tap, tethered children think differently about themselves. They are not quite alone.

Always-on connectivity removes the urgency for teenagers to manage their emotions. Parents-on-tap can make it hard to assess a teenager's level of maturity. The tethered teenager looks confident, but knows there is a backup and a check-in. When a parent checks in with a child, the call can be just that, dispensing with all preliminaries. Moreover, in cell culture, the "check-in call" has become a universal genre. It is how we have learned to talk to each other on our cells, partly in deference to the fact that one often takes a call while doing other things. Similarly, the text message with emoticons is almost by nature a check-in, but ambiguous in destination, sometimes meant for one, but acknowledging in its design that it perhaps will be seen by many. Emoticons are a performance art of the virtual body, meant to communicate an emotional state quickly. They are not meant to open a dialogue about complexity of feeling. Although the culture that grows up around the cell is a talk culture (in shopping malls, supermarkets, city streets, cafés, playgrounds, and parks, cells are out and people are talking into them), it is not necessarily a culture in which talk contributes to self-reflection. A culture of shared self-reflection depends on having an emotion, experiencing it, electing to share it with another person, and struggling with the difficulties that this entails. It does not thrive easily in the world of check-ins, emoticons, and rapid response.

Today's adolescents have no less need than previous generations to learn empathic skills, to define identities, to manage and express feelings, to handle being lonely and sad. But technology has changed the rules of engagement with these developmental tasks and perhaps their resolution. When the inter-changes to develop empathy are reduced to the shorthand of emoticon-emotions, questions such as, "Who am I?" and "Who are you?" are refor-matted for the small screen, flattened and disambiguated in the process. High technology, with all of its potential range and richness, has been put at the service of telegraphic speed and brevity.

Adult ambivalence about cell culture takes the form of devotion to the devices paired with complaints, some born of their grown-up memories of life in a sometimes-on (rather than always-on) communications culture. They feel stressed by new responsibilities to e-mail, a nagging sense of always being behind, the inability to take a vacation without bringing the office with them, the feeling that they are being asked to respond immediately to situations at work, even when no response might be preferable or when wise response requires taking time, time that is no longer available. Teens growing up with always-on communications technology are primed to receive a quick message to which they are expected to give a rapid response. They may never know another way. Their experience raises the question for all of us: Are we leav-ing enough time to take one's time?

Our technology is generated by our values but also comes to shape them. If we think of a telephone call as a quick response system enabled by always-on technology, we can forget that there is a difference between a scheduled call and the call you make in reaction to a fleeting emotion or because some-one crossed your mind or left you a message. The self that is shaped by this world of rapid response cultivates what we already acknowledge as multi-tasking. This self measures success by calls made, e-mails answered, contacts reached. This self is calibrated on the basis of what the technology proposes, by what it makes possible, by what it makes easy. But in the buzz of activity, there are losses that we are perhaps not ready to sustain.

We insist that our world is increasingly complex, yet we have created a communications culture that has decreased the time available for us to sit and think, uninterrupted. To make more time means turning off our devices, dis-engaging from the always-on culture. But this is not a simple proposition since our devices have become more closely coupled to our sense of our bod-ies and increasingly feel like extensions of our minds.

In the 1990s, as the Internet became part of everyday life, people began to create multiple online avatars and used them to shift gender, age, race, and class. The effort was to create richly rendered virtual selves through which one could experiment with identity by playing out parallel lives in constructed worlds. The world of avatars and games continues for some, but now, increasingly comfortable with being virtual and always-on, we are content to play ourselves. The way we are being shaped by today's communications technology is far subtler than what came before. Now it follows from our always-on, increasingly intimate connection to our devices. They provide a social and psychological GPS, a navigation system for tethered selves. One television producer, accustomed to being linked to the world via her cell and Palm Pilot, revealed that for her, the Palm's inner spaces were where her self resides: "When my Palm crashed it was like a death. It was more than I could handle. I felt as though I had lost my mind."[2]

---

[2] Presentation at MIT Initiative on Technology and Self, October 2001.